Pages and Pictures

Otsego Hall,

Residence of J. Fenimore Cooper

J. Fenimore Cooper

PAGES AND PICTURES,

FROM

THE WRITINGS

OF

JAMES FENIMORE COOPER,

WITH NOTES

BY

SUSAN FENIMORE COOPER.

Illustrated, on Steel and Wood, from Original Drawings.

CASTLE BOOKS

PREFACE.

THE earlier works of every national literature must always possess an interest peculiar to themselves; an interest which may even, to a certain degree, be independent of any merit of their own, and naturally connected with the period to which they belong. There can be nothing, of course, of the peculiar charm of remote time connected with any work dating with the present century: if, in the quaint ballad, the rude chronicle of early English writing, the figures all move, as it were, amid the long shadows of the dawn, thrown into high and picturesque relief by the morning light, we are prepared for something far less striking and peculiar in the form of any literature coming into being in the noontide of full civilization. Still, there will always be something of a peculiar movement and coloring connected with the first intellectual work of every independent people; something which gives claim to a degree of especial attention to the earlier volumes of every national library, however brilliant may be those which fill succeeding shelves. And while a dozen years of American history, at this period of time, effect the changes which have required centuries with older nations, the fact gives already to works of the last fifty years, something of the interest of a past condition of existence. The writings of Mr. Fenimore Cooper, from

their date and their spirit, must always hold this position to the American reader.   They possess another claim, also, which to the present hour
is peculiar; they flow from a fountain more copious than any other
opened, until now, on the same soil; it is believed that no author this
side of the Atlantic has written so fully.   A long succession of works
possessing merit in themselves, reaching to so large a number, and covering, in their composition, so long a period of time, must always possess
a degree of importance which cannot belong to any isolated book.   Each
work, in a series of this nature, appears not only in its individual character, but also as a member of a group; if the writings have any merit
singly, they carry with them additional value in their full literary company; each, like the pearl in a chain, giving and receiving something of
light and worth, as it is found linked with others.

The volume now open before the reader, contains a selection of
episodes from the writings of Mr. Fenimore Cooper, illustrated, it is
scarcely necessary to observe, by artists of acknowledged merit.   Connected with the extracts, will be found notes relating to the different
works whence the pages have been drawn.   It was at first the intention
to give a passage from each of the different works of the imagination
from the same pen; but the size and nature of the volume, so copiously
illustrated, have rendered it necessary to omit a portion of the series,
and among these, several favorite works.   It is hoped, however, that the
book is sufficiently complete in its present form to give pleasure to the
reader from the variety of its passages, while the notes may afford him
a clearer idea than he has yet received, of a long and important series
connected with American literature.

S. F. C.

COOPERSTOWN, *Sep. 15th*, 1860.

CONTENTS.

ILLUSTRATIONS.

ENGRAVINGS ON STEEL.

ENGRAVINGS ON WOOD.

ONE HUNDRED AND TWENTY HEAD AND TAIL-PIECE VIGNETTE EMBELLISHMENT
Drawn by F. O. C. DARLEY. Engraved by P. F. Annin.

LAKE OTSEGO FROM HYDE.

I.

INTRODUCTION.

WHEN the year 1820 opened on Mr. Cooper, it found him living a quiet rural life, on a small farm in Scarsdale, some five-and-twenty miles from New York. He was at that time in his thirty-first year, having been born on the 15th of September, 1789, at Burlington, New Jersey; and, as yet, there was no clue to be gathered among his pursuits at the moment, or from his previous career, which might lead to the opinion that he would ever become known as a great writer.

Active life had commenced early with him. In 1805, he had received a midshipman's warrant, but soon after his marriage, which took place in 1811, he had left the navy. Had his friends been called upon to predict his future career, many would probably have anticipated a return to the profession of his early youth, for which he still continued to cherish a very warm partiality; or others might have conjectured that the lively interest he had often shown in public questions would be likely to lead him eventually to fix his attention on political life. Beyond the facts that he was known in society to possess unusual talent, and that he had received all the advantages of education which the country afforded at that period, there appeared no grounds for believing that he would ever attain distinction as a literary man.

A farmer's life was that to which he himself looked forward. The cottage he then occupied had been recently built, and he took very great pleasure in the improvements required by a new place. At that period landscape-gardening was in its very earliest stages in America, where very little indeed had yet been done toward giving beauty of design, or finish of detail, to pleasure grounds of any kind. The educated men of the country had indeed shown judgment and taste in placing their houses, the positions of which were often very beautiful; a pleasing view was always considered desirable, and the advantages of a grove, or a stream of water, were seldom overlooked. Many of the oldest places in the country possess very great natural beauties in this way, more particularly those on the banks of rivers first peopled by the colonists, and those within reach of the civilizing influences of the older towns. But, beyond this single fact of a choice of position, very little had been attempted. Straight rows of trees shading the house, or forming an avenue from the gates, or lining the nearer fences, were then the general form of ornamental planting practised by our country gentlemen. Many were the noble elms, the fragrant locusts, the exotic willows, and poplars, thus ranged, like sentinels, about houses which within doors possessed much of the elegance and luxury of the same class of dwellings beyond the sea; while the drawing-rooms were rich in expensive woods, gilded mirrors, choice carpetings, delicate porcelain, the gardens and lawns of the same establishments were but little superior to those of the laboring farmer who had no leisure for finish of improvement. Horticulture and landscape-gardening are the growth of an older and a much higher civilization than that which flows from commerce alone. The early dawn of improvement in pleasure-grounds was just then, however, beginning to open upon the country, and some of the gentlemen in Westchester county were giving much of their attention to subjects of this kind; English books had led the way, returning travellers suggested new ideas, and people were beginning to talk about grouping trees, and shrubbery, and grading lawns. The improvement of his grounds became a task into which Mr. Cooper entered with instinctive good taste, and with all the animation and warmth of interest peculiar to his character. The position of the house was fine, commanding a beautiful view over the farms and woods of the adjoining country, in whose varied groves hickory and tulip-tree, cedar and sassafras, grew luxuriantly; a broad reach of Sound stretched beyond, always dotted with the white sails the sailor's eye loved to follow in their graceful movements to and fro, while the low shores of Long Island, with the famous pippin orchards of Newtown, formed the distant background. Planning a lawn, building a ha-ha fence, then a novelty in the country, and ditching a swamp, were the tasks of the moment;

while the friends who followed his movement often smiled at the almost boyish eagerness with which he watched the growth of shrubs, or they shook their heads sagely at the size of the trees he was engaged in transplanting.   Active in all his habits, and full of vigorous health, he superintended the work going on, in all its stages, often undertaking some light task himself, and never failing to shorten the time by chatting with his laborers—picking up amusement or practical information in this way.

The height on which the cottage was built had received the name of Angevine.   Early in the history of the county, a colony of Huguenots had settled on the shores of Long Island Sound, at the village of New Rochelle. They were a very respectable and interesting people, with a high character for industry, honesty, and for simple fidelity to their religious duties.   A touching instance of the last characteristic has been preserved, as a tradition of the neighborhood.   In the earlier days of the little colony there was no minister of the gospel among them, and no place of public worship where the services were held in French, nearer than the church of the St. Esprit, in New York.   With the earliest hours of Sunday, by starlight or moonlight, a little band of simple-hearted pilgrims, men and women, old and young together, were in the habit of setting out on foot, walking from their cottage homes, more than twenty miles, to join in the public worship of the Lord's day, in their mother tongue.   At a rather later period, a little stone church, rude and quaint, with pointed roof, was built in their village; and within its square walls the households of the Anglican communion, for many miles around, attended the services, until the building was pronounced unsafe and taken down.   Many families from this little colony were scattered over the adjoining country, among the farms of Mamaroneck, Rye, and Scarsdale, where Huguenot names are still very common; one of these households had settled, as tenants, nearly a hundred years earlier, on the height alluded to, in Scarsdale.   When Mr. Cooper came to examine the ground for the site of a house, he found their rude graves, a rough field-stone marking the head and foot of each, lining one of the fences, as was so frequently the custom on American farms at that period; a kindly feeling of regard for the Huguenot colony, and respect for their graves, which of course remained unmolested, led to the name of Angevine being given to the new place.

Reading, which always enters so naturally into country life, was a regular resource for the evening hours, and rainy days, at Angevine.   It is needless to observe that the books on every table were, at that day, almost exclusively English.   The roll of all the contemporary authors in the country, of any note, might have been called over in a trice; and if, among these, there were already

several brilliant pens, yet the united influence of the whole class on the nation
was still very slight indeed.   The American people, in the forty-fifth year
of their independence, were in fact living on English literature almost as exclusively as they had done a century earlier, in a state wholly colonial.   The very
brilliancy of that epoch, so remarkable in British literature, was in one sense
discouraging, and unfavorable to the birth of original writing in America; the
idea of publishing in the same language, and on the same day, with Scott, with
Byron, with Burns, with Wordsworth, thus boldly challenging the world to
comparisons the most critical, might almost have sufficed in itself, one would
suppose, to silence all literary labor on the part of a people still so provincial at
heart as we then were.

     At that period there came sailing into the harbor of New York, with each
returning month, one or two packet ships, from London or Liverpool, their
arrival in the lower bay being duly announced to Wall street by the unwieldy
arms of the wooden telegraph on Staten Island; and, among bales of English
calicos and broadcloths, there never failed to be some smaller package of far
greater and more lasting value—some volume fresh from the London press, high
in merit, full of interest, a work whose appearance had been already heralded,
and whose arrival was eagerly expected by every reader in the country.   Perhaps it was a romance of the Waverley series, still a delightful mystery as
regarded their origin, or a brilliant canto of Byron, or a charming social tale by
Miss Edgeworth, or a valuable religious work by Mr. Wilberforce, or Miss More.
With the next day's papers the news of the arrival spread through the country-
houses of Westchester.   Orders were immediately sent to the bookseller in New
York.   At that day each village on the Sound had its own sloop, plying two or
three times a week to and fro, through the perils of Hell-Gate, carrying the
produce of the farms to Fulton Market, and bringing back sugar and tea, and
good things of all sorts, to the rustic wharf.   Among other imported luxuries
came the last new book.   Or perchance it was the mail-coach, which, as it
travelled eastward along the winding roads of Westchester, dropped the precious
parcel at the quiet village post-office.   Lucky was that household deemed which
could first cut the pages of the new volume; and long did its contents, rich in
entertainment or instruction, offer subject for social talk and clever discussion,
about the firesides of the whole neighborhood.   The most imposing living personages of the day, moving through the great cities and over the battlefields of
old Europe, scarcely filled a wider space in familiar household talk than the
brilliant figures on the many-colored canvas of Sir Walter Scott.   Kings and
queens, of ancient abdicated dynasties and the newly-crowned alike, victorious

The Deerslayer: "Here he first helped him to take an attitude in which he could appease his burning thirst."

marshals and generals, successful statesmen, cabinet ministers and court beauties, were compelled to share the honors of fireside fame with Dominie Sampson, and Edie Ochiltree, and Jennie Deans, and Meg Merrilies.

It is quite needless to declare that Mr. Cooper took great delight in the Waverley novels; when the secret of their authorship was still a subject for discussion, he was among those who never doubted that they were written by Walter Scott, the poet. He read aloud delightfully. His voice was very fine; deep, clear and expressive. Good reading was, with him, a natural gift, the impulse of the moment, an instinct of genius. During those quiet country evenings, he often read aloud; there was one who listened with affectionate interest—one for whom, through a long life, he read with especial pleasure. Poetry was occasionally chosen: his reading of verse was particularly good, accurate, and full of deep poetic feeling. For Shakespeare he was always ready; entering with unfeigned delight into the spirit of his works, whether comedy or tragedy. Pope, Thomson, Gray, were also in favor. But he could seldom be induced to read more than a page or two of Milton, at a time; the great epic poet he considered too correctly cold and classical in spirit, for his theme; and this opinion continued unchanged through life. "Shakespeare should have written Paradise Lost. What a poem he would have given to the world!" was a remark he repeatedly made. But new books were, of course, in particular request; and rapidly as the great Scotch novels succeeded each other, something more was needed to fill up all those quiet evening hours at Angevine. Unfortunately those English packets brought trash, as well as treasures literary, from beyond the sea. On one occasion, a new novel chanced to lie on the table; he was asked to read. The title and look of the book were not to his taste; he opened it, however, and began. Suddenly, after wading through a few pages, it was thrown aside in disgust:

"I can write you a better book than that, myself!" was his exclamation.

The consequences of that careless declaration made half in jest, were, indeed, little foreseen. He was playfully challenged to make good his promise. And when urged to commence at once, immediately began throwing together the outline of a tale, something in the style of the rejected volume. Ere long, the first pages of "Precaution" were written.

The idea of writing a book was certainly, under the circumstances, a very bold one. Hitherto no man could have shown himself farther from any inclination for authorcraft. He was not one of those people who like the feeling of foolscap, the sight of pen and ink, who indulge secret partialities for note-books, diaries and extracts. His portfolio was wholly empty; scarcely, indeed, provided with letter-paper for an occasional correspondent. The mere mechanical drudgery of writing was irksome to him; so much so, that in a letter dated only a year or two earlier, he made use of the words: "Much as I dislike writing in general," &c. But, how often the latent tastes, the dormant inclinations, the undeveloped thought and feeling which are yet to shape the future course, lie unobserved, until unexpectedly aroused into action! Some occasional act, some isolated flash of temper, some sudden gleam of intelligence, are, in such cases, often found, however, to reveal character and ability more clearly than the quiet tenor of the daily course. Such had been the case with Mr. Cooper. As a boy, he had taken great delight in certain old-fashioned heroic romances, a taste inherited, perhaps, from his mother, who was much given to reading works of imagination. When about eleven years old, he pored over several strange old tales of this class, with a playfellow of his own age; and among others was one bearing the title of "Don Belianis of Greece," now, doubtless, wholly forgotten. These produced a great impression, and he had barely finished them when he gravely informed his comrade that he should write a book himself! He should begin at once. It was to be a great heroic romance, with knights, and squires, and horses, and ladies, and castles, and banners. "Don Belianis of Greece" was, of course, to be the model. There was, however, one formidable difficulty in the way; the penmanship was a part of the task for which he had not the least partiality. After due deliberation, an idea occurred which removed this obstacle entirely. It was agreed that the new work should be printed without the usual preliminary labor of writing it. There was, at that time, a little blue newspaper, called the *Otsego Herald*, published in Cooperstown, by the father of his companion, who was its editor. It was agreed that while the press was resting from its weekly labors, the projected romance should be dictated and printed in the office by the two boys. This new Beaumont and Fletcher production was accordingly commenced, and several chapters were printed, when, as might have been foreseen, the young author became weary of his task, and threw it aside. Such was the first composition of which any record has been preserved, and for years it appears to have remained an isolated production.

On another occasion, however, after reaching manhood, Mr. Cooper had actually committed himself more publicly in print, and that in verse, too. In his youth he occasionally wrote verses, such as most young men are in the habit of producing—sometimes sentimental, sometimes of a comic character. These are said to have been generally cleverly imagined, and not without a degree of merit, though he attached no value whatever to them himself. On one occasion, when he was in the printing-office of the *Herald*, at Cooperstown, a poor fellow subject to epileptic fits, came in to ask charity from a group of gentlemen he found there. The man's certificates were particularly good, and his story excited much interest. He proved to be a strolling ballad-singer, a vocation now quite obsolete in the country. A purse was made up for him, when, looking about the circle, he remarked that if some gentleman would write him a few verses, something new, it would be worth far more to him than the silver he had just received. Mr. Cooper offered to try his hand at verse-making, and inquired what subject would be preferred. "There's nothing sells like ballads!" was the answer. A ballad was promised. The last war with England was then drawing to a close; and Buffalo, at that time a small frontier village, had been recently burnt by the troops under Colonel Murray. Some thirty or forty stanzas of doggerel were immediately written, bearing the imposing title of, "Buffalo Burnt, or the Dreadful Conflagration!" The catastrophe was, of course described in the most pathetic manner. A number of copies were printed, and the poor stroller went off with his wallet full. Some months later he appeared again in the village; he came to beg another ballad. "Buffalo Burnt, or the Dreadful Conflagration," had been wonderfully successful in the farm-houses of the neighboring counties. A second ballad was written, whose title has been forgotten; but as the poor stroller never applied again to his poet, it was probably less successful than the first effort. Some four or five years later, the writer of the ballad being in a neighboring village, was invited to a tea-party; music was proposed; a young lady was handed to the piano, and to the amazement and horror of Mr. Cooper, very gravely began singing "Buffalo Burnt, or the Dreadful Conflagration!"

Such were the very few preliminary steps in composition when "Precaution" was commenced. As the story advanced, the writer became amused and interested in his task. It was not, however, until it had made some progress that the idea of publishing was suggested. Without this proposition the book would probably never have been completed; but the idea of appearing in a character so unexpected, of taking his friends by surprise in this way, was in itself amusing, and gave zest to the task. The MS. was read in portions to several persons; to Mr. Charles Wilkes, of New York, a friend of long standing, in whose highly cultivated taste he had great confidence; to Mr. James Atcheson, of Otsego county, an Englishman, a man of learning and talent, but of eccentricity of character, in whose society Mr. Cooper took much pleasure; and to the family of Governor Jay, at Bedford, with whom he had from childhood been on terms of intimacy. These partial friends all advised the publication of the tale. Probably one of the greatest compliments the book ever received came from an excellent lady, a guest in the house, present at the Bedford readings: she was convinced that Mr.

Cooper spoke in pleasantry when he declared the MS. to be original; he was clearly making fun of his audience—she was quite confident that she had heard that very tale some years earlier. And so well were the general tone and character of the school he imitated kept up, that, even after the publication of the " Spy " and " Pioneers," the same excellent lady persisted in the opinion that Mr. Cooper could never have written " Precaution." It was clearly a woman's book.

Meanwhile the tale was printed. On the 25th of August, 1820, it was published by Mr. A. T. Goodrich, of New York, under the title of " Precaution; or, Prevention is Better than Cure." The original publications of a New York house of that day were, of course, very few in number. The book attracted a degree of attention. Its literary merits were considered respectable, though not in the least brilliant. The characters were declared natural, and the moral tone was pronounced excellent. Quite as a matter of course, it was supposed, at first, to have been written in England, and by a woman. The publisher, however, declared that it was an American work, and written by a gentleman of New York. Surprise was expressed, and a degree of curiosity excited in society; but most of those who read the book continued quite incredulous. And when, at length, the name of Mr. Cooper began to be whispered in connection with the tale, incredulity rather increased—the very suggestion was considered a piece of pleasantry. What American naval officer, it was asked, would be likely to write a book so English, and so womanly in tone and execution? In the sense of an elaborate imitation, at least, " Precaution" may be said to have been thoroughly successful. For a long time it was attributed to an English lady, a near connection of Mr. Cooper's.

The reading world has shown itself much given to indulging in fancies of its own regarding the authorship of a new book. One day it is pleased to ascribe a volume to some pen which is perhaps as yet wholly innocent of bookcraft; at another moment it pertinaciously insists on giving a new work to a distinguished writer, who has, in fact, never read a line of it. In short, it likes to prove itself particularly sagacious in these matters, not easily blinded, very capable of penetrating at a glance mysteries of this sort. It professes to know intuitively the impossibility of this or that individual writing this or that passage, or to trace the sign manual of some well-known and skilful pen on every page of the last anonymous volume. It enjoys vastly showing itself wiser than its neighbor in this way. It would like to be convinced that Homer never wrote the Iliad, and quite recently it has even shown an inclination to assert that William Shakespeare, of Stratford, had very little to do with Othello and Hamlet. The authorship of Junius, we may rest assured, will never be settled beyond all cavil, even should Junius himself be proved to have thrown off his own mask. In fact, however, like all who are prone to indulging conceits, the reading world may be quite easily misled. It is little aware of the great facility with which the pen of a clever writer assumes different characters—ay, characters often the very opposite of that most natural to the individual who writes. Your grave man, perhaps, shall write very gayly; few courtiers of the great Louis so truly sober in mood, we are told, as the witty and humorous author of the "Bourgeois Gentilhomme." Few worthies have made their friends laugh more heartily than "Gilpin," that "citizen of credit and renown;" and yet it was the heavy-hearted Cowper who seated him on horseback. Good-natured tempers may be very capable of writing bitter satire and sharp controversy. Boileau is said to have been an amiable man. Miss Hannah More was blessed with a very happy natural temper, and she has left it on record that controversy could have a certain intellectual charm for her; after several very severe letters, admirable in their way, and in answer to the attacks of an opponent, she confesses that the task had given her too much pleasure; she must refrain from any similar work in future. And thus it is that men may assume on paper a quiet womanly tone, and that women may write, if they please, bold and daring pages, quite at variance with the spirit of their own daily life. And in all this there is no hypocrisy. It is simply a work of the intellect, literally *jeu d'esprit;* the mind is amused with the task it has set itself, and takes pleasure in playing out its own game; is often, perhaps, led onward far beyond its first intention.

There are two different fountains whence inspiration flows to the writer—the intellect and the heart, thought and feeling. Thought makes the best artist, has greater foresight, a wiser command of means, gives greater completeness, higher finish. But heart has a power even beyond this, a power of life and soul, more entirely swaying human sympathy and action; it has more freshness, more originality, more sincerity — its highest influences are even more enduring Thought sees truth, and reveals it, or often may conceal it. Heart feels truth itself, and, with a generous fulness of eloquence all its own, to which no *enthousiasme de commande* can ever attain, compels conviction. Many a highly-polished classic sonnet lies in cold neglect on the library shelf, while the humble ballad, full of true natural feeling, is preserved in affectionate living remembrance. These two great influences, intellect and feeling, are found acting in partial independence of each other. What a man writes with the intellect only, may be entirely foreign to his own life—work wholly artificial; what he really writes from the heart, must necessarily have the same coloring as his character—flowing from his own inmost nature, and carry with it something of the inherent force of truth. "Have a heart and know it," is the advice of the great Polish poet. It is, however, where both powers are called into action, in all their fulness, that the noblest writings are produced. Where a strong intellect plans, and a generous, upright heart works, there we may look for a great book. Imitation can never, for this reason, attain to the very highest and most effective excellence —it is a work of the head only; it may be very skilful, quite faultless, very successful in its way, but the soul and spirit must ever be wanting. Genius, like the wonderful thrush of the American wood, may have its many voices, it may even condescend to sing its lays to borrowed tunes; the careless wayfarer is deceived; passing along, he fancies that he hears the robin, or the ground-sparrow; but when the rare creature pours forth its own noble song, he pauses, with upward gaze, and lingers, lost in delight, listening to those "native wood-notes wild.'

"Precaution" was soon reprinted in England, and received much as an English book of the same class might have been. While this tale was written under an assumed name, it must be understood that there were two particulars in which it was perfectly sincere. The author's reverence for the Christian religion, and his respect for purity of female character, were entirely unfeigned. Throughout a long life he was never known to trifle with either subject.

The book was very imperfectly printed on the coarse, dark paper of the day, with almost countless faults of punctuation, and a list of errata closely covering an entire page, at the end of the volume. A copy of the first edition may be considered as a curiosity at the present day, showing the wonderful progress made since then in American typography.

A brief extract from "Precaution" is given, rather that the reader may be enabled to compare the passage with other pages which are to follow, than from any particular merit of its own.

I.

CHARITY.

"I AM sorry, aunt, Mr. Denbigh is not rich," said Emily to Mrs. Wilson, after they had retired in the evening, almost unconscious of what she uttered. The latter looked at her niece in surprise, at a remark so abrupt, and one so very different from the ordinary train of Emily's reflections, as she required an explanation. Emily, slightly coloring at the channel her thoughts had insensibly strayed into, gave her aunt an account of their adventure in the course of the morning's drive, and touched lightly on the difference in the amount of the alms of her brother and those of Mr. Denbigh.

"The bestowal of money is not always an act of charity," observed Mrs. Wilson, gravely, and the subject was dropped: though neither ceased to dwell on it in her thoughts, until sleep closed the eyes of both.

The following day Mrs. Wilson invited Grace and Emily to accompany her in a walk; the gentlemen having preceded them in pursuit of their differen. avocations. Francis had his regular visits of spiritual consolation; John had gone to the hall for his pointers and fowling-piece, the season for woodcock having arrived; and Denbigh had proceeded no one knew whither. On gaining the high-road, Mrs. Wilson desired her companions to lead the way to the cottage where the family of the mendicant gardener had been lodged, and thither they soon arrived. On knocking at the door, they were immediately admitted to an outer room, in which they found the wife of the laborer who inhabited the building, engaged in her customary morning employ- ments. They explained the motives of the visit, and were told that the family they sought were in an adjoining room, but she rather thought at that moment engaged with a clergyman who had called a quarter of an hour before. "I expect, my lady, it's the new rector, who every body says is so good to the poor and needy; but I have not found time yet to go to church to hear his reverence preach, ma'am," courtseying and handing the fresh-dusted chairs to her unexpected visitors. The ladies seated themselves, too delicate to interrupt Francis in his sacred duties, and were silently waiting his appearance, when a voice was distinctly heard through the thin partition, the first note of which undeceived them as to the character of the gardener's visitor.

"It appears then, Davis, by your own confession," said Denbigh, mildly, but in a tone of reproof, "that your frequent acts of intemperance have at least given ground for the steward's procuring your discharge, if it has not justified him in doing that which his duty to your common employer required."

"It is hard, sir," replied the man, sullenly, "to be thrown on the world with a family like mine, to make way for a younger man with but one child."

"It may be unfortunate for your wife and children," said Denbigh, "but just, as respects yourself. I have already convinced you, that my interference or reproof is not an empty one: carry the letter to the person to whom it is directed, and I pledge you, you shall have a new trial; and should you conduct yourself soberly, and with propriety, continued and ample support; the second letter will gain your children immediate admission to the school I mentioned; and I now leave you, with an earnest injunction to remember that habits of intemperance not only disqualify you to support those who have such great claims on your protection, but inevitably lead to a loss of those powers which are necessary to insure your own eternal welfare."

"May Heaven bless your honor," cried the woman, with fervor, and evidently in tears, "both for what you have said, and what you have done. Thomas only wants to be taken from temptation to become a sober man again—an honest one he has ever been, I am sure."

"I have selected a place for him," replied Denbigh, "where there is no exposure through improper companions, and every thing now depends upon himself, under Providence."

Mrs. Wilson had risen from her chair on the first intimation given by Denbigh of his intention to go, but had paused at the door to listen to this last speech; when, beckoning her companions, she hastily withdrew, having first made a small present to the woman of the cottage, and requested her not to mention their having called.

"What becomes now of the comparative charity of your brother and Mr. Denbigh, Emily?" asked Mrs. Wilson, as they gained the road on their return homeward. Emily was not accustomed to hear any act of John slightly spoken of without at least manifesting some emotion, which betrayed her sisterly regard; but on the present occasion she chose to be silent; while Grace, after waiting in expectation that her cousin would speak, ventured to say timidly:

"I am sure, dear madam, Mr. Moseley was very liberal, and the tears were in his eyes while he gave the money. I was looking directly at them the whole time."

"John is compassionate by nature," continued Mrs. Wilson, with an almost imperceptible smile. "I have no doubt his sympathies were warmly enlisted in behalf of this family; and possessing much, he gave liberally. I have no doubt he would have undergone personal privation to have relieved their distress, and endured both pain and labor, with such an excitement before him. But what is all that to the charity of Mr. Denbigh?"

Grace was unused to contend, and, least of all, with Mrs. Wilson; but, unwilling to abandon John to such censure, with increased animation, she said:

"If bestowing freely, and feeling for the distress you relieve, be not commendable, madam, I am sure I am ignorant what is."

J. Hamilton sc.t

J. M.c Gahey sculp.t

The Pathfinder: Going Down the Rapids

"That compassion for the woes of others is beautiful in itself, and the want of it an invariable evidence of corruption from too much, and an ill-governed intercourse with the world, I am willing to acknowledge, my dear Grace," said Mrs. Wilson, kindly; "but the relief of misery, where the heart has not undergone this hardening ordeal, is only a relief to our own feelings: this is compassion; but Christian charity is a higher order of duty: it enters into every sensation of the heart; disposes us to judge, as well as to act, favorably to our fellow-creatures; is deeply seated in the sense of our own unworthiness; keeps a single eye, in its dispensations of temporal benefits, to the everlasting happiness of the objects of its bounty; is consistent, well regulated; in short"—and Mrs. Wilson's pale cheek glowed with an unusual richness of color—"it is an humble attempt to copy after the heavenly example of our Redeemer, in sacrificing ourselves to the welfare of others, and does and must proceed from a love of his person, and an obedience to his mandates."

"And Mr. Denbigh, aunt," exclaimed Emily, the blood mantling to her cheeks with a sympathetic glow, while she lost all consideration for John in the strength of her feelings, "his charity you think to be of this description?"

"So far, my child, as we can understand motives from the nature of the conduct, such appears to have been the charity of Mr. Denbigh."

Grace was silenced, if not convinced; and the ladies continued their walk, lost in their own reflections, until they reached a bend in the road which hid the cottage from view.

II.

THE SPY.

To a spirit naturally so free and active as that of the writer of "Precaution" imitation must soon become wearying and irksome in the extreme. Disguise was now thrown off—and forever.

"I will try another book!" he exclaimed, supposing that this second narrative should prove the last.

A field wholly new was chosen. A tale was soon planned. It was to be in one sense historical, yet a book entirely American in scenery, in the characters, and in its spirit. Works of historical romance, brilliant with the proud pageantry of European story, were at that moment filling the eye of the civilized world with their dazzling glamour, displaying figures the most picturesque, yet charmingly natural, thrown into striking groups by a hand the most powerful, the most skilful, which had yet woven the web of English fiction. What materials were there, in our own brief annals, to compare with these treasures of tradition; what was there in our own bare and homely provincial life which could delight the reader's imagination; what hope had the young American sailor, untutored in authorcraft, when entering the field held by the veteran writer already great in achievement and fame? The question was soon to be decided.

Patriotism was to be the soul of the new book, and the fact that he was about to move over home ground gave new zest to the work. In his warmly-generous nature, still in the glow of youth, love of country flowed from fountains clear, deep and full, and he was perhaps unconscious himself of all the life and spirit which the feeling was about to infuse into the pages of the new tale. The scene was laid in Westchester county, where he was living at the time—a part of the country to which he was always partial; the society found in the different gentlemen's houses scattered over the county was particularly good, and to one as thoroughly social as himself, in all his tastes and habits, a source of much enjoyment. The genial, temperate climate was also pleasant, while the sea-breezes, even when sweeping over the country in the form of the local "three-days' storm," had their own charm for a sailor's senses.

Many lesser incidents of the Revolution, now wholly forgotten, were at that day still living facts in the minds of the people, scarcely yet remote enough for the shadowy perspective of history. Many of those who had taken an active part in the great struggle were still coming in and going out of their children's doors—aged men, telling tales of the different events of the conflict, with all the glow of personal interest. Many a gray-haired housewife, as she sat at the wheel, spinning her thread of flax or wool, could talk of the armies she had seen in her girlhood passing her father's door, marching to and fro, on their way to this or that victory, or retreating, perchance, from this or that defeat. Westchester was full of such recollections. There was no portion of the country whose soil, during the eight eventful years of the war, was so often trodden by friend and foe, alike in arms. The city of New York, unlike any other in the country, was held, from the very first to the very latest days of the war, by strong garrisons of one party or the other. Abandoned by General Washington after the defeat on Long Island, it became from that hour the permanent head-quarters of the British commander-in-chief; while American armies, now standing aloof in conscious weakness of numbers, now advancing nearer with returning strength of reinforcement, kept constant watch, their eyes fixed on that important point. Of course, smaller bodies of troops, of both parties, were in unceasing movement over the adjacent country, foraging, reconnoitring, skirmishing, as the occasion required. Scarce a narrow lane of the many winding roads of the county, fenced with rude stone walls, hedged with brier and vine, shaded with cedar and oak, as they are, along which trim British troops and ragged American soldiers had not marched and countermarched by the light of sun or star. Scarce a farm-house door which had not been darkened by Cow-boy, Hessian, or Skinner, on errand of pillage or violence. Scarce a barnyard which had not been harried, scarce a larder, whether high or low, which had not, time and again, been rifled. Here and there still darker work had been done—homes had been destroyed by fire, good yeoman blood had been shed, life had been taken, husband, father, or brother had fallen in some unrecorded skirmish, the hero of a rustic neighborhood. The entire country between the American outposts on the skirts of the Highlands, and the British works on the island of Manhattan—the Neutral

Ground, as it was called by both parties—probably suffered more in this way than the same extent of country in any part of the Union. Scarsdale and Mamaroneck lay within this region. The battlefield of White Plains was close at hand; Fort Washington had stood on a neighboring height; Dobb's Ferry, so long a central point of interest for the American forces, lay only a few miles beyond. On the daily drive from Angevine to the nearest post-office at Mamaroneck, a spot was passed connected with one of the many local traditions of the neighborhood; in a pretty thicket, covering a piece of swampy land, a cave was shown in which one of the partisans of the day had lain for some time concealed, fed secretly by friendly hands with food stealthily brought at night, until escape was effected. And again, on the way to the little Huguenot church at New Rochelle, the road wound at the foot of a hill, shaded by a pretty grove, which, in spite of its quiet, sunny aspect at the present hour, enjoyed the gloomy honors of a haunted wood—a sharp skirmish had taken place there in the years of the Revolution, and ever and anon, at solemn midnight hours, ghosts were dimly seen gliding to and fro, aye, it was even whispered that the clashing of their swords had been faintly heard, more than once, on some stormy night; in vain might proud incredulity shake its head, the inmates of certain old gray cottages, with moss-grown shingled walls, and projecting ovens, knew better; they believed the fact most firmly.

At the foot of the hill on which stood the cottage of Angevine, there was a small farm-house, remarkable in one architectural particular, its four walls showing each a different color to the face of the sun—red, yellow, brown, and white. In this comfortable polychromatic dwelling lived a small farmer who came frequently to Angevine, telling his tales of "Godfrey's Cave," and the "haunted wood," or talking over past scenes, in which figured "continentals," "regulars," "rebels," and "refugees"—words carrying strange sounds to our ears to-day. "Uncle John H——" was but one of the number of the yeoman neighbors— some of Huguenot, some of English stock—who gladly came to pass a cheerful evening hour with the master of the house, fighting the county battles over with fresh interest, aroused by the spirited questions, the intelligent sympathy of their host. All, as they drank their glass of cider, picked over their hickory-nuts, or pared their Newtown pippin, had countless deeds of violence, more or less flagrant, to relate, of Cow-boy and Skinner; all had some family tradition to repeat, of hairbreadth escape, of daring feat, of harried fields, and houses burned. There was one very remarkable tale-teller of the region, long since deceased, while his family have also passed away, far surpassing most narrators, since the days of the celebrated German, whose reputation in this way was well established in the county ; his anecdotes, however, were chiefly confined to the prowess of a near relative, " Major Brom B——," a hero of the great war, who would assuredly have deserved half a dozen pensions had he ever claimed one. This champion commanded, according to the narrator, a family troop, small in number, but most redoubtable in their feats ; all related by blood to " Major Brom," all in uniform of silver gray, and numbering twenty-seven martial spirits in one company. The major was, moreover, the happy owner of a negro, " Bonny," almost as famous as himself, while his gun, " the Buccaneer," had not its fellow on the continent. The various adventures of " Major Brom B.," the twenty-seven silver-grays, Bonny the negro, and Buccaneer the gun, were an un- failing source of entertainment at many firesides in Westchester at that day.

But it was from sources far higher than these, that the leading idea of the new book was derived. Visits to Bedford were very frequent at that period. One summer's afternoon, while sitting on the broad piazza of the house, Judge Jay and Mr. Cooper were listening with respectful attention to the remarks of the vener- able Governor Jay, as he related different facts connected with the history of the Revolution. The conversation turned more particularly on the spirit of true patriotism, as shown by all classes of the people, during the struggle. Governor Jay then observed that there were men whose services at critical moments, in obtaining information for the use of the commander-in-chief had been of the greatest importance, and that repeatedly such services had been undertaken at imminent personal risks, from the most disinterested love of country. He then proceeded to relate a remarkable incident of this nature, with which he had been himself connected. It was from this interesting conversation, that the idea of the character of Harvey Birch was now drawn, as the reader will find, in looking over an ensuing extract referring to the incident.

Strolling peddlers, staff in hand, and pack at the back, were more common visitors at the country-houses of that day than at the present hour, when these per- sonages usually keep their coaches, and may be called speculators, and wandering traders, rather than old-fashioned peddlers. It was after the visit of one of these men, a Yankee peddler of the old sort, to the cottage at Angevine, that Harvey's lot in life was decided—he was to be a spy, and a peddler. Always rapid in his work, the outline had scarcely been conceived, when the first pages were written. On this occasion, as on all others when writing a book, he first adopted some general leading idea, sketched vaguely in his mind a few of the more prominent characters, and then immediately began his work in its final shape, leaving the details to suggest and develop themselves during the progress of the volume. Excepting when writing history, he is not known to have ever drawn up a written plan, and in one or two instances only were a few brief notes thrown on paper, regarding some particular chapter. In all the details he depended in a great measure on the thought and feeling of the moment. While writing "The Spy," and one or two of his earliest works, some intimate friend was occasionally consulted. But, ere long, he became quite independent in his action on these matters; and during thirty years of professional writing, there was but one with whom he habitually talked over his plot and characters—one only, who was ever his chief counsellor, one in whose taste and judgment he had great confidence.

On the 17th of September, 1821, "The Spy, a Tale of the Neutral Ground," was published in New York, by Wiley and Halsted. The book immediately attracted general attention, probably beyond what any American volume had yet done. It was read with delight. The strikingly original character of Harvey Birch, so clearly conceived, so thoroughly carried out, riveted attention, while the glow pervading the whole narrative, gave interest to every chapter. The critics were taken by surprise—they held their breath. That a book so full of talent, should have been written by an author as yet unrecognized among them, was strange indeed. A few ventured to praise. Many waited for the word of command from England, ere committing themselves, the common course of things in all literary matters at that day. Meanwhile in society, the work was meeting with brilliant success. It was found on every table, and enjoyed by all classes of readers. Ere long the character of Harvey Birch became so vividly impressed on the public mind, that people expected to see his thin, stooping figure, gliding across their path, as they drove about the hills and valleys of Westchester.

In Europe, "The Spy" had also great success, the interest inherent in the book being naturally increased by its coming from a country whence so little was then expected, in the way of original literature. In England it was well received; Mr. Cooper was much gratified by a compliment from Miss Edgeworth, who, after expressing the pleasure she had received from the book, sent him a message through a mutual friend, declaring that she liked "Betty Flanagan" particularly, and that an Irish pen could not have drawn her better. French translation soon followed. Some very ludicrous mistakes occur in the first French versions. The name given to the Wharton place, "The Locusts" proved a puzzle; the word was rendered as it was found in the dictionary, "Les Sauterelles"—the Grasshoppers. This might have answered very well, but for one unfortunate fact—a dragoon of Lawton's troop is represented as tying his horse to one of the locusts on the lawn. Here was a difficulty; the worthy translator, however, belonging evidently to the class "traduttori, traditori," seems to have taken it for granted, that trans-atlantic grasshoppers must necessarily be of gigantic proportions; nothing daunted, he proceeds gravely to state the remarkable fact, that the dragoon secured his charger by fastening the bridle to one of the grasshoppers before the door—apparently standing there for that purpose! In another chapter, when giving the passage in which Colonel Wellmere is represented as drawing figures on the dining-table with the wine spilled from his glass, as the gentlemen are sitting over their nuts and Madeira, the sage translator takes occasion to insert a note, in which he calls the reader's attention to a fact showing so clearly the rude style of living in America at that day—even in the house of a man in Mr. Wharton's position table-linen was unknown. It was soon reported in New York, among Mr. Cooper's friends, that the book was his own. An amusing incident occurred not long after its publication. The writer was walking in Broadway, when he saw a gentleman, well known to him, cross the street, and advance to meet him; it was a prominent merchant, a man of money, very well known in Wall street. He came on a friendly errand, to congratulate his acquaintance on the new book, and its success. He was loud in its praises.

"An admirable book—never read any thing more full of spirit and interest in my life!"

"I am glad you like it."

"Like it—to be sure I do. From the moment I opened the first volume I could not leave my chair until I had gone through the last chapter. I sat up all night to read it through!"

"My friend Harvey is much obliged to you."

"I have one criticism to make, however. You dont object to criticism I hope! I like the book as a whole exceedingly—it is full of interest, every page of it—the character of Harvey is excellent too in most particulars—but there lies the difficulty—you have made one capital mistake in drawing Harvey's character!"

"Indeed, and what may that be?"

"Why, my dear sir, you have given the man no motive! The character is well drawn in other particulars; but so much the greater pity that you failed on that point. Just look at the facts; here is a man getting into all kinds of scrapes, running his neck into the noose, of his own accord, and where, pray, is his motive? Of course I thought until the last page, that he would be well paid for his services—but just as I expected to see it all made clear as day, he refuses to take the gold General Washington offers him. There was your great mistake—you should have given Harvey some motive!"

At a later day, when revising "The Spy" for the last edition, the author was dissatisfied with many things in his work, and once remarked that he should like to write it entirely anew. On several occasions he expressed a regret that he should have introduced General Washington, personally, into a work of fiction, veneration for the character of the great man increasing with his own years.

The following account of the Spy is given in Mr. Cooper's words:

"The author has often been asked if there were any foundation in real life, for the delineation of the principal character in this book. He can give no clearer answer to the question, than by laying before his readers a simple statement of the facts connected with its original publication.

"Many years since, the writer of this volume was at the residence of an illustrious man, who had been employed in various situations of high trust during the darkest days of the American Revolution. The discourse turned upon the effects which great political excitement produce on character, and the purifying consequences of a love of country, when that sentiment is powerfully and generally awakened in a people. He, who, from his years, his services, and his knowledge of men, was best qualified to take the lead in such a conversation, was the principal speaker. After dwelling on the marked manner in which the great struggle of the nation, during the war of 1775, had given a new and honorable direction to the thoughts and practices of multitudes whose time had formerly been engrossed by the most vulgar concerns of life, he illustrated his opinions by relating an anecdote, the truth of which he could attest as a personal witness.

" The dispute between England and the United States of America, though not strictly a family quarrel, had many of the features of a civil war. The people of the latter were never properly and constitutionally subject to the people of the former, but the inhabitants of both countries owed allegiance to a common king. The Americans, as a nation, disavowed this allegiance, and the English, choosing to support their sovereign in the attempt to regain his power, most of the feelings of an internal struggle were involved in the conflict. A large proportion of the emigrants from Europe, then established in the colonies, took part with the crown; and there were many districts in which their influence, united to that of the Americans who refused to lay aside their allegiance, gave a decided preponderance to the royal cause. America was then too young, and too much in need of every heart and hand, to regard these partial divisions, small as they were in actual amount, with indifference. The evil was greatly increased by the activity of the English in profiting by these internal dissensions; and it became doubly serious when it was found that attempts were made to raise various corps of provincial troops, who were to be banded with those from Europe, to reduce the young republic to subjection. Congress named an especial and a secret committee, therefore, for the express purpose of defeating this object. Of this committee Mr. ——, the narrator of the anecdote, was chairman.

" In the discharge of the novel duties which had now devolved on him, Mr. —— had occasion to employ an agent whose services differed but little from those of a common spy. This man, as will easily be understood, belonged to a condition in life which rendered him the least reluctant to appear in so equivocal a character. He was poor, ignorant, so far as the usual instruction was concerned; but cool, shrewd, and fearless by nature. It was his office to learn in what part of the country the agents of the crown were making their secret efforts to embody men, to repair to the place, enlist, appear zealous in the cause he affected to serve, and otherwise to get possession of as many of the secrets of the enemy as possible. The last he of course communicated to his employers, who took all the means in their power to counteract the plans of the English, and frequently with success.

" It will readily be conceived that a service like this was attended with great personal hazard. In addition to the danger of discovery, there was the daily risk of falling into the hands of the Americans themselves, who invariably visited sins of this nature more severely on the natives of the country than on the Europeans who fell into their hands. In fact, the agent of Mr. —— was several times arrested by the local authorities; and, in one instance, he was actually condemned by his exasperated countrymen to the gallows. Speedy and private orders to his gaoler alone saved him from an ignominious death. He was permitted to escape; and this seeming, and indeed actual peril was of great aid in supporting his assumed character among the English. By the Americans, in his little sphere,

he was denounced as a bold and inveterate tory.   In this manner he continued
to serve his country in secret during the early years of the struggle, hourly
environed by danger, and the constant subject of unmerited opprobrium.

"In the year ——, Mr.—— was named to a high and honorable employment
at a European court.   Before vacating his seat in Congress, he reported to that
body an outline of the circumstances related, necessarily suppressing the name of
his agent, and demanding an appropriation in behalf of a man who had been of
so much use, at so great risk.   A suitable sum was voted, and its delivery was
confided to the chairman of the secret committee.

"Mr.—— took the necessary means to summon his agent to a personal interview.   They met in a wood at midnight.   Here Mr. —— complimented his
companion on his fidelity and adroitness ; explained the necessity of their communications being closed ; and finally tendered the money.   The other drew
back, and declined receiving it.   "The country has need of all its means," he
said ; "as for myself, I can work, or gain a livelihood in various ways."   Persuasion was useless, for patriotism was uppermost in the heart of this remarkable
individual ; and Mr. —— departed, bearing with him the gold he had brought,
and a deep respect for the man who had so long hazarded his life, unrequited, for
the cause they served in common.

"The writer is under an impression that, at a later day, the agent of Mr. ——
consented to receive a remuneration for what he had done ; but it was not until
his country was entirely in a condition to bestow it.

"It is scarcely necessary to add, that an anecdote like this, simply but forcibly
told by one of its principal actors, made a deep impression on all who heard it.
Many years later, circumstances which it is unnecessary to relate, and of an
entirely adventitious nature, induced the writer to publish a novel, which proved
to be, what he little foresaw at the time, the first of a tolerably long series.   The
same adventitious causes which gave birth to the book, determined its scene and
its general character.   The former was laid in a foreign country ; and the latter
embraced a crude effort to describe foreign manners.   When this tale was published, it became matter of reproach among the author's friends, that he, an
American in heart as in birth, should give to the world a work which aided perhaps, in some slight degree, to feed the imagination of the young and unpractised
among his own countrymen, by pictures drawn from a state of society so different
from that to which he belonged.   The writer, while he knew how much of what
he had done was purely accidental, felt the reproach to be one that, in a measure,
was just.   As the only atonement in his power, he determined to inflict a second
book, whose subject should admit of no cavil, not only on the world, but on him-

self. He chose patriotism for his theme; and to those who read this introduction and the book itself, it is scarcely necessary to add, that he took the hero of the anecdote just related as the best illustration of his subject.

"Since the original publication of "The Spy," there have appeared several accounts of different persons who are supposed to have been in the author's mind while writing the book. As Mr. —— did not mention the name of his agent, the writer never knew any more of his identity with this or that individual than has been here explained. Both Washington and Sir Henry Clinton had an unusual number of secret emissaries; in a war that partook so much of a domestic character, and in which the contending parties were people of the same blood and language, it could scarcely be otherwise.

"The style of the book has been revised by the author in this edition. In this respect, he has endeavored to make it more worthy of the favor with which it has been received; though he is compelled to admit there are faults so interwoven with the structure of the tale that, as in the case of a decayed edifice, it would cost perhaps less to reconstruct than to repair. Five-and-twenty years have been as ages with most things connected with America. Among other advances, that of her literature has not been the least. So little was expected from the publication of an original work of this description, at the time it was written, that the first volume of "The Spy" was actually printed several months before the author felt a sufficient inducement to write a line of the second. The efforts expended on a hopeless task are rarely worthy of him who makes them, however low it may be necessary to rate the standard of his general merit.

"One other anecdote connected with the history of this book, may give the reader some idea of the hopes of an American author, in the first quarter of the present century. As the second volume was slowly printing, from manuscript that was barely dry when it went into the compositor's hands, the publisher intimated that the work might grow to a length that would consume the profits. To set his mind at rest, the last chapter was actually written, printed, and paged, several weeks before the chapters which precede it were even thought of. This circumstance, while it cannot excuse, may serve to explain the manner in which the actors are hurried off the scene.

"A great change has come over the country since this book was originally written. The nation is passing from the gristle into the bone, and the common mind is beginning to keep even pace with the growth of the body politic. The march from Vera Cruz to Mexico was made under the orders of that gallant soldier who, a quarter of a century before, was mentioned with honor in the last chapter of this very book. Glorious as was that march, and brilliant as were its results in a military point of view, a stride was then made by the nation, in a moral sense, that has hastened it, by an age, in its progress toward real independence and high political influence.   The guns that filled the valley of the Aztecs with their thunder, have been heard in echoes on the other side of the Atlantic, producing equally hope or apprehension.

"There is now no enemy to fear, but the one that resides within.   By accustoming ourselves to regard even the people as erring beings, and by using the restraints that wisdom has adduced from experience, there is much reason to hope that the same Providence which has so well aided us in our infancy, may continue to smile on our manhood.

"COOPERSTOWN, *March* 29, 1849."

The Spy: "Berry well now look him trough" he said,
peeping over the housekeeper's shoulder, as he held a
long lank candle of yellow tallow, in such a manner as
to throw its feeble light on the volume.

BIRCH IN HIS COTTAGE.

THE possessions of Mr. Wharton extended to some distance on each side of the house in which he dwelt, and most of his land was unoccupied. A few scattering dwellings were to be seen in different parts of his domains, but they were fast falling to decay, and were untenanted. The proximity of the country to the contending armies had nearly banished the pursuits of agriculture from the land. It was useless for the husbandman to devote his time, and the labor of his hands, to obtain over-flowing garners, that the first foraging party would empty. None tilled the earth with any other view than to provide the scanty means of subsistence, except those who were placed so near to one of the adverse parties as to be safe from the inroads of the light troops of the other. To these the war offered a golden harvest, more especially to such as enjoyed the benefits of an access to the royal army. Mr. Wharton did not require the use of his lands for the purposes of subsistence, and willingly adopted the guarded practice of the day, and limited his attention to such articles as were soon to be consumed within his own walls, or could be easily secreted from the prying looks of the foragers. In consequence, the ground on which the action was fought had not a single inhabited building, besides the one belonging to the father of Harvey Birch. This stood between the places where the cavalry had met, and the charge had been made on the party of Wellmere.

To Katy Haynes, it had been a day fruitful in incidents to furnish an inexhaustible theme to her after-life. The prudent housekeeper had kept her political feelings in a state of rigid neutrality; her own friends had espoused the cause of the country, but the maiden never lost sight of the moment when she herself was to be espoused to Harvey Birch. She did not wish to fetter the bonds of Hymen with any other clogs than those with which nature had already so amply provided them. Katy could always see enough to embitter the marriage bed, without calling in the aid of political contention; and yet, at times, the prying spinster had her doubts of which side she should be, to escape this dreaded evil. There was so much of practised deception in the conduct of the peddler, that the housekeeper frequently arrested her own words when most wishing to manifest her sympathy. His lengthened absences from home had commenced immediately after the hostile armies had made their appearance in the country; previously to that event, his returns had been regular and frequent.

The battle of the Plains had taught the cautious Washington the advantages possessed by his enemy, in organization, arms, and discipline. These were difficulties to be mastered by his own vigilance and care. Drawing off his troops to the heights, in the northern part of the county, he bid defiance to the attacks of the royal army, and Sir William Howe fell back to the enjoyments of his barren conquests, a deserted city and the adjacent islands. Never afterward did the opposing armies make the trial for success within the limits of Westchester; yet hardly a day passed that the partisans did not make their inroads; or a sunrise, that the inhabitants were spared the relation of the excesses that the preceding darkness had served to conceal. Most of the movements of the peddler through the country were made at the hours which others allotted to repose. The evening sun would frequently leave him at one extremity of the district, and the morning find him at the other. His pack was his never-failing companion, and there were those who closely studied him in his moments of traffic, who thought his only purpose was the accumulation of gold. He would be often seen near the Highlands with a body bending under the weight it carried; and again near the Harlem River, travelling, with lighter steps, with his face toward the setting sun. But these glances at him were uncertain and fleeting. The intermediate time no eye could penetrate. For months he disappeared, and no traces of his course were ever known.

Strong parties held the heights of Harlem, and the northern end of Manhattan Island was bristled with the bayonets of the English sentinels, yet the peddler glided among them unnoticed and uninjured. His approaches to the American lines were also frequent; but generally so conducted as to baffle pursuit. Many a sentinel, placed in the gorges of the mountains, spoke of a strange figure that had been seen gliding by them in the mists of the evening. The stories reached the ears of the officers, and, as we have related, in two instances, the trader fell into the hands of the Americans. The first time he escaped from Lawton, shortly after his arrest; but the second he was condemned to die. On the morning of his intended execution, the cage was opened, but the bird had flown. This extraordinary escape had been made from the custody of a favorite officer of Washington, and sentinels who had been thought worthy to guard the person of the commander-in-chief. Bribery and treason could not approach the characters of men so well esteemed, and the opinion gained ground among the common soldiery, that the peddler had dealings with the dark one. Katy, however, always repelled this opinion with indignation; for within the recesses of her own bosom, the housekeeper, in ruminating on the events, concluded that the evil spirit did not pay in gold. Nor, continues the wary spinster in her cogitations, does Washington; paper and promises were all that the leader of the American troops could dispense to his servants, until after the receipt of supplies from France; and even then, although the scrutinizing eyes of Katy never let any opportunity of examining into the deer-skin purse pass unimproved, she was never able to detect the image of Louis, intruding into the presence of the well-known countenance of George III.

The house of Harvey had been watched at different times by the Americans, with a view to his arrest, but never with success; the reputed spy possessed a secret means of intelligence, that invariably defeated their schemes. Once, when a strong body of the Continental army held the Four Corners for a whole summer, orders had been received from Washington himself, never to leave the door of Harvey Birch unwatched; the command was rigidly obeyed, and during this long period the peddler was unseen; the detachment was withdrawn, and the next night Birch re-entered his dwelling. The father of Harvey had been greatly molested, in consequence of the suspicious character of the son. But, notwithstanding the most minute scrutiny into the conduct of the old man, no fact could be substantiated against him to his injury, and his property was too small to keep alive the zeal of professed patriots; its confiscation and purchase would not reward them for their trouble. Age and sorrow were now about to spare him from further molestation, for the lamp of life had begun to be drained of its oil. The separation of the father and son had been painful, but in obedience to what both thought a duty. The old man had kept his situation a secret from the neighborhood, in order that he might have the company of his child in his last moments. The confusion of the past day, and his increasing dread that Harvey might be too late, helped to hasten the event he would fain arrest for yet a little while. As night set in, his illness increased to such a degree, that the dismayed housekeeper had sent a truant boy, who had been shut up with them for the day rather than trust himself in the presence of the combatants, to the Locusts, in quest of a companion to cheer her desolate situation. Cæsar was the only one who could be spared, and, loaded with eatables and cordials by the kind-hearted Miss Peyton, the black had been dispatched on this duty. The dying man was past the use of such articles, and his chief anxiety seemed to centre in a meeting with his absent child.

The noise of the chase had been heard by the group in the house, but its cause not understood; and as both the black and Katy were apprised of the detachment of American horse being below them, with its discontinuance all apprehension from this disturbance ceased. They heard the dragoons, as they moved slowly by the building, but in compliance with the prudent injunction of the black, the housekeeper forbore to indulge her curiosity by taking a view of the pageant. The old man had closed his eyes, and his attendants supposed him to be asleep. The house contained two large rooms, and as many small ones. One of the former served for kitchen and parlor; in the other, lay the father of Birch; of the latter, one was the sanctuary of the vestal, and the other contained the provisions for subsistence. A huge chimney of stone rose in the centre of the building, serving, of itself, for a partition between the larger rooms; and fire-places of corresponding dimensions were in each apartment. A bright fire was burning in that of the common room, and within the very jambs of its monstrous jaws sat Cæsar and Katy, at the time of which we write. The African was impressing his caution on the housekeeper to suppress an idle curiosity that might prove dangerous.

"Best nebber tempt a Satan," said Cæsar, rolling up his eyes significantly, till the whites glistened by the glare of the fire; "I like to lose an ear, only for carrying a little bit of a letter; but I wish Harvey get back."

"It is very disgraceful in him to be away at such times," said Katy, imposingly. "Suppose now his father wanted to make his last will in the testament, who is there to do such a thing for him? Harvey is a very wasteful and a very disregardful man."

"Perhaps he make him afore," said the black, inquiringly.

"It would not be a wonderment if he had," returned the housekeeper; "he is whole days looking into the Bible."

"Then he read a good book," said the black, solemnly. "Miss Fanny read him to Dinah berry often."

"Yes," continued the inquisitive spinster; "but he would not be forever studying it, if it didn't hold something more as common."

She rose from her seat, and stealing softly to a chest of drawers in the room where lay the sick, took from it a large Bible, heavily bound, and secured with strong clasps of brass, with which she returned to the expecting African. The volume was opened, and she proceeded instantly to the inquiry. Katy was far from an expert scholar, and to Cæsar the characters were absolutely strangers. For some time the housekeeper was occupied with finding out the word Matthew, which she at last saw in large Roman letters crowning one of the pages, and instantly announced her discovery to the attentive Cæsar.

"Berry well, now look him all through," said the black, peeping over the damsel's shoulder, as he held a long, lank candle of yellow tallow in his hand, in such a manner as to throw its feeble light on the volume.

"Yes, but I must begin with the book," replied the other, turning the leaves carefully back, until, moving two at once, she lighted upon a page covered with the labors of a pen. "Here," said the housekeeper with impatience, and shaking with the eagerness of expectation, "here is the very words themselves; now I would give the world to know who he has left them big silver shoe-buckles to."

"Read 'em," said Cæsar, laconically.

"And the black-walnut drawers; for Harvey could never want them."

"Why no want 'em as well as he fader?" asked the black, dryly.

"And the six silver tablespoons; for Harvey always uses the iron."

"I guess he say," continued the African, pointing significantly to the writing, and listening eagerly, as the other thus opened the store of the elder Birch's wealth.

Thus repeatedly advised, and impelled by her own curiosity, Katy commenced her task. Anxious to come to the part which most interested herself, she dipped at once into the centre of the subject.

"*Chester Birch, born September 1st*, 1754;" read the spinster, with great deliberation.

"Well," cried the impatient Cæsar, "what he give him?"

"*Abigail Birch, born July, 12th*, 1757;" continued the housekeeper, in the same tone.

"I guess he give her a spoons," interrupted the black.

"*June 1st*, 1760. *On this awful day, the judgment of an offended God lighted on my house——*" a heavy groan from the adjoining room made the spinster instinctively close the book, and Cæsar, for a moment, shook with fear. Neither possessed sufficient resolution to go and examine the condition of the sufferer, but his heavy breathing continued as usual. Katy dared not, however, reopen the Bible, and carefully securing its clasps, it was laid on the table in silence. Cæsar took his chair again, and after looking timidly round the room, remarked—

"I tought he 'bout to go."

"No," said Katy, solemnly, "he will live till the tide is out, or the first cock crows in the morning."

"Poor man!" continued the black, nestling still farther into the chimney corner; "I hope he lay quiet after he die."

"'Twould be no astonishment to me if he didn't," returned Katy, glancing her eyes round the room, and speaking in an under voice; "for they say an unquiet life makes an uneasy grave."

"Johny Birch a berry good man," said the black, quite positively.

"Ah! Cæsar," said the housekeeper, in the same voice, "he is good, only, who does good—can you tell me, Cæsar, why honestly-gotten gold should be hidden in the bowels of the earth?"

"If he know where he be, why don't he dig him up?" asked the black, promptly.

"There may be reasons not comprehendible to you," said Katy, moving her chair so that her clothes covered the charmed stone, underneath which lay the secret treasures of the peddler, unable to refrain speaking of that which she would have been very unwilling to reveal; "but a rough outside often holds a smooth inside." Cæsar stared around the building, unable to fathom the hidden meaning of the damsel, when his roving eyes suddenly became fixed, and his teeth chattered with affright. The change in the countenance of the black was instantly perceived by Katy, and turning her face, she saw the peddler himself, standing within the door of the room.

"Is he alive?" asked Birch, tremulously, and seemingly afraid to receive an answer to his own question.

"Surely," said the maiden, rising hastily and officiously offering her chair to the peddler, "he must live till day or the tide is down."

Disregarding all but her assurance, the peddler stole gently to the room of his dying parent. The tie which bound this father and son together was one of no ordinary kind. In the wide world they were all to each other. Had Katy but read a few lines farther in the record, she would have seen the sad tale of their misfortunes. At one blow competence and kindred had been swept from before them, and from that day to the present hour, persecution and distress had followed their wandering steps. Approaching the bedside, Harvey leaned his body forward, and said, in a voice nearly choked by his feelings:

"Father, do you know me?"

The parent slowly opened his eyes, and a smile of satisfaction passed over his pallid features, leaving behind it the impression of death in still greater force, by the contrast. The peddler gave a restorative he had brought with him to the parched lips of the sick man, and for a few minutes new vigor seemed to be imparted to his frame. He spoke, but slowly and with difficulty. Curiosity kept Katy silent; awe had the same effect on Cæsar; and Harvey seemed hardly to breathe, as he listened to the language of the departing spirit.

"My son," said the father, in a hollow voice, "God is as merciful as he is just; if I threw the cup of salvation from my lips when a youth, he graciously offers it to me in mine age. He chastiseth to purify, and I go to join the spirits of our lost family. In a little while, my child, you will be alone. I know you too well not to foresee you will be a lone pilgrim through life. The bruised reed may endure, but it will never rise. You have that within you, Harvey, that will guide you aright; persevere as you have begun, for the duties of life are never to be neglected—and——." A noise in the adjoining room interrupted the dying man, and the impatient peddler hastened to learn the cause, followed by Katy and the black. The first glance of his eye on the figure in the doorway told the trader but too well, both his errand, and the fate that probably awaited himself. The intruder was a man still young in years, but his lineaments bespoke a mind long agitated by evil passions. His dress was of the meanest materials, and so ragged and unseemly, as to give him the appearance of studied poverty. His hair was prematurely whitened, and his sunken, lowering eye, avoided the bold, forward look of innocence. There was a restlessness in his movements, and an agitation in his manner, that proceeded from the workings of the foul spirit within him, and which was not less offensive to others than distressing to himself. This man was a well-known leader of one of those gangs of marauders who infested the county with a semblance of patriotism, and were guilty of every grade of offence, from simple theft up to murder. Behind him stood several other figures clad in a similar manner, but whose countenances expressed nothing more than the callous indifference of brutal insensibility. They were all well armed with muskets and bayonets, and provided with the usual implements of foot soldiers. Harvey knew resistance to be vain, and quietly submitted to their directions. In the twinkling of an eye both he and Cæsar were stripped of their decent garments, and made to exchange clothes with two of the filthiest of the band. They were then placed in separate corners of the room, and, under the muzzles of the muskets, required faithfully to answer such interrogatories as were put to them.

"Where is your pack?" was the first question to the peddler.

"Hear me," said Birch, trembling with agitation; "in the next room is my father, now in the agonies of death; let me go to him, receive his blessing, and close his eyes, and you shall have all—aye, all."

"Answer me as I put the questions, or this musket shall send you to keep the old driveller company; where is your pack?"

"I will tell you nothing, unless you let me go to my father," said the peddler, resolutely.

His persecutor raised his arm with a malicious sneer, and was about to execute his threat, when one of his companions checked him, and cried—

"What would you do? you surely forget the reward. Tell us where are your goods, and you shall go to your father."

Birch complied instantly, and a man was dispatched in quest of the booty; he soon returned, throwing the bundle on the floor, swearing it was as light as feathers."

"Aye," cried the leader, "there must be gold somewhere for what it did contain; give us your gold, Mr. Birch; we know you have it; you will not take continental, not you."

"You break your faith," said Harvey, sullenly.

"Give us your gold," exclaimed the other, furiously, pricking the peddler with his bayonet until the blood followed his pushes in streams. At this instant a slight movement was heard in the adjoining room, and Harvey cried imploringly—

"Let me—let me go to my father, and you shall have all."

"I swear you shall go then," said the skinner.

"Here take the trash," cried Birch, as he threw aside the purse, which he had contrived to conceal, notwithstanding the change in his garments.

"The robber raised it from the floor with a hellish laugh, as he said coolly—

"Aye, but it shall be to your Father in heaven."

"Monster!" exclaimed Birch, "have you no feeling, no faith, no honesty?"

"Why, to hear him, one would think there was not a rope round his neck already," said the other, malignantly. "There is no necessity of your being uneasy, Mr. Birch;

if the old man gets a few hours the start of you in the journey, you will be sure to follow him before noon to-morrow."

This unfeeling communication had no effect on the peddler, who listened with gasping breath to every sound from the room of his parent, until he heard his own name spoken in the hollow, sepulchral tones of death. Birch could endure no more, but shrieking out—

"Father, hush—father, I come—I come:" he darted by his keeper, and was the next moment pinned to the wall by the bayonet of another. Fortunately, his quick motion had caused him to escape a thrust aimed at his life, and it was by his clothes only that he was confined.

"No, Mr. Birch," said the skinner, "we know you too well for a slippery rascal, to trust you out of sight—your gold, your gold."

"You have it," said the peddler, writhing with the agony of his situation.

"Ay, we have the purse; but you have more purses. King George is a prompt paymaster, and you have done him many a piece of good service. Where is your hoard? without it you will never see your father."

"Remove the stone underneath the woman," cried the peddler, eagerly—remove the stone."

"He raves, he raves," said Katy, instinctively, moving her position to another stone than the one on which she had been standing. In a moment it was torn from its bed, and nothing but earth was seen under it.

"He raves; you have driven him from his right mind," continued the trembling spinster, "would any man in his senses think of keeping gold under a hearth-stone?"

"Peace, babbling fool," cried Harvey. "Lift the corner stone, and you will find what will make you rich, and me a beggar."

"And then you will be depiseable," said the housekeeper, bitterly. "A peddler without goods and without money is sure to be despiseable."

"There will be enough left to pay for his halter," cried the skinner, as he opened upon a store of English guineas. These were quickly transferred to a bag, notwithstanding the declarations of the spinster, that her dues were unsatisfied, and that, of right, ten of the guineas should be her property.

Delighted with a prize that greatly exceeded their expectations, the band prepared to depart, intending to take the peddler with them, in order to give him up to some of the American troops above, and to claim the reward offered for his apprehension. Every thing was ready, and they were about to lift Birch in their arms, for he refused to move an inch, when a figure entered the room that appalled the group: around his body was thrown the sheet of the bed from which he had just risen, and his fixed eye and haggard face gave him the appearance of a being from another world. Even Katy and Cæsar thought it was the spirit of the elder Birch, and they both fled the house, followed by the alarmed skinners.

The excitement, which had given the sick man strength, soon vanished, and the peddler, lifting him in his arms, reconveyed him to his bed. The reaction of the system which followed hastened to close the scene.

The glazed eye of the father was fixed upon his son; his lips moved, but his voice was unheard. Harvey bent down, and, with his parting breath, received the dying benediction of his parent. A life of privation, of care, and of wrongs, embittered most of the future hours of the peddler. But under no sufferings, in no misfortunes, the subject of poverty and biting obloquy, the remembrance of that blessing never left him; it constantly gleamed over the images of the past, shedding a holy radiance around his saddest hours of despondency; it cheered the prospect of the future with the prayers of a pious spirit for his well-being; and it brought assurance to his soul, of having discharged faithfully and truly the sacred offices of filial love.

THE HIGHLANDS.

THEY now reached the highest point in their toilsome progress to the summit, and Frances seated herself on a rock to rest and to admire. Immediately at her feet lay a deep dell, but little altered by cultivation, and dark with the gloom of a November sunset. Another hill rose opposite to where she sat, at no great distance, along whose rugged sides nothing was to be seen but shapeless rocks, and oaks whose stinted growth proved the absence of soil.

To be seen in their perfection, the Highlands must be passed immediately after the fall of the leaf. The picture is then in its chastest keeping, for neither the scanty foliage which the summer lends the trees, nor the snows of winter, are present to conceal the minutest objects from the eye. Chilling solitude is the characteristic of the scenery, nor is the mind at liberty, as in March, to look forward to a renewed vegetation that is soon to check, without improving the view.

The day had been cloudy and cool, and thin fleecy clouds hung around the horizon, often promising to disperse, but as frequently disappointing the maid in her expectation of a parting beam from the setting sun. At length a solitary gleam of light struck on the base of the mountain on which she was gazing, and moved gracefully up its side, until, reaching the summit, it stood for a minute, forming a crown of glory to the sombre pile beneath. So strong were the rays, that what was before indistinct, now clearly opened to the view. With a feeling of awe at being thus unexpectedly admitted, as it were, into the secrets of that desert place, Frances gazed intently, until, among the scattered trees and fantastic rocks, something like a rude structure was seen. It was low, and so obscured by the color of its materials, that but for its roof, and the glittering of a window, it must have escaped her notice. While yet lost in the astonishment created by discovering a habitation for man in such a spot, on moving her eyes she perceived another object that increased her wonder. It apparently was a human figure, but of singular mould and unusual deformity. It stood on the edge of a rock but a little above the hut, and it was no difficult task for our heroine to fancy it was gazing at the vehicles that were ascending the side of the mountain beneath her. The distance, however, was too great for her to distinguish with precision. After looking at it a moment in breathless wonder, Frances had just come to the conclusion that it was ideal, and that what she saw was a part of the rock itself, when the object moved swiftly from its position, and glided into the hut, at once removing any doubts

The Spy: The Journey over the Highlands — Frances Wharton

as to the nature of either. Whether it was owing to the recent conversation that she had been holding with Katy, or to some fancied resemblance that she discerned, Frances thought, as the figure vanished from her view, that it bore a marked likeness to Birch, moving under the weight of his pack. She continued to gaze in breathless silence toward the mysterious residence, when the gleam of light passed away, and at the same instant the tones of a bugle rang through the glens and hollows, and were re-echoed in every direction. Springing on her feet in alarm, the maid heard the trampling of horses, and directly a party in the well-known uniform of the Virginians came sweeping round the point of a rock near her, and drew up at a short distance from where she stood. Again the bugle sounded a lively strain, and before the agitated girl had time to rally her thoughts, Dunwoodie dashed by the party of dragoons, threw himself from his charger, and advanced to the side of his mistress.

III.

THE PIONEERS.

THE earliest years of the author of "The Spy" were passed in the little village on the shores of Lake Otsego.   Although born at Burlington, he was carried when an infant a few weeks old, to the hamlet then growing up at the eastern sources of the Susquehanna.   His childish recollections were all closely connected with the forests and hills, the fresh clearings, new fields and homes on the banks of the Otsego.   It was here his boy's strength was first tried in those sports to which gray-headed men, amid the cares of later life, delight to look back.   From the first bow-and-arrow, kite, and ball, to later feats in fishing, riding, shooting, skating, all were connected with his highland home.   It was on the waters of the Otsego that he first learned to handle an oar, to trim a sail.   Healthy and active, he delighted in every exercise of the kind—a brave, blithe-hearted, impetuous, most generous and upright boy, as he is remembered by those who knew him in childhood.

Master Oliver Cory kept the village school in those days, and for many years later. He was a man remarkably well qualified for that honorable post, laborious, upright, firm in discipline, yet patient and kindly by nature. His training of the boys under his care was excellent. Every Saturday was devoted to religious instruction, while morals and manners were the subject of careful, though quiet attention on his part. Among his pupils was the youngest son of Judge Cooper, considered by his master as a very promising and intelligent lad. The school was kept in an ambitious edifice called the Academy, described as "one of those tasteless buildings that afflict all new countries." It served many different purposes in its day; political meetings, religious services and the public courts were held under its roof, varied by an occasional ball. Those were not the times of lectures or concerts. Master Cory and his pupils, however, seem to have had a taste for music; Judge Cooper had brought from Philadelphia a large upright barrel-organ, of more than common power and dignity of exterior, altogether the most imposing musical instrument which had yet found its way to the shores of the Otsego; it was put up in the hall of the mansion-house, where for years it went on playing reels, and country dances, almost every evening, to say nothing of its many graver performances. The arrival of this organ in the village, produced a sensation which might be compared to the appearance of some brilliant musical star, some *prima donna assoluta* in a large town, at the present day; when carefully put in its position, and duly prepared for performance, a sort of rehearsal was held; the weather was warm, the broad doors and ample windows of the house were all open as usual, and as Master Oliver Cory soon learned to his cost. The Academy stood on the street adjoining the grounds of Otsego Hall, and as the first strains of Hail Columbia poured into the school-room, the effect on the children was electrical, never before had they heard such music. Jenny Lind could scarcely have delighted the students of a German university in a higher degree. Astonishment, inattention, confusion, succeeded each other; at length disorder and disorganization threatened the whole school; fortunately Master Cory, equal to the emergency, saw clearly the only course to be taken:

"Boys, that organ is a remarkable instrument. You have never heard the like of it before. I give you half an hour's intermission; go into the street, and listen to the music!"

But Master Cory and his pupils were not always content to play audience; they chose to be performers themselves sometimes. Annual exhibitions took place, during which the Academy was thronged, to hear the speeches of Coriolanus and Iago, of Brutus and Cassius, delivered by raw lads from the village and adjoining farms, equipped in the local militia uniform, hats of the date of 1776, blue coats faced with red, and matross swords, exhibitions which are still a subject for merriment among the few who remember them. The future author of "The Pioneers," then a child some eight years old, was much commended on one of these occasions for his moving recitation of the "Beggars' Petition," in the character of an old man, wrapped in a faded cloak, and bending over his staff; it is to be feared that Master Cory, half a century later still indulged in certain emotions of undue pride when dwelling on the correctness of his little pupil's pathetic performance on that occasion.

Ere long, however, a school of higher aims, in the way of instruction, was deemed necessary. The youngest son of the house was sent from home. This first eventful journey was made under the care of a worthy farmer of the neighborhood, who was carrying toward the Hudson, a load of wheat, from the new fields of Otsego, then considered a great grain country. The route taken was the turnpike, a great western thoroughfare at that day, running between the valley of the Hudson and the Chenango River. This road had been only recently completed as far as Cherry Valley, and wonders were expected from it; the young traveller had heard this new triumph of civilization so much discussed at his father's table, by the gentlemen visiting at the house, that his curiosity to see it was extreme. Directors and stockholders were endeavoring to solve the difficult question of what should be done with the proceeds of the tolls, a dividend of ten per cent. being all that was allowed by the charter; stone bridges were planned; nay, some visionary spirits even talked of the necessity of lighting the road at night, as a means of disposing of the surplus fund. At length they arrived at the famous turnpike; the school-boy's eyes were gratified with actual observation of its magnificent breadth, its scientific construction, the directness of its course, the excellence of its condition—merits which to one who reached it by the primitive, irregular, corduroy tracks then the common highways of the region, were very impressive, indeed. As they trotted slowly along, the former pointed out among other marvels, the taverns which were springing up within sight of each other, throughout the sixty miles between Albany and Lake Otsego: "A tavern for every mile!" as it was boastfully proclaimed; a fact certainly remarkable, showing clearly as it does the very rapid strides with which civilization moved over new ground at that period. A long train of farm wagons, heavily laden with the precious wheat, then higher than ever in value, owing to the great European wars, were rolling slowly eastward, and the number of emigrant teams, crowded with growing families and household gear, moving in the opposite direction toward the lake shores, were all full of interest for the young traveller, and seemed to promise ample prosperity to the new road, and the county. But, alas for the great turnpike; its track is now quiet and all but deserted, its toll-gates have been thrown down, its stone bridges were never built, its lamps were never lighted! Traffic from the quiet shores of the Otsego now moves northward, following the trail of the old Indian portage toward the valley of the Mohawk. In 1798, there was movement enough, however, on the new road to render it no unworthy approach to the capital of the state. Ere long the young traveller reached Albany.

He was set down at the door of St. Peter's Rectory. Here he became a pupil of the Rev. Mr. Ellison, an English clergyman of high scholarship, who received three or four boys into his family. The young lad from Otsego soon became a favorite with his tutor, who took pleasure in instructing him. Had Mr. Ellison lived, his pupil's career might have been different; though it is scarcely probable that one so active in body, as well as in mind, would have been satisfied with the quiet and comparative monotony of a student's life. In 1802, Mr. Ellison died. His pupil soon after entered Yale College, at the early age of thirteen. At the close of three years more he went to sea, his first voyages being made before the mast, to England and to Spain. In 1805, he entered the navy. Some years later his marriage gave him an interest in another part of the country; but in all the wanderings of early life, and still at a later day, the home of his childhood, the highland valley where his father's hearth-stone lay, was never forgotten by him.

And now that a new career was opening before him, his eyes were again turned toward the forest-clad hills at the sources of the Susquehanna. The Spy was just finished; the glow of success was still fresh upon him when he again resolved to "try one more book!" The new narrative, like that which had preceded it, was to be connected in one sense with the history of the country; it should follow the first steps of civilization in its conquests over the wilderness, and its scenes should be enacted in the valley of the Otsego. Affection for the ground, interest in the people, the pleasing character of the natural scenery, all united to point out the banks of the highland lake as fitting frame-work for his pictures. The new book was immediately commenced, and Natty Bumppo, with his silent footfall, stepped from beneath the shadows of the old pines into the winter sunlight.

There was an old hunter by the name of Shipman living in the Otsego hills during the first years of the little colony, who came frequently to offer his game at Judge Cooper's door, and whose rude equipment, dogs, and rifle, had much attraction for the lads of the house. But even then, at the close of the first ten or fifteen years of clearing, game was no longer as abundant as it had been. The wild creatures were already bounding away before the sound of the axe. Occasionally, it is true, a bear was seen feasting on the wild fruits which usually grow in profusion on the borders of newly-cleared ground, or mayhap he was surprised by the hunters in one of the shallow caves of those hills, where he had lain down for his long winter nap. The peculiar wailing cry of the sharp-toothed panther, so like the voice of woman in distress, was still heard at times by the wanderer on the quiet wood-roads. Now and then the howl of the wolf came across the icy field of the Otsego, in the winter nights. The deer lingered last; they were not unfrequently seen, bounding through the forest, or drinking at familiar springs, during the first three or four years of this century. One autumn day, the future author of "The Pioneers," then a pupil under Master Cory's charge, was at play in his father's garden, when suddenly he was surprised by a deer which came leaping over the fence from the street, almost brushing his face, as it bounded away into the pine-wood in the rear of the house, dogs and men in hot pursuit. The incident was even then so unusual as to make a great impression on the boy. In after years, when walking with his children over the same ground, Mr. Cooper repeatedly spoke of it. And this is said to have been one of the last of those beautiful creatures driven in chase through the village, and over ground where so very lately they had roamed at will. They still continued, however, to be hunted among the hills, and in the lake, for several years longer. At length they gradually took flight, retreating to the wilder mountains to the southward, where Shipman and his brother hunters were compelled to follow them, or else exchange the rifle for the axe. A vague recollection of Shipman seems to have lingered in the mind of the writer, and to have suggested the idea of the principal character in "The Pioneers." And yet to call this man the original of Natty Bumppo, would be clearly an error. The assertion is true only just so far as the barest resemblance in outline may go—in pursuit, something in rude accoutrement, and in the ground over which they both hunted. Here all similarity ceases. In every higher sense of the words, the character of Natty is wholly original; in all that gives worth, and dignity, and poetry, and soul, to the conception, it comes in full freshness and freedom, direct from the mind of the author.

Many of the figures filling the canvas of "The Pioneers" are said to have once lived on the same ground. But there is no one instance in which this assertion is strictly true. There is no character in the book which the writer aimed at copying closely from real life; some vague resemblance may be traced here and there, but in most instances the personages are wholly fictitious. Classes were represented, and not individuals.

Chingachgook, old Indian John, is supposed to have been drawn from life; but this again is an error. The character is imaginary. The head-waters of the Susquehanna were favorite hunting-ground with the neighboring tribes, but they had no permanent village on the ground. Their forts, or "castles," as these were so strangely miscalled by the whites, and their burial-places, lay on either hand, north or south, in the valley of the Mohawk, or on the southern banks of the Susquehanna. They did not, therefore, linger on the shores of the Otsego, as at some other points; when the white man appeared with his team, his plough, and his axe, they abandoned their canoes on the lake, gave up its choice fish to his steel hook and twine net, and followed the flying game farther toward the setting sun; or, in diminished numbers, they still wandered to and fro, over ground rendered sacred to them by older traditions connected with their lodges, and the graves of their fathers. Occasionally only they came in family groups, or in small parties, to taste the bass, or tap the maples in the forest, during the first years of the village. But it is not known that any one individual remained long enough to fill the position ascribed to Chingachgook in "The Pioneers."

An Indian alarm, however, occurred quite as a matter of course in connection with the early days of most American frontier hamlets. In the annals of the village, the year 1794, or that following the date given in the opening chapter of "The Pioneers," is especially remembered for an incident of this kind. A large party of Indians—of what tribe, we are not told—were seen lurking in the woods within a short march of the village. As they did not show themselves openly, but sought or affected concealment, their movements naturally excited suspicion. Their numbers were, of course, exaggerated; the women and children were thrown into great alarm, and some of the good people seem to have actually feared a repetition of the horrors of Cherry Valley, so thoroughly impressed on the household memories of the county.

It was deemed prudent to take steps for defence; weapons were prepared for action, and scouts were sent out into the woods to watch the red men. Meanwhile, with well-barred doors and windows, the women and children were gathered in their homes. Suddenly, in the dead of night, the report of firearms was heard, and the tramp of horse and foot passed along the quiet street. Had the scouts returned! Were the Indians upon them! The whole village was aroused and thrown into strange alarm. The men hurried into the street to face a possible foe; they were met by a party of constables, who had gone out in pursuit of a gang of counterfeiters, and now, returning at midnight with their prisoners, had fired off their pistols on entering the village, thus throwing the little community into great agitation. It was not until the next day that the alarm subsided. The Indians, not long after, passed noiselessly on their way through the forest; the object of their approach was never known. This is said to have been the last occasion on which the red men drew near the village in sufficient numbers to assume in any way the aspect of a war-party, moving over old forest pathways of their own, so long familiar to their race, but now wholly effaced by the plough of the white man. Whatever may have been their object, whatever feeling of secret enmity may have lurked in their hearts, this party could never have actually plotted any work of general violence against the little colony; the day for massacre had wholly passed away. The horrors of Cherry Valley dated nearly twenty years back in time, and a century in facts.

It has been said that the character of Mr. Grant, the missionary, was drawn from life. The assertion is entirely unfounded. The author of "The Pioneers" had much too strong a personal regard for the venerable clergyman supposed to be referred to under the name of Mr. Grant, to have wished to introduce him into a work of fiction. On the contrary, he has filled the position actually occupied by him with a figure purely imaginary, and, in many personal particulars, directly the opposite of Father Nash. The trials and difficulties of missionary life at that day, on frontier ground, were great; and probably not one of his brethren suffered more privations from poverty, and the many hardships of a new country, than the venerable man whose sincere piety, earnest zeal, courage, and perseverance were greatly blessed to the many parishes of that region, springing up under his laborious itinerant ministry. But between Mr. Grant, the missionary of "The Pioneers," and Father Nash, there is absolutely no resemblance whatever to be traced, beyond that of position, and the peculiar trials connected with it. This was precisely what the writer aimed at representing, purposely avoiding any approach to individual portraiture of character or person. A single glance at the household circle of each will show how little the author of "The Pioneers" aimed at presenting his honored friend to the public under a feigned name; instead of being the sad, subdued, bereaved man, with one living child remaining of a large family, which Mr. Grant is represented, Father Nash, at the same period of his missionary labors, full of life and vigor himself, was blessed with a most worthy and diligent wife, and surrounded with a large flock of young children, most of whom survived him.

In one particular, however, the trials of real life were even greater, perhaps, than those of the fictitious narrative. It seems to us, of the present hour, almost incredible that suffering for want of food should have ever been known, by any but the very improvident, in this land of plenty. Such, however, was not the case. Scarcity was repeatedly felt by all during the first years of settlement, more especially by the families of the farmers, living beyond the village; and it is well known that the poor missionary family suffered severely in this way, on more than one occasion. There were those at hand however, always ready to offer relief, where privation was known. The most severe trial of this kind occurred during the season still remembered as "the starving time," in the traditions of the country, and which fell upon the whole region, for many miles beyond the lake shores. It was at an early day when the green fields were yet very few, when there were no roads through the forest, and no mills to grind the little corn among the stores of the colonists. The hamlet was then literally in the heart of a wilderness, and the number of newly arrived emigrants increasing beyond the amount of food within reach, something approaching to actual famine was felt in many a cabin. Families accustomed to abundance, in the homes they had left farther eastward, were now pining for the want of daily bread, the poor hungry children feeding on the scrapings of the iron pots in which their sapaen had been prepared. In this emergency, the leader of the little colony exerted himself to the utmost; grain was purchased at a distance, brought up the Mohawk in boats, thence on pack horses through the forest, from Canajoharie and Fort Plain, out dealt and liberally to the people. Most happily shoals of herring came up the Susquehanna, from the Chesapeake, at the same moment, filling the lake so abundantly, that they were actually dipped out of the water, by the bucketful. Salt was sent for in great quantities, and the fish were cured, and carried into the cabins of the people, scattered through the neighboring woods. The pigeons also came in large flocks, and after a period of great distress for some weeks, plenty was once more restored to the half famished people.

The number of foreigners finding their way to the shores of this quiet inland
lake at that early day, was quite remarkable. Among these, were several Frenchmen, driven from their own country by the terrors of the Revolution. A few
incidents of border life, connected with their history are given in the words of
Mr. Cooper:

"In the course of the winter of 1789–90, during one of the periodical visits
of Colonel Frey [Colonel Hendrick Frey, of Frey's Bush, on the Mohawk], a
large lumber-sleigh was fitted out, with four horses, and the whole party sallied
out upon the lake, for a morning drive. An ex-officer of the French army, a
Monsieur Ebbal, resided by himself, on the western bank of the lake. Perceiving the sleigh, and four horses approaching his house, this gentleman with the
courtesy of his nation, went forth upon the ice, to greet the party, of whose
character he was not ignorant, by the style in which it appeared. Mr. Cooper
invited his French friend to join him, promising him plenty of game, with copious
libations of Madeira, by way of inducement. Though a good table companion in
general, no persuasion could prevail on the Frenchman to accept the offer that
day, while, provoked by his obstinacy, the party laid violent hands on him, and
brought him to the village by force.

"Monsieur Ebbal took his captivity in good part, and was soon as buoyant
and gay as any of his companions. He habitually wore a long-skirted surtout,
which at that time was almost a mark of a Frenchman, and this surtout he pertinaciously refused to lay aside, even when he took his seat at table. On the contrary, he kept it buttoned to the very throat, as it might be in defiance. The
Christmas joke, a plentiful board, and abundant potations, however, threw the
guest off his guard. Warmed with wine and the blazing fire, he incautiously
unbuttoned; when his delighted companions discovered that the accidents of a
frontier life, the establishment of a bachelor who kept no servant, and certain irreg-
ularities in washing-days, that were attendant on both circumstances, coupled with
his *empressement* to salute his friends, had induced the gallant Frenchman to come
abroad without a shirt. He was uncased on the spot, amid the roars of the

convives, and incontinently put into linen. "Cooper was so polite," added the mirth-loving Hendrick Frey, when he repeated the story for the hundredth time, ' that he supplied a shirt with ruffles at the wristbands, which made Ebbal very happy for the rest of the evening. How his hands did go, after he got the ruffles !'

"These wags told Monsieur Ebbal, that if chased by a bear, the most certain mode of escape was to throw away his hat or his coat, to induce the animal to stop and smell at it, and then to profit by the occasion, and climb a sapling that was too small to enable his enemy to fasten its claw in it, in the way it is known to ascend a tree. The advice was well enough ; but the advised having actually an occasion to follow it the succeeding autumn, scrambled up a sapling first, and began to throw away his clothing afterward. The bear, a she one, with cubs, tore to pieces garment after garment, without quitting the spot, keeping poor Ebbal treed throughout a cool autumnal night, almost as naked as when he uncased at the celebrated Christmas banquet. It appears that the real name of this person was *L'Abbe de Raffcourt*."

* * * * * * *

"In 1801, a man dressed in a sailor's jacket, without stockings, or neckcloth, but cleanly, and otherwise of respectable appearance, and who seemed of middle age, presented himself to Judge Cooper, with a request to know whether a small piece of low meadow land, that lies between ' Fenimore' and the village, was to be sold. The answer was in the affirmative, but the applicant was informed that on account of its position, the price would be relatively high, amounting to a considerable sum. The stranger requested that a deed might immediately be made of it, and he counted down the money, in gold, giving his name as Esaias Hausman. Mr. Hausman left the hall the owner of the lot in question, which has ever since been known as the ' Hausman lot.' The habits, attainments and character of this man soon attracted attention. He spoke five or six of the living languages, and had a tolerable knowledge of the classics. He lived entirely alone, in a small house he had caused to be built on his purchase, and in the rudest manner. Occasionally he would disappear, and his absences sometimes extended to months. He frequently spoke of his past life, though it is not known that he ever gave any explicit or connected history of his origin, or of the events that led him to America. According to his own account of his adventures, he had served in the French imperial army, and he was once heard to say that the death of Robespierre alone saved him from the block. Casual remarks of this kind increased curiosity, when Hausman became more reserved, and soon ceased to touch at all on the events of his past life. Some time about the year 1805, he had been absent for several months, when it was discovered that he was teaching Hebrew to the president of one of the Eastern Colleges. This occupation did not last long, however, for he was soon back again, in his hut on the lake shore. In this manner, this singular man passed many years, apparently undetermined in his purposes, rude, and even coarse in many of his habits, but always cour. teous and intelligent. He died at Herkimer, in 1812, and without making any revelations concerning himself, or his family. As he died intestate, his property escheated, the lot on the lake shore being sold by the public. It is said that a considerable sum in gold was found in a purse, worn between his shoulder-blades.

" Nothing farther was ever known of Esaias Hausman. He was certainly shrewd and observant, and his acquisitions, which were a little exaggerated, probably, by vulgar report, were of that kind which denote, in Europe, a respect-able education. He had not the appearance or manner of a Polish gentleman, though he called himself a Pole, and the most probable conjecture concerning him, a conjecture which we believe is sustained by some of his own remarks, made him a Jew. The name is German, but the people of that persuasion often assume new appellations."

    *   *   *   *   *   *   *

" M. Le Quoy excited a good deal of interest during his stay in the place, as he was a man altogether superior to his occupation, which was little more than that of a country grocer ; an interest that was much increased by the following circumstance.

" Among the early settlers in Otsego county was M. Louis de Villers, a French gentleman of respectable extraction and good manners. M. de Villers was at Cooperstown, about the year 1793, at a moment when a countryman, a M. Renouard, who afterward established himself in the county, had recently reached the place. M. Renouard was a seaman, and had the habit of using tobacco. Inquiring of M. de Villers where he could make a purchase of the weed, M. de Villers directed him to the shop of M. Le Quoy, telling him he could help a countryman by making his purchase there. In a few minutes M. Renouard returned from the shop, agitated and pale. M. de Villers inquired if he were unwell. ' Who is the man who sold me this tobacco ?' demanded M. Renouard. ' M. Le Quoy is a countryman of ours. ' Yes ; M. Le Quoy de Mersereau !' ' I know nothing about the de Mersereau ; he calls himself Le Quoy. Do you know any thing of him ?' ' When I went to Martinique, to be port-captain of St Pierre,' answered M. Renouard, ' this man was the civil governor of the island, and refused to confirm my appointment.'

"Subsequent inquiry confirmed this story, M. Le Quoy explaining that the influence of a lady had stood in the way of M. Renouard's preferment.

"The history of M. Le Quoy has since been ascertained to be as follows: When governor of Martinique, he had it in his power to do a friendly office to Mr. John Murray, of New York, by liberating one of his ships; Mr. Murray being at the head of the old and highly respectable commercial house of John Murray and Sons, then one of the principal firms of the country, this act brought about an exchange of civilities between Mr. Murray and M. Le Quoy, which continued for years. When the French Revolution drove M. Le Quoy from the island, he repaired to New York, and sought his friend Mr. Murray, to whom he stated that he had a small sum of money, which he wished to invest in a country store, until his fortunes might revive. Between Mr. Murray and Judge Cooper there existed an intimacy, and to the latter gentleman M. Le Quoy was referred. Under the advice of Judge Cooper, M. Le Quoy established himself in Cooperstown, where he remained a year or two. At the end of that time he made his peace with the new French government, and quitting his retreat, he was employed for some months in superintending the accounts of the different French consulates in this country. It is said that he soon after returned to Martinique in his old capacity, and died the first season of yellow fever. . . . The following letter appears to have been written by him soon after he left Cooperstown, and at the moment he commenced his consular duties:

"'PHILADELPHIA, *October* 10, 1794.

" ' DEAR SIR :—I have experienced too much of your friendship to believe you will not hear of my fate with some degree of concern. I am to go to Charleston, S. C., about some business which will keep me most all the winter. I hope for a more permanent employment than what I have at present; if not, I know where to find peace, good business, good friends. I shall always consider you among the number.

" 'I wish you and all your family health and happiness.

" ' And I remain, dear sir, your most humble servant,

" ' F. T. LE QUOY.

" 'MONS. W. COOPER, in Cooperstown, Otsego county.' "

The singular name of this gentleman, who is said to have died without representatives, was given to the French emigrant of "The Pioneers," the character of the latter, however, was entirely imaginary

In the chapter selected for this volume from "The Pioneers," the reader will find an allusion to a piece of artillery, very famous in its day among the good people on the lake shores, and to whose report the Otsego hills have a thousand times re-echoed on days of rejoicing. This was the "Cricket," so thoroughly enjoyed by all the lads of the village.

The following account of the "Cricket" is given in Mr. Cooper's words:

"The present site of Cooperstown is connected with an event of some interest, which occurred during the war of the Revolution. An expedition having been commanded to proceed under the orders of General Sullivan, against the Indians who then dwelt in the vicinity of Seneca Lake, a brigade employed in the duty, under Brigadier-General James Clinton, father of the celebrated De Witt Clinton, marched from Albany for that purpose. After ascending the Mohawk as far as Fort Plain, this brigade cut a road through the forest to the head of Lake Otsego, whither it transported its boats. Traces of this road exist, and are still known by the name of the Continental Road. Embarking at the head of the lake, the troops descended to the outlet, where they encamped on the site of the present village. General Clinton's quarters are said to have been in a small building of hewn logs, which then stood in what are now the grounds of Otsego Hall, and which it is thought was erected by Colonel Croghan, as a place in which he might hold his negotiations with the Indians, as well as for a commencement of the settlement.

"This building, which was about fifteen feet square, and intended for a sort of block-house, was undoubtedly the first ever erected on this spot. It was subsequently used by some of the first settlers as a dwelling, and by Judge Cooper as a smoke-house. There were found the graves of two white men in the same grounds, which were believed to contain the bodies of deserters, who were shot at the time the troops were encamped there. These graves are supposed to have been the first of any civilized men in the township of Otsego. All traces of them have now disappeared.

"As soon as encamped, the troops of General Clinton commenced the construction of a dam at the outlet, and when the water had risen to a sufficient height in the lake, the obstruction was removed, the current clearing the bed of the river of flood-wood. After a short delay for this purpose, the troops embarked and descended the river as far as the junction with the Tioga, where they were met by another brigade commanded by General Sullivan in person. On this occasion the Susquehanna below the dam is said to have been so much reduced that a man could jump over it. Traces of the dam still exist, and for many years they were very obvious.

"At a later day, in digging the cellar of the house first occupied by Judge Cooper, a large iron swivel was discovered, which was said to have been buried by the troops, who found it was useless for their service. This swivel was the only piece of artillery used for the purposes of salutes and merry-makings in the vicinity of Cooperstown for years after the settlement of the country. It is well and affectionately remembered by the name of the "Cricket," and was bursted lately in the same good cause of rejoicing on the fourth of July. At the time of its final disaster, for it met with many vicissitudes by field and flood, having actually been once thrown into the lake, it is said that there was no very perceptible difference in size between its touch-hole and its muzzle."

With a few more remarks from Mr. Cooper's pen, these notes to "The Pioneers" must close:

"In order to prevent mistake, it may be well to say that the incidents of this tale are purely a fiction. The literal facts are chiefly connected with the natural and artificial objects, and the customs of the inhabitants. The academy, and court-house, and jail, and inn, and most similar things, are tolerably exact. They have all, long since, given place to buildings of a better character. There is some liberty taken with the truth in the description of the principal dwelling; the real building had no 'firstly' or 'lastly.' It was of bricks, and not of stone; and its roof exhibited none of the beauties of the 'composite order.' It was erected in an age too primitive for that ambitious school of architecture. But the author indulged his recollections freely when he had fairly entered the door. Here all is literal, even to the severed vase of Wolfe, and the urn which held the ashes of Queen Dido."

"The author has elsewhere said that the character of Leather-Stocking is a creation, rendered probable by such auxiliaries as were necessary to produce that effect. Had he drawn still more upon fancy, the lovers of fiction would not have so much cause for their objections to his work. Still the picture would not have been in the least true, without some substitute for most of the other personages. The great proprietor resident on his lands and giving his name to, instead of receiving it from his estates, as in Europe, is common over all New York. The physician with his theory, rather obtained than corrected by experiments on the human constitution; the pious, self-denying, laborious, and ill-paid missionary; the half-educated, litigious, envious, and disreputable lawyer, with his counterpoise, a brother of the profession, of better origin and of better character; the shiftless, bargaining, discontented seller of his "betterments;" the plausible carpenter, and most of the others, are familiar to all who have ever dwelt in a new country."

"It may be well to say here, a little more explicitly, that there was no intention to describe with particular accuracy any real characters in this book. It has been repeatedly said—and in published statements—that the heroine of this book was drawn after a sister of the writer, who was killed by a fall from a horse now nearly half a century since. So ingenious is conjecture, that a personal resemblance has been discovered between the fictitious character and the deceased relative. It is scarcely possible to describe two females of the same class in life, who would be less alike, personally, than Elizabeth Temple and the sister of the author, who met with the deplorable fate mentioned. In a word, they were as unlike in this respect as in history, character, and fortunes."

"Circumstances rendered this sister singularly dear to the author. After a lapse of half a century, he is writing this paragraph with a pain that would induce him to cancel it, were it not still more painful to have it believed that one whom he regarded with a reverence that surpassed the love of a brother, was converted by him into the heroine of a work of fiction."

"From circumstances which, after this introduction, will be obvious to all, the author has had more pleasure in writing "The Pioneers" than the book will, probably, ever give any of its readers. He is quite aware of its numerous faults, some of these he has endeavored to repair in this edition; but, as he has, in intention, at least—done his full share in amusing the world, he trusts to its good nature for overlooking this attempt to please himself."

NATTY BUMPPO'S CAVE.

PIGEON-SHOOTING.

From this time to the close of April, the weather continued to be a succession of great and rapid changes. One day, the soft airs of spring would seem to be stealing along the valley, and, in unison with an invigorating sun, attempting, covertly, to rouse the dormant powers of the vegetable world; while on the next, the surly blasts from the north would sweep across the lake, and erase every impression left by their gentle adversaries. The snow, however, finally disappeared, and the green wheat-fields were seen in every direction, spotted with the dark and charred stumps that had, the preceding season, supported some of the proudest trees of the forest. Ploughs were in motion, wherever those useful implements could be used, and the smokes of the sugar-camps were no longer seen issuing from the summits of the woods of maple. The lake had lost all the characteristic beauty of a field of ice, but still a dark and gloomy covering concealed its waters, for the absence of currents left them yet hid under a porous crust, which, saturated with the fluid, barely retained enough of its strength to preserve the contiguity of its parts. Large flocks of wild geese were seen passing over the country, which hovered, for a time, around the hidden sheet of water, apparently

The Pioneers: "It's far easier to call names than to hit a buck on the spring; but the cretur came by his end from a younger hand than either yourn or mine as I said before."

searching for an opening, where they might find a resting-place; and then, on finding themselves excluded by the chill covering, would soar away to the north, filling the air with their discordant screams, as if venting their complaints at the tardy operations of nature.

For a week, the dark covering of the Otsego was left to the undisturbed possession of two eagles, who alighted on the centre of its field, and sat proudly eyeing the extent of their undisputed territory. During the presence of these monarchs of the air, the flocks of migrating birds avoided crossing the plain of ice, by turning into the hills, apparently seeking the protection of the forests, while the white and bald heads of the tenants of the lake were turned upward, with a look of majestic contempt, as if penetrating to the very heavens with the acuteness of their vision. But the time had come when even these kings of birds were to be dispossessed. An opening had been gradually increasing, at the lower extremity of the lake, and around the dark spot where the current of the river had prevented the formation of ice, during even the coldest weather; and the fresh southerly winds, that now breathed freely up the valley, obtained an impression on the waters. Mimic waves began to curl over the margin of the frozen field, which exhibited an outline of crystallizations, that slowly receded toward the north. At each step the power of the winds and the waves increased, until, after a struggle of a few hours, the turbulent little billows succeeded in setting the whole field in an undulating motion, when it was driven beyond the reach of the eye, with a rapidity that was as magical as the change produced in the scene by this expulsion of the lingering remnant of winter. Just as the last sheet of agitated ice was disappearing in the distance, the eagles rose over the border of crystals, and soared with a wide sweep far above the clouds, while the waves tossed their little caps of snow into the air, as if rioting in their release from a thraldom of five months' duration.

The following morning Elizabeth was awakened by the exhilarating sounds of the martins, who were quarrelling and chattering around the little boxes that were suspended above her windows, and the cries of Richard, who was calling, in tones as animating as the signs of the season itself—

"Awake! awake! my lady fair! the gulls are hovering over the lake already, and the heavens are alive with the pigeons. You may look an hour before you can find a hole through which to get a peep at the sun. Awake! awake! lazy ones! Benjamin is overhauling the ammunition, and we only wait for our breakfasts, and away for the mountains and pigeon-shooting."

There was no resisting this animated appeal, and in a few minutes Miss Temple and her friend descended to the parlor. The doors of the hall were thrown open, and the mild, balmy air of a clear spring morning was ventilating the apartment, where the vigilance of the ex-steward had been so long maintaining an artificial heat with such unremitted diligence. The gentlemen were impatiently waiting for their morning's repast, each being equipt in the garb of a sportsman. Mr. Jones made many visits to the southern door, and would cry—

"See, cousin Bess! see, 'duke, the pigeon-roosts of the south have broken up! They are growing more thick every instant. Here is a flock that the eye cannot see the end of. There is food enough in it to keep the army of Xerxes for a month, and feathers enough to make beds for the whole county. Xerxes, Mr. Edwards, was a Grecian king, who—no, he was a Turk, or a Persian, who wanted to conquer Greece, just the same as these rascals will overrun our wheat-fields, when they come back in the fall. Away! away! Bess; I long to pepper them from the mountain."

In this wish both Marmaduke and young Edwards seemed equally to participate, for the sight was most exhilarating to a sportsman; and the ladies soon dismissed the party, after a hasty breakfast.

If the heavens were alive with pigeons, the whole village seemed equally in motion, with men, women, and children. Every species of fire-arms, from the French ducking-gun, with its barrel of near six feet in length, to the common horseman's pistol, was to be seen in the hands of the men and boys; while bows and arrows, some made of the simple stick of a walnut sapling, and others in a rude imitation of the ancient cross-bows, were carried by many of the latter.

The houses and the signs of life apparent in the village, drove the alarmed birds from the direct line of their flight, toward the mountains, along the sides and near the bases of which they were glancing in dense masses, that were equally wonderful by the rapidity of their motion, as by their incredible numbers.

We have already said, that across the inclined plane which fell from the steep ascent of the mountains to the banks of the Susquehanna, ran the highway, on either side of which a clearing of many acres had been made at a very early day. Over those clearings, and up the eastern mountain, and along the dangerous path that was cut into its side, the different individuals posted themselves, as suited their inclinations; and in a few moments the attack commenced.

Among the sportsmen was to be seen the tall, gaunt form of Leather-Stocking, who was walking over the field, with his rifle hanging on his arm, his dogs following close at his heels, now scenting the dead or wounded birds, that were beginning to tumble from the flocks, and then crouching under the legs of their master, as if they participated in his feelings at this wasteful and unsportsmanlike execution.

The reports of the fire-arms became rapid, whole volleys rising from the plain, as flocks of more than ordinary numbers darted over the opening, covering the field with darkness, like an interposing cloud; and then the light smoke of a single piece would issue from among the leafless bushes on the mountain, as death was hurled on the retreat of the affrighted birds, who were rising from a volley, for many feet into the air, in a vain effort to escape the attacks of man. Arrows, and missiles of every kind, were seen in the midst of the flocks; and so numerous were the birds, and so low did they take their flight, that even long poles, in the hands of those on the sides of the mountain, were used to strike them to the earth.

During all this time, Mr. Jones, who disdained the humble and ordinary means of destruction used by his companions, was busily occupied, aided by Benjamin, in making arrangements for an assault of a more than ordinary fatal character. Among the relics of the old military excursions, that occasionally are discovered throughout the different districts of the western part of New York, there had been found in Templeton, at its settlement, a small swivel, which would carry a ball of a pound weight. It was thought to have been deserted by a war-party of the whites, in one of their inroads into the Indian settlements, when, perhaps, their convenience or their necessities induced them to leave such an incumbrance behind them in the woods. This miniature cannon had been released from the rust, and being mounted on little wheels, was now in a state for actual service. For several years, it was the sole organ for extraordinary rejoicings that was used in those mountains. On the mornings of the Fourths of July, it would be heard, with its echoes ringing among the hills, and telling forth its sounds, for thirteen times, with all the dignity of a two-and-thirty pounder; and even Captain Hollister, who was the highest authority in that part of the country on all such occasions, affirmed that, considering its dimensions, it was no despicable gun for a salute. It was somewhat the worse for the service it had performed, it is true, there being but a trifling difference in size between the touch-hole and the muzzle. Still, the grand conceptions of Richard had suggested the importance of such an instrument, in hurling death at his nimble enemies. The swivel was dragged by a horse into a part of the open space, that the sheriff thought most eligible for planting a battery of the kind, and Mr. Pump proceeded to load it. Several handfuls of duck-shot were placed on top of the powder, and the major-domo soon announced that his piece was ready for service.

The sight of such an implement collected all the idle spectators to the spot, who, being mostly boys, filled the air with their cries of exultation and delight. The gun was pointed on high, and Richard, holding a coal of fire in a pair of tongs, patiently took his seat on a stump, awaiting the appearance of a flock that was worthy of his notice.

So prodigious was the number of the birds, that the scattering fire of the guns, with the hurling of missiles, and the cries of the boys, had no other effect than to break off small flocks from the immense masses that continued to dart along the valley, as if the whole creation of the feathered tribe were pouring through that one pass. None pretended to collect the game, which lay scattered over the fields in such profusion as to cover the very ground with the fluttering victims.

Leather Stocking was a silent but uneasy spectator of all these proceedings, but was able to keep his sentiments to himself until he saw the introduction of the swivel into the sports.

"This comes of settling a country!" he said—"here have I known the pigeons to fly for forty long years, and, till you made your clearings, there was nobody to skear or to hurt them. I loved to see them come into the woods, for they were company to a body; hurting nothing; being, as it was, as harmless as a garter-snake. But now it gives me sore thoughts when I hear the frighty things whizzing through the air, for I know it's only a motion to bring out all the brats in the village at them. Well! the Lord won't see the waste of his creaters for nothing, and right will be done to the pigeons, as well as others, by and by. There's Mr. Oliver, as bad as the rest of them, firing into the flocks as if he was shooting down nothing but the Mingo warriors."

Among the sportsmen was Billy Kirby, who, armed with an old musket, was loading, and without even looking into the air, was firing and shouting as his victims fell even on his own person. He heard the speech of Natty, and took upon himself to reply—

"What's that, old Leather-Stocking?" he cried, "grumbling at the loss of a few pigeons!" If you had to sow your wheat twice, and three times, as I have done, you wouldn't be so massyfully feeling'd to'ards the divils. Hurrah, boys! scatter the feathers. This is better than shooting at a turkey's head and neck, old fellow."

"It's better for you, maybe, Billy Kirby," replied the indignant old hunter, "and all them as don't know how to put a ball down a rifle-barrel, or how to bring it up ag'in with a true aim; but it's wicked to be shooting into flocks in this wasty manner; and none do it, who know how to knock over a single bird. If a body has a craving for pigeon's flesh, why! it's made the same as all other creater's, for man's eating, but not to kill twenty and eat one. When I want such a thing, I go into the woods till I find one to my liking, and then I shoot him off the branches without touching a feather of another, though there might be a hundred on the same tree. But you couldn't do such a thing, Billy Kirby—you couldn't do it if you tried."

"What's that you say, you old, dried cornstalk! you sapless stub!" cried the wood-chopper. "You've grown mighty boasting, sin' you killed the turkey; but if you're for a single shot, here goes at that bird which comes on by himself."

The fire from the distant part of the field had driven a single pigeon below the flock to which it had belonged, and, frightened with the constant reports of the muskets, it was approaching the spot where the disputants stood, darting first from one side, and then to the other, cutting the air with the swiftness of lightning, and making a noise with its wings, not unlike the rushing of a bullet. Unfortunately for the wood-chopper, notwithstanding his vaunt, he did not see his bird until it was too late for him to fire as it approached, and he pulled his trigger at the unlucky moment when it was darting immediately over his head. The bird continued its course with incredible velocity.

Natty lowered the rifle from his arm, when the challenge was made, and, waiting a moment, until the terrified victim had got in a line with his eyes, and had dropped near the bank of the lake, he raised it again with uncommon rapidity, and fired. It might have been chance, or it might have been skill, that produced the result; it was probably a union of both; but the pigeon whirled over in the air, and fell into the lake, with a broken wing. At the sound of his rifle, both his dogs started from his feet, and in a few minutes the "slut" brought out the bird, still alive.

The wonderful exploit of Leather-Stocking was noised through the field with great rapidity, and the sportsmen gathered in to learn the truth of the report.

"What," said young Edwards, "have you really killed a pigeon on the wing, Natty, with a single ball?"

"Haven't I killed loons before now, lad, that dive at the flash?" returned the hunter. "It's much better to kill only such as you want, without wasting your powder and lead, than to be firing into God's creaters in such a wicked manner. But I come out for a bird, and you know the reason why I like small game, Mr. Oliver, and now I have got one I will go home, for I don't relish to see these wasty ways that you are all practysing, as if the least thing wasn't made for use, and not to destroy."

"Thou sayest well, Leather-Stocking," cried Marmaduke, "and I begin to think it time to put an end to this work of destruction."

"Put an ind, judge, to your clearings. An't the woods his work as well as the pigeons? Use, but don't waste. Wasn't the woods made for the beasts and birds to harbor in? and when man wanted their flesh, their skins, or their feathers, there's the place to seek them. But I'll go to the hut with my own game, for I wouldn't touch one of the harmless things that kiver the ground here, looking up with their eyes on me, as if they only wanted tongues to say their thoughts."

With this sentiment in his mouth, Leather-Stocking threw his rifle over his arm, and, followed by his dogs, stepped across the clearing with great caution, taking care not to tread on one of the wounded birds that lay in his path. He soon entered the bushes on the margin of the lake, and was hid from view.

Whatever impression the morality of Natty made on the judge, it was utterly lost on Richard. He availed himself of the gathering of the sportsmen, to lay a plan for one "fell swoop" of destruction. The musket-men were drawn up in battle array, in a line extending on each side of his artillery, with orders to await the signal of firing from himself.

"Stand by, my lads," said Benjamin, who acted as an aide-de-camp on this momentous occasion; "stand by, my hearties, and when Squire Dickens heaves out the signal for to begin firing, d'ye see, you may open upon them in a broadside. Take care and fire low, boys, and you'll be sure to hull the flock."

"Fire low!" shouted Kirby—"hear the old fool! If we fire low, we may hit the stumps, but not ruffle a pigeon."

"How should you know, you lubber?" cried Benjamin, with a very unbecoming

heat for an officer on the eve of battle—"how should you know, you grampus?
Haven't I sailed aboard of the Boadishy for five years? and wasn't it a standing order
to fire low, and to hull your enemy? Keep silence at your guns, boys, and mind the
order that is passed."

The loud laughs of the musket-men were silenced by the authoritative voice of
Richard, who called to them for attention and obedience to his signals.

Some millions of pigeons were supposed to have already passed, that morning, over
the valley of Templeton; but nothing like the flock that was now approaching had
been seen before. It extended from mountain to mountain in one solid blue mass, and
the eye looked in vain over the southern hills to find its termination. The front of this
living column was distinctly marked by a line but very slightly indented, so regular
and even was the flight. Even Marmaduke forgot the morality of Leather-Stocking as
it approached, and, in common with the rest, brought his musket to his shoulder.

"Fire!" cried the sheriff, clapping his coal to the priming of the cannon. As half
of Benjamin's charge escaped through the touch-hole, the whole volley of the musketry
preceded the report of the swivel. On receiving this united discharge of small arms,
the front of the flock darted upward, while, at the same instant, myriads of those in
their rear rushed with amazing rapidity into their places, so that when the column of
white smoke gushed from the mouth of the little cannon, an accumulated mass of objects was gliding over its point of direction. The roar of the gun echoed along the
mountains, and died away to the north, like distant thunder, while the whole flock of
alarmed birds seemed, for a moment, thrown into one disorderly and agitated mass.
The air was filled with their irregular flights, layer rising over layer, far above the tops
of the highest pines, none daring to advance beyond the dangerous pass; when,
suddenly, some of the leaders of the feathered tribe shot across the valley, taking their
flight directly over the village, and the hundreds of thousands in their rear followed
their example, deserting the eastern side of the plain to their persecutors and their
fallen.

"Victory!" shouted Richard, "victory! we have driven the enemy from the field."

"Not so, Dickon," said Marmaduke; "the field is covered with them; and, like
the Leather-Stocking, I see nothing but eyes, in every direction, as the innocent sufferers
turn their heads, in terror, to examine my movements. Full one half of those that have
fallen are yet alive: and I think it is time to end the sport; if sport it be."

"Sport!" cried the sheriff; it is princely sport! There are some thousands of the
blue-coated boys on the ground, so that every old woman in the village may have a
pot-pie for the asking."

Well, we have happily frightened the birds from this side of the valley," said
Marmaduke, "and our carnage must of necessity end, for the present. Boys, I will
give you a sixpence a hundred for the pigeons' heads only: so go to work, and bring
them into the village, where I will pay you."

This expedient produced the desired effect, for every urchin on the ground went industriously to work to wring the necks of the wounded birds. Judge Temple retired toward his dwelling with that kind of feeling, that many a man has experienced before him, who discovers, after the excitement of the moment has passed, that he has purchased pleasure at the price of misery to others. Horses were loaded with the dead; and, after the first burst of sporting, the shooting of pigeons became a business, for the remainder of the season, more in proportion to the people. Richard, however, boasted for many a year, of his shot with the "cricket;" and Benjamin gravely asserted, that he thought they killed nearly as many pigeons on that day, as there were Frenchmen destroyed on the memorable occasion of Rodney's victory.

IV.

THE PILOT.

THE idea of writing a romance connected with the sea, was accidentally suggested by a conversation at the table of Mr. Charles Wilkes. The author of Waverley had recently published "The Pirate," and, as usual with every fresh volume from his pen, the book and its characters entered largely into the table-talk of the hour. The admiration of the landsmen of the party was much excited by the nautical passages of the narrative; and some of the guests doubted whether Sir Walter Scott, the legal man, the poet of past centuries, could have drawn marine touches so correctly; the fact was given as a reason for doubting his identity with the author of Waverley. No man admired the genius of Sir Walter Scott more than the author of "The Pioneers;" but on this occasion he maintained the opinion that "The Pirate" was not thoroughly satisfactory to a nautical reader; he added that a man accustomed to ships, and the sea, could have accomplished far more with the same materials as those employed in "The Pirate." His companions differed from him; they considered the proportion of nautical matter as a proof of the author's skill; they held that similar scenes introduced very freely into a work of fiction must necessarily become tedious from their monotony, that they could not long be made really interesting to the general reader; professional men might take pleasure in them, but for a landsman, occasional passages by way of brief episodes, admitted for the sake of novelty and variety, must always be sufficient. More than this must necessarily become an error of judgment in any work of fiction. Mr. Cooper opposed this view of the subject with his usual spirit and animation. He admitted that as yet very little had been done in the way of nautical fiction; but he maintained that a work of this nature, with the scene laid on the ocean, whose machinery should be ships and the waves, whose principal characters should be seamen, acting and talking as such, might be written with perfect professional accuracy, and yet possess equal interest with a similar book connected with the land. The general opinion of the company was very strongly against him. And in a conversation on the same subject with his host, prolonged after they had left table, the same views were very clearly expressed by Mr. Wilkes, for whose general taste and judgment Mr. Cooper had the highest respect. On this occasion, however, the friends differed. Before the conversation had turned to other subjects, Mr. Cooper had already resolved to prove the justness of his own opinion, although no declaration to that effect was made. The same evening, on his way home from the house of Mr. Wilkes, the outline of a nautical romance was vaguely sketched in his own mind.

"I must write one more book—a sea tale—to show what can be done in this way by a sailor!" he exclaimed, little foreseeing that the freshly-planned story should be only the first of a series of similar narratives.

It was the intention to blend history and nautical fiction in the new work—or to introduce at least some one striking historical character, believing that the reader's attention could thus be more readily attracted. No necessity for any such historical figure would seem really to have existed; at a later day many were the incidents of sea life to which the same pen gave deep interest, and in which the characters were all imaginary. The new book, however, was to be a first attempt, a bold experiment with elements as yet untried. It was conceived necessary to connect with the narrative some historical name which should give it importance, and for the same reason the struggles of the Revolution were chosen for the date of the tale. The nautical annals of that period were brief, and a rapid glance was sufficient to show that among the historical figures of the time, that of the bold adventurer Paul Jones stood prominent as one of the few adapted to a work of fiction. His cruise in the Ranger, and his singularly daring descents upon Whitehaven and St. Mary's Isle, suggested the plot of "The Pilot."

Two ships, a frigate, and a schooner, were chosen as the nautical machinery of the tale. The name of the larger vessel was purposely omitted, with the idea of vaguely connecting her cruise, in the reader's mind, with that of some one of the few American men-of-war of the same date. To the schooner he gave the name of the Ariel, so well adapted to the peculiar character of an American craft of that size. Let us open the volume and see with what prospect of success the two vessels are first brought into view:

" ' But wha ha ye gotten here? That chiel has an ow'r liking to the land for a seafaring body ; an' if the bottom o' the sea be any thing like the top o' it, he's in grat danger o' a shipwrack !'

"This unexpected change in the discourse drew all eyes on the object toward which the staff of the observant drover was pointed. To the utter amazement of every individual present, a small vessel was seen moving slowly round a point of land that formed one of the sides of the little bay, to which the field in which the laborers were, composed the other. There was something very peculiar in the externals of this unusual visitor, which added in no small degree to the surprise created by her appearance in that retired place. None but the smallest vessels, and those rarely, or at long intervals a desperate smuggler, were ever known to venture so close to the land, amid the sand-bars and sunken rocks with which that immediate coast abounded. The adventurous mariners who now attempted this dangerous navigation in so wanton, and, apparently, so heedless a manner, were in a low black schooner, whose hull seemed utterly disproportioned to the raking masts it upheld, which, in their turn, supported a lighter set of spars, that tapered away until their upper extremities appeared no larger than the lazy pennant that in vain endeavored to display its length in the light breeze.

"The short day of that high northern latitude was already drawing to a close, and the sun was throwing his parting rays obliquely across the waters, touching the gloomy waves here and there with streaks of pale light. The stormy winds of the German Ocean were apparently lulled to rest ; and, though the incessant rolling of the surge on the shore heightened the gloomy character of the hour and the view, the light ripple that ruffled the sleeping billows was produced by a gentle air, that blew directly from the land. Notwithstanding this favorable circumstance, there was something threatening in the aspect of the ocean, which was speaking in hollow, but deep murmurs, like a volcano on the eve of an eruption, that greatly heightened the feelings of amazement and dread with which the peasants beheld this extraordinary interruption to the quiet of their little bay. With no other sails spread to the action of the air than her heavy mainsail, and one of those light jibs that projected far beyond her bows, the vessel glided over the water with a grace and a facility that seemed magical to the beholders, who turned their wondering looks from the schooner to each other in silent amazement. At length, the drover spoke in a low, solemn voice—

" ' He's a bold chiel that steers her ! And if that bit craft has wood in her bottom, like the brigantines that ply between Lon'on and the Frith o' Leith, he's more in danger than a prudent man could wish. Ay ! he's by the big rock that shows his head when the tide runs low, but it's no mortal mon who can steer long in the road he's journeying, and not speedily find land wi' water a top o't.'

"The little schooner, however, still held her way among the rocks and sand-pits, making such slight deviations in her course as proved her to be under the direction of one who knew his danger, until she had entered as far into the bay as prudence could at all justify, when her canvas was gathered into folds, seemingly without the agency of hands, and the vessel, after rolling for a few minutes on the long billows that hove in from the ocean, swung round in the currents of the tide, and was held by her anchor.

"The peasants now began to make their conjectures more freely concerning the character and objects of their visitor; some intimating that she was engaged in contraband trade, and others that her views were hostile, and her business war. A few dark hints were hazarded on the materiality of her construction, for nothing of artificial formation, it was urged, would be ventured by men in such a dangerous place, at a time when even the most inexperienced landsmen were enabled to foretell the certain gale. The Scotchman, who, to all the sagacity of his countrymen added no small portion of their superstition, leaned greatly to the latter conclusion, and had begun to express this sentiment warily and with reverence, when the child of Erin, who appeared not to possess any very definite ideas on the subject, interrupted him, by exclaiming—

"'Faith! there's two of them! A big and a little! Sure the bogles o' the sea likes good company the same as any other Christians.'

"'Twa!' echoed the drover; 'twa! Ill luck bides o' some o' ye. Twa craft a sailing without hand to guide 'em, in sic a place as this, whar eyesight is na guid enough to show the dangers, bodes evil, to a' that luik thereon. Hoot! she's na the yearling, the tither! Luik! mon, luik! she's a gallant boat and a gr'at!' He paused, raised his pack from the ground, and first giving one searching look at the objects of his suspicions, he nodded with great sagacity to the listeners, and continued, as he moved slowly toward the interior of the country: 'I should na wonder if she carried King George's commission about her; weel, weel, I wull journey, and ha' a crack wi' the guid mon; for they craft have a suspeecious aspect, and the sma' bit thing wu'ld nab a mon quite easy, and the big one wu'ld hold us a', and no feel we war' in her.'

"This sagacious warning caused a general movement of the party, for the intelligence of a hot press was among the rumors of the times. The husband-men collected their implements of labor, and retired homeward; and though many a curious eye was bent on the movements of the vessels, from the distant

hills, but very few of those not immediately interested in the mysterious visitors
ventured to approach the rocky cliffs that lined the bay.

"The vessel that caused these cautious movements was a gallant ship, whose
huge hull, lofty masts, and square yards, loomed in the evening haze, above the
sea, like a distant mountain, rising from the deep. She carried but little sail, and
though she warily avoided the near approach to the land that the schooner had
attempted, the similarity of their movements was sufficiently apparent to warrant
the conjecture that they were employed on the same duty. The frigate, for the
ship belonged to this class of vessels, floated across the entrance of the little
bay majestically, in the tide, with barely enough motion through the water to
govern her movements, until she arrived opposite to the place where her consort
lay, when she hove up heavily into the wind, squared the enormous yards on her
mainmast, and attempted, in counteracting the power of her sails by each other,
to remain stationary; but the light air, that had at no time swelled her heavy
canvas to the utmost, began to fail, and the long waves that rolled in from the
ocean ceased to be ruffled with the breeze from the land. The currents and
billows were fast sweeping the frigate toward one of the points of the estuary,
where the black heads of the rocks could be seen running far into the sea, and, in
their turn, the mariners of the ship dropped an anchor to the bottom, and drew
her sails in festoons to the yards. As the vessel swung round to the tide, a heavy
ensign was raised to her peak, and a current of air opening for a moment its folds,
the white field and red cross that distinguish the flag of England, were dis-
played to view."

"The Pilot" was written in New York in 1823, and published by Mr. Charles

Wiley, on the 29th of December of that year. There could be no doubt as to its success. All that interest which the writer had believed it possible to throw around a naval narrative, was fully aroused; the opinion declared some months earlier at the table of Mr. Wilkes was proved to be correct. The pictures placed before the reader were drawn with so much spirit and poetical feeling, with so much clearness and fidelity, as to command attention, and fill the public mind for the moment. The success of the book in England was also decided. Ere long, indeed, the tale was translated into French, and German, and Italian, in spite of the many technical difficulties of the subject—a most convincing proof of the interest of the work; the flag of the little Ariel was carried triumphantly into the Bay of Biscay, aye, into the classic waters of the Mediterranean.

With the character of Paul Jones, as given in "The Pilot," Mr. Cooper, at a later day, was himself dissatisfied. It was not sufficiently true to reality. The pilot of the frigate was represented as a man of higher views and aims, in a moral sense, than the facts of the life of Paul Jones would justify. The commander of the Ranger was in truth a bold and daring adventurer, a skilful seaman, a brave partisan, an ambitious man—but he was scarcely the enthusiast in private feeling, in political views, described in the pilot of the frigate. The author would gladly have severed entirely the slight historical link between the two, and left the pilot as vaguely connected with the annals of the country, as the ship he steered.

With Long Tom Coffin, also, he was, in his own last years, less satisfied than many of his readers. As he looked back at the character, in the maturity of long experience, he saw it with a clearer view, a greater fulness of conception, a more complete finish of detail—he considered it as a sketch only, and would gladly have wrought up the sketch of the old salt, a man after his own heart, to a finished picture, as he has done with Natty Bumppo. Of the two characters he considered that of Boltrope better, perhaps, as a piece of workmanship than that of the old Nantucket hero.

A few remarks on the origin of "The Pilot," given in Mr. Cooper's words, are inserted here:

"It is probable a true history of human events would show that a far larger proportion of our acts are the results of sudden impulses and accident, than of that reason of which we so much boast. However true or false this opinion may be in more important matters, it is certainly and strictly correct as relates to the conception and execution of this book.

"'The Pilot' was published in 1823. This was not long after the appearance of 'The Pirate,' a work which it is hardly necessary to remind the reader has a direct connection with the sea. In a conversation with a friend, a man of polished taste and extensive reading, the authorship of the Scottish novels came under discussion. The claims of Sir Walter were a little distrusted, on account of the peculiar and minute information that the romances were then very generally thought to display. 'The Pirate' was cited as a very marked instance of this universal knowledge, and it was wondered where a man of Scott's habits and associations could have become so familiar with the sea. The writer had frequently observed that there was much looseness in this universal knowledge, and that the secret of its success was to be traced to the power of creating that *vraisemblance*, which is so remarkably exhibited in those world-renowned fictions, rather than to any very accurate information on the part of their author. It would have been hypercritical to object to 'The Pirate' that it was not strictly nautical or true in its details; but, when the reverse was urged as a proof of what, considering the character of other portions of the work, would have been most extraordinary attainments, it was a sort of provocation to dispute the seamanship of 'The Pirate,' a quality to which the book has certainly very little just pretension. The result of this conversation was a sudden determination to produce a work which, if it had no other merit, might present truer pictures of the ocean and ships than any that are to be found in 'The Pirate.' To this unpremeditated decision, purely an impulse, is not only 'The Pilot' due, but a tolerably numerous school of nautical romances that have succeeded it.

"The author had many misgivings concerning the success of the undertaking, after he had made some progress in the work; the opinions of his different friends being any thing but encouraging. One would declare that the sea could not be made interesting; that it was tame, monotonous, and without any other movement than unpleasant storms, and that, for his part, the less he got of it the better. The women very generally protested that such a book would have the odor of bilge-water, and that it would give them the *maladie de mer*. Not a single individual among all those who discussed the merits of the project, within the range of the author's knowledge, either spoke or looked encouragingly. It is probable that all these persons anticipated a signal failure.

"So very discouraging did these ominous opinions get to be, that the writer was, once or twice, tempted to throw his manuscript aside, and turn to something new. A favorable opinion, however, coming from a very unexpected quarter, put a new face on the matter, and raised new hopes. Among the intimate friends of the writer, was an Englishman, who possessed most of the peculiar qualities of the educated of his country. He was learned even, had a taste that was so just as always to command respect, but was prejudiced, and particularly so in all that related to this country and its literature. He could never be persuaded to admire Bryant's 'Water-Fowl,' and this mainly because if it were accepted as good poetry, it must be placed at once amongst the finest fugitive pieces of the language. Of the 'Thanatopsis' he thought better, though inclined to suspect it of being a plagiarism. To the tender mercies of this one-sided critic, who had never affected to compliment the previous works of the author, the sheets of a volume of 'The Pilot' were committed, with scarce an expectation of his liking them. The reverse proved to be the case—he expressed himself highly gratified, and predicted a success for the book which it probably never attained.

"Thus encouraged, one more experiment was made, a seaman being selected for the critic. A kinsman, a namesake, and an old messmate of the author, one now in command on a foreign station, was chosen, and a considerable portion of the first volume was read to him. There is no wish to conceal the satisfaction with which the effect on this listener was observed. He treated the whole matter as fact, and his criticisms were strictly professional and perfectly just. But the interest he betrayed could not be mistaken. It gave a perfect and most gratifying assurance that the work would be more likely to find favor with nautical men, than with any other class of readers."

In the pages chosen for illustration of "The Pilot," the reader will find brought together two very different chapters from the same pen. In the first is given the historical record of the celebrated battle of the Bon Homme Richard, one of the most remarkable in the brief annals of American naval warfare, and written with all the conscientious accuracy of detail which was in the power of the historian to give it. The second passage is drawn from one of the opening chapters of "The Pilot," the first of many storm scenes sketched by the same hand. The reader may be interested in comparing the two—history and fiction flowing in parallel, yet thoroughly distinct currents, from the same pen.

BATTLE OF THE BON HOMME RICHARD.

THE pilot-boat had hardly left the Bon Homme Richard when the leading ships of a fleet of more than forty sail were seen stretching out from behind Flamborough Head, on a bowline, evidently with the intention of turning down toward the Straits of Dover. From previous intelligence this fleet was immediately known to contain the Baltic ships, under the convoy of the Serapis, forty-four, Captain Richard Pearson, and a hired ship that had been put into the king's service, called the Countess of Scarborough. The latter was commanded by Captain Piercy, and mounted twenty-two guns. As the interest of the succeeding details will chiefly centre in the Serapis and the Richard, we shall give a more minute account of the actual force of the former.

At the period of which we are now writing, forty-fours were usually built on two decks. Such, then, was the construction of this ship, which was new, and had the reputation of being a fast vessel. On her lower gun-deck she mounted twenty eighteen-pound guns; on her upper gun-deck, twenty nine-pound guns; and on her quarter-deck and forecastle, ten six-pound guns; making an armament of fifty guns in the whole. She had a regularly trained man-of-war's crew of three hundred and twenty souls, fifteen of whom, however, were said to have been Lascars.

When the squadron made this convoy, the men-of-war were inshore astern and to leeward, probably with a view to keep the merchantmen together. The bailiffs of Scarborough, perceiving the danger into which this little fleet was running, had sent a boat off to the Serapis to apprise her of the presence of a hostile force, and Captain Pearson fired two guns, signaling the leading vessels to come under his lee. These orders were disregarded, however, the headmost ships standing out until they were about a league from the land.

J. Hamilton fecit

J. M. Griffin Sculpt

The Pilot: Wreck of the Ariel

Commodore Jones having ascertained the character of the fleet in sight, showed a signal for a general chase, another to recall the lieutenant in the pilot-boat, and crossed royal yards on board the Richard. These signs of hostility alarmed the nearest English ships, which hurriedly tacked together, fired alarm guns, let fly their top-gallant sheets, and made other signals of the danger they were in, while they now gladly availed themselves of the presence of the ships-of-war, to run to leeward, or sought shelter closer in with the land. The Serapis, on the contrary, signaled the Scarborough to follow, and hauled boldly out to sea, until she had got far enough to windward, when she tacked and stood inshore again, to cover her convoy.

The Alliance being much the fastest vessel of the American squadron, took the lead in the chase, speaking the Pallas as she passed. It has been proved that Captain Landais told the commander of the latter vessel on this occasion, that if the stranger proved to be a fifty, they had nothing to do but to endeavor to escape. His subsequent conduct fully confirmed this opinion, for no sooner had he run down near enough to the two English vessels-of-war to ascertain their force, than he hauled up and stood off from the land again. All this was not only contrary to the regular order of battle, but contrary to the positive command of Commodore Jones, who had kept the signal to form a line abroad, which should have brought the Alliance astern of the Richard, and the Pallas in the van. Just at this time the Pallas spoke the Richard, and inquired what station she should take, and was also directed to form the line. But the extraordinary movements of Captain Landais appear to have produced some indecision in the commander of the Pallas, as he too, soon after tacked, and stood off from the land. Captain Cottineau, however, was a brave man, and subsequently did his duty in the action, and this manœuvre has been explained by the Richard's hauling up suddenly for the land, which induced him to think that her crew had mutinied and were running away with the ship. Such was the want of confidence that prevailed in a force so singularly composed, and such were the disadvantages under which this celebrated combat was fought!

So far, however, from meditating retreat or mutiny, the people of the Bon Homme Richard had gone cheerfully to their quarters, although every man on board was conscious of the superiority of the force with which they were about to contend; and the high, unconquerable spirit of the commander appears to have communicated itself to the crew.

It was now getting to be dark, and Commodore Jones was compelled to follow the movements of the enemy by the aid of a night-glass. It is probable that the obscurity which prevailed added to the indecision of the commander of the Pallas, for from this time until the moon rose, objects at a distance were distinguished with difficulty, and even after the moon appeared, with uncertainty. The Richard, however, stood steadily on, and about half-past seven, she came up with the Serapis, the Scarborough being a short distance to leeward. The American ship was to windward, and as she drew slowly near, Captain Pearson hailed. The answer was equivocal, and both ships delivered their entire broadsides nearly simultaneously. The water being so smooth, Commodore Jones had relied materially on the eighteens that were in the gun-room; but at this discharge two of the six that were fired bursted, blowing up the deck above, and killing or wounding a large proportion of the people that were stationed below. This disaster caused all the heavy guns to be instantly deserted, for the men had no longer sufficient confidence in their goodness to use them. It, at once, reduced the broadside of the Richard to about a third less than that of her opponent, not to include the disadvantage of the manner in which the metal that remained was distributed among light guns. In short, the combat was now between a twelve-pounder and an eighteen-pounder frigate; a species of contest in which, it has been said, we know not with what truth, the former has never been known to prevail. Commodore Jones informs us himself, that all his hopes, after this accident, rested on the twelve-pounders that were under the command of his first lieutenant.

The Richard, having backed her topsails, exchanged several broadsides, when she filled again, and shot ahead of the Serapis, which ship luffed across her stern and came up on the weather quarter of her antagonist, taking the wind out of her sails, and, in her turn, passing ahead. All this time, which consumed half an hour, the cannonading was close and furious. The Scarborough now drew near, but it is uncertain whether she fired or not. On the side of the Americans it is affirmed that she raked the Richard at least once; but, by the report of her own commander, it would appear that, on account of the obscurity and the smoke, he was afraid to discharge his guns, not knowing which ship might be the friend, or which the foe. Unwilling to lie by, and to be exposed to shot uselessly, Captain Piercy edged away from the combatants, exchanged a broadside or two, at a great distance, with the Alliance, and shortly afterward was engaged at close quarters by the Pallas, which ship compelled him to strike, after a creditable resistance of about an hour.

Having disposed of the inferior ships, we can confine ourselves to the principal combatants. As the Serapis kept her luff, sailing and working better than the Richard, it was the intention of Captain Pearson to pay broad off across the latter's forefoot, as soon as he had got far enough ahead; but making the attempt, and finding he had not room, he put his helm hard down to keep clear of his adversary, when the double movement brought the two ships nearly in a line, the Serapis leading. By these uncertain evolutions, the English ship lost some of her way, while the American, having kept her sails trimmed, not only closed, but actually ran aboard of her antagonist, bows on, a little on her weather quarter. The wind being light, much time was consumed in these different manœuvres, and near an hour had elapsed between the firing of the first guns, and the moment when the vessels got foul of each other in the manner just described.

The English now thought that it was the intention of the Americans to board them, and a few minutes passed in the uncertainty which such an expectation would create; but the positions of the vessels were not favorable for either party to pass into the opposing ship. There being at this moment a perfect cessation of the firing, Captain Pearson demanded, "Have you struck your colors?" "I have not yet begun to fight," was the answer.

The yards of the Richard were braced aback, and, the sails of the Serapis being full, the ships separated. As soon as far enough asunder, the Serapis put her helm hard down, laid all aback forward, shivered her after-sails, and wore short round on her heel, or was box-hauled, with a view, most probably, of luffing up athwart the bow of her enemy, in order to again rake her. In this position the Richard would have been fighting her starboard, and the Serapis her larboard guns; but Commodore Jones, by this time, was conscious of the hopelessness of success against so much heavier metal, and after having backed astern some distance, he filled on the other tack, luffing up with the intention of meeting the enemy as she came to the wind, and of laying her athwart hause. In the smoke, one party or the other miscalculated the distance, for the two vessels came foul again, the bowsprit of the English ship passing over the poop of the American. As neither had much way, the collision did but little injury, and Commodore Jones, with his own hands, immediately lashed the enemy's head-gear to his mizzen-mast. The pressure on the after sails of the Serapis, which vessel was nearly before the wind at the time, brought her hull round, and the two ships gradually fell close alongside of each other, head and stern, the jib-boom of the Serapis giving way with the strain. A spare anchor of the English ship now hooked in the quarter of the American, and additional lashings were got out on board the latter to secure her in this position.

Captain Pearson, who was as much aware of his advantage in a regular combat as his opponent could be of his own disadvantage, no sooner perceived the vessels foul than he dropped an anchor, in the hope that the Richard would drift clear of him. But such an expectation was perfectly futile, as the yards were interlocked, the hulls were pressed close against each other, there were lashings fore and aft, and even the ornamental work aided in holding the ships together. When the cable of the Serapis took the strain, the vessels slowly tended, with the bows of the Serapis and the stern of the Richard to the tide. At this instant the English made an attempt to board, but were repulsed without loss.

All this time the battle raged. The lower ports of the Serapis having been closed, as the vessel swung, to prevent boarding, they were now blown off, in order to allow the guns to be run out; and cases actually occurred in which the rammers had to be thrust into the ports of the opposite ship in order to be entered into the muzzles of their proper guns. It is evident that such a conflict must have been of short duration. In effect, the heavy metal of the Serapis, in one or two discharges, cleared all before it, and the main-deck guns of the Richard were in a great measure abandoned. Most of the people went on the upper-deck, and a great number collected on the forecastle, where they were safe from the fire of the enemy, continuing to fight by throwing grenades and using muskets.

In this stage of the combat the Serapis was tearing her antagonist to pieces below, almost without resistance from her enemy's batteries, only two guns on the quarter-deck, and three or four of the twelves, being worked at all. To the former, by shifting a gun from the larboard side, Commodore Jones succeeded in adding a third, all of which were used with effect, under his immediate inspection, to the close of the action. He could not muster force enough to get over a second gun. But the combat would now have soon terminated, had it not been for the courage and activity of the people aloft. Strong parties had been placed in the tops, and, at the end of a short contest, the Americans had driven every man belonging to the enemy below; after which they kept up so animated a fire, on the quarter-deck of the Serapis in particular, as to drive nearly every man off it that was not shot down.

Thus, while the English had the battle nearly all to themselves below, their enemies had the control above the upper deck. Having cleared the tops of the Serapis, some American seamen lay out on the Richard's mainyard, and began to throw hand-grenades upon the two upper decks of the English ship; the men on the forecastle of their own vessel seconding these efforts, by casting the same combustibles through the ports of the Serapis. At length one man, in particular, became so hardy as to take his post on the extreme end of the yard, whence, provided with a bucket filled with combustibles, and a match, he dropped the grenades with so much precision that one passed through the main-hatchway. The powder-boys of the Serapis had got more cartridges up than were wanted, and, in their hurry, they had carelessly laid a row of them on the main-deck, in a line with the guns. The grenade just mentioned set fire to some loose powder that was lying near, and the flash passed from cartridge to cartridge, beginning abreast of the mainmast and running quite aft.

The effect of this explosion was awful. More than twenty men were instantly killed, many of them being left with nothing on them but the collars and wristbands of their shirts, and the waistbands of their duck trowsers; while the official returns of the ship, a week after the action, show that there were no less than thirty-eight wounded on board, still alive, who had been injured in this manner, and of whom thirty were said to have been then in great danger. Captain Pearson described this explosion as having destroyed nearly all the men at the five or six aftermost guns. On the whole, near sixty of the Serapis's people must have been instantly disabled by this sudden blow.

The advantage thus obtained, by the coolness and intrepidity of the topmen, in a great measure restored the chances of the combat, and, by lessening the fire of the enemy, enabled Commodore Jones to increase his. In the same degree that it encouraged the crew of the Richard, it diminished the hopes of the people of the Serapis.

One of the guns under the immediate inspection of Commodore Jones had been pointed some time against the mainmast of his enemy, while the two others had seconded the fire of the tops, with grape and canister. Kept below decks by this double attack, where a scene of frightful horror was present in the agonies of the wounded, and the effects of the explosion, the spirits of the English began to droop, and there was a moment when a trifle would have induced them to submit. From this despondency they were temporarily raised by one of those unlooked-for events that ever accompany the vicissitudes of a battle.

After exchanging the ineffective and distant broadsides already mentioned with the Scarborough, the Alliance had kept standing off and on, to leeward of the two principal ships, out of the direction of their shot, when, about half-past eight, she appeared crossing the stern of the Serapis and the bow of the Richard, firing at such distance as to render it impossible to say which vessel would suffer the most. As soon as she had drawn out of the range of her own guns, her helm was put up, and she ran down near a mile to leeward, hovering about, until the firing had ceased between the Pallas and Scarborough, when she came within hail and spoke both of these vessels. Captain Cottineau of the Pallas earnestly entreated Captain Landais to take possession of his prize, and allow him to go to the assistance of the Richard, or to stretch up to the windward in the Alliance himself, and succor the commodore.

After some delay, Captain Landais took the important duty of assisting his consort, into his own hands, and making two long stretches, under his topsails, he appeared, about the time at which we have arrived in the narration of the combat, directly to windward of the two ships, with the head of the Alliance to the westward. Here the latter ship once more opened her fire, doing equal damage at least, to friend and foe. Keeping away a little, and still continuing her fire, the Alliance was soon on the larboard quarter of the Richard, and, it is even affirmed, that her guns were discharged until she had got nearly abeam.

Fifty voices now hailed to tell the people of the Alliance that they were firing into the wrong ship, and three lanterns were shown, in a line, on the off side of the Richard, which was the regular signal of recognition for a night action. An officer was directed to hail, and to order Captain Landais to lay the enemy aboard, and the question being put, whether the order was comprehended, the answer was in the affirmative.

As the moon had been up some time, it was impossible not to distinguish between the vessels, the Richard being all black, while the Serapis had yellow sides, and the impression seems to have been general in the former vessel, that they had been attacked intentionally. At the discharge of the first guns of the Alliance, the people left one or two of the twelves on board the Richard, which they had begun to fight again, saying that the Englishmen in the Alliance had got possession of the ship, and were helping the enemy. It appears that this discharge dismounted a gun or two, extinguished several lanterns on the main deck, and did a good deal of damage aloft.

The Alliance hauled off to some distance, keeping always on the off side of the Richard, and soon after she reappeared edging down on the larboard beam of her consort, hauling up athwart the bows of that ship and the stern of her antagonist. On this occasion, it is affirmed that her fire recommenced, when, by possibility, the shot could only reach the Serapis through the Richard. Ten or twelve men appear to have been killed and wounded on the forecastle of the latter ship, which was crowded at the time, and among them was an officer of the name of Caswell, who, with his dying breath, maintained that he had received his wound by the fire of the friendly vessel.

After crossing the bows of the Richard, and the stern of the Serapis, delivering grape as she passed, the Alliance ran off to leeward, again standing off and on, doing nothing, for the remainder of the combat.

The fire of the Alliance added greatly to the leaks of the Richard, which ship by this time had received so much water through the shot-holes, as to begin to settle. It is even affirmed by many witnesses, that the most dangerous shot-holes on board the Richard were under her larboard bow, and larboard counter, in places where they could not have been received from the fire of the Serapis. This evidence, however, is not unanswerable, as it has been seen that the Serapis luffed upon the larboard-quarter of the Richard in the commencement of the action, and, forging ahead, was subsequently on her larboard-bow, endeavoring to cross her fore foot. It is certainly possible that shot may have struck the Richard in the places mentioned, on these occasions, and that, as the ship settled in the water from other leaks, the holes then made may have suddenly increased the danger. On the other hand, if the Alliance did actually fire while on her bow and quarter of the Richard, as appears by a mass of uncontradicted testimony, the dangerous shot-holes may very well have come from that ship.

Let the injuries have been received from what quarter they might, soon after the Alliance had run to leeward, an alarm was spread in the Richard that the ship was sinking. Both vessels had been on fire several times, and some difficulty had been experienced in extinguishing the flames, but here was a new enemy to contend with, and as the information came from the carpenter, whose duty it was to sound the pump-wells, it produced a good deal of consternation. The Richard had more than a hundred English prisoners on board, and the master-at-arms, in the hurry of the moment, let them all up from below, in order to save their lives. In the confusion of such a scene at night, the master of a letter-of-marque, that had been taken off the north of Scotland, passed through a port of the Richard into one of the Serapis, when he reported to Captain Pearson that a few minutes would probably decide the battle in his favor, or carry his enemy down, he himself having been liberated in order to save his life. Just at this instant the gunner, who had little to occupy him at his quarters, came on deck, and not perceiving Commodore Jones or Mr. Dale, both of whom were occupied with the liberated prisoners, and believing the master, the only other superior he had in the ship, to be dead, he ran up on the poop to haul down the colors. Fortunately the flag-staff had been shot away, and, the ensign already hanging in the water, he had no other means of letting his intention to submit be known, than by calling out for quarter. Captain Pearson now hailed to inquire if the Richard demanded quarter, and was answered by Commodore Jones himself in the negative. It is probable that the reply was not heard, or, if heard, supposed to come from an unauthorized source, for, encouraged by what he had learned from the escaped prisoner, by the cry, and by the confusion that prevailed in the Richard, the English captain directed his boarders to be called away, and, as soon as mustered, they were ordered to take possession of the prize. Some of the men actually got on the gunwale of the latter ship, but finding boarders ready to repel boarders, they made a precipitate retreat. All this time the topmen were not idle, and the enemy were soon driven below again with loss.

In the meanwhile Mr. Dale, who no longer had a gun that could be fought, mustered the prisoners at the pumps, turning their consternation to account, and probably keeping the Richard afloat by the very blunder that had come so near losing her. The ships were now on fire again, and both parties, with the exception of a few guns on each side, ceased fighting, in order to subdue this dangerous enemy. In the course of the combat the Serapis is said to have been set on fire no less than twelve times, while toward its close, as will be seen in the sequel, the Richard was burning all the while.

As soon as order was restored in the Richard, after the call for quarter, her chances of success began to increase, while the English, driven under cover, almost to a man, appear to have lost, in a great degree, the hope of victory. Their fire materially slackened, while the Richard again brought a few more guns to bear; the mainmast of the Serapis began to totter, and her resistance, in general, to lessen. About an hour after the explosion, or between three hours and three hours and a half after the first gun was fired, and between two hours and two hours and a half after the ships were lashed together, Captain Pearson hauled down the colors of the Serapis with his own hands, the men refusing to expose themselves to the fire of the Richard's tops.

As soon as it was known that the colors of the English had been lowered, Mr. Dale got upon the gunwale of the Richard, and laying hold of the main-brace pendant, he swung himself on board the Serapis. On the quarter-deck of the latter he found Captain Pearson, almost alone, that gallant officer having maintained his post throughout the whole of this close and murderous conflict. Just as Mr. Dale addressed the English captain, the first-lieutenant of the Serapis came up from below to inquire if the Richard had struck, her fire having entirely ceased. Mr. Dale now gave the English officer to understand that he was mistaken in the position of things, the Serapis having struck to the Richard, and not the Richard to the Serapis. Captain Pearson confirming this account, his subordinate acquiesced, offering to go below and silence the guns that were still playing upon the American ship. To this Mr. Dale would not consent, but both the English officers were immediately passed on board the Richard. The firing was then stopped below. Mr. Dale had been closely followed to the quarter-deck of the Serapis by Mr. Mayrant, a midshipman, and a party of boarders, and as the former struck the quarter-deck of the prize, he was run through the thigh, by a boarding-pike, in the hands of a man in the waist, who was ignorant of the surrender. Thus did the close of this remarkable combat resemble its other features in singularity, blood being shed and shot fired, while the boarding officer was in amicable discourse with his prisoners!

As soon as Captain Pearson was on board the Richard, and Mr. Dale had received a proper number of hands in the prize, Commodore Jones ordered the lashings to be cut, and the vessels to be separated, hailing the Serapis, as the Richard drifted from alongside of her, and ordering her to follow his own ship. Mr. Dale now had the head sails of the Serapis braced sharp aback, and the wheel put down, but the vessel refused both her helm and her canvas. Surprised and excited at this circumstance, the gallant lieutenant sprang from the binnacle on which he had seated himself, and fell at his length on the deck. He had been severely wounded in the leg, by a splinter, and until this moment had been ignorant of the injury. He was replaced on the binnacle, when the master of the Serapis came up and acquainted him with the fact that the ship was anchored.

By this time, Mr. Lunt, the second lieutenant, who had been absent in the pilot-boat, had got alongside, and was on board the prize. To this officer Mr. Dale now consigned the charge of the Serapis, the cable was cut, and the ship followed the Richard, as ordered.

Although this protracted and bloody combat had now ended, neither the danger nor the labors of the victors were over. The Richard was both sinking and on fire. The flames had got within the ceiling, and extended so far that they menaced the magazine, while all the pumps, in constant use, could barely keep the water at the same level. Had it depended on the exhausted people of the two combatants, the ship must have soon sunk, but the other vessels of the squadron sent hands on board the Richard, to assist at the pumps. So imminent did the danger from the fire become, that all the powder was got on deck, to prevent an explosion. In this manner did the night of the battle pass, with one gang always at the pumps, and another contending with the flames, until about ten o'clock in the forenoon of the 24th, when the latter were got under. After the action, eight or ten Englishmen in the Richard stole a boat from the Serapis, and ran away with it, landing at Scarborough. Several of the men were so alarmed with the condition of their ship, as to jump overboard and swim to the other vessels.

When the day dawned, an examination was made into the condition of the Richard. Abaft, on a line with the guns of the Serapis that had not been disabled by the explosion, the timbers were found to be nearly all beaten in, or beaten out, for in this respect there was little difference between the two sides of the ship; and it was said that her poop and upper decks would have fallen into the gun-room, but for a few fut-tocks that had been missed. Indeed, so large was the vacuum, that most of the shot fired from this part of the Serapis, at the close of the action, must have gone through the Richard without touching any thing. The rudder was cut from the stern-post, and the transoms were nearly driven out of her. All the after-part of the ship, in particular, that was below the quarter-deck, was torn to pieces, and nothing had saved those stationed on the quarter-deck but the impossibility of elevating guns that almost touched their object.

The result of this examination was to convince every one of the impossibility of carrying the Richard into port, in the event of its coming on to blow. Commodore Jones was advised to remove his wounded while the weather continued moderate, and he reluctantly gave the order to commence. The following night and the morning of the succeeding day were employed in executing this imperious duty, and about nine o'clock, the officer of the Pallas, who was in charge of the ship, with a party at the pumps, finding that the water had reached the lower deck, reluctantly abandoned her. About ten, the Bon Homme Richard wallowed heavily, gave a roll, and settled slowly into the sea, bows foremost.

THE FRIGATE IN A STORM.

The extraordinary activity of Griffith, which communicated itself with promptitude to the crew, was produced by a sudden alteration in the weather. In place of the well-defined streak along the horizon, that has been already described, an immense body of misty light appeared to be moving in with rapidity from the ocean, while a distinct but distant roaring announced the sure approach of the tempest, that had so long troubled the waters. Even Griffith, while thundering his orders through the trumpet, and urging the men, by his cries, to expedition, would pause, for instants, to cast anxious glances in the direction of the coming storm; and the faces of the sailors who lay on the yards were turned, instinctively, toward the same quarter of the heavens, while they knotted the reef-points, or passed the gaskets, that were to confine the unruly canvas to the prescribed limits.

The pilot alone, in that confused and busy throng, where voice rose above voice, and cry echoed cry, in quick succession, appeared as if he held no interest in the important stake. With his eyes steadily fixed on the approaching mist, and his arms folded together in composure, he stood calmly waiting the result.

The ship had fallen off, with her broadside to the sea, and was become unmanageable, and the sails were already brought into the folds necessary to her security, when the quick and heavy fluttering of canvas was thrown across the water, with all the gloomy and chilling sensations that such sounds produce, where darkness and danger unite to appal the seaman.

"The schooner has it!" cried Griffith; "Barnstable has held on, like himself, to the last moment—God send that the squall leave him cloth enough to keep him from the shore!"

"His sails are easily handled," the commander observed, "and she must be over the principal danger. We are falling off before it, Mr. Gray; shall we try a cast of the lead?"

The pilot turned from his contemplative posture, and moved slowly across the deck before he returned any reply to this question—like a man who not only felt that every thing depended on himself, but that he was equal to the emergency.

"'Tis unnecessary," he at length said; "'twould be certain destruction to be taken aback, and it is difficult to say, within several points, how the wind may strike us."

"'Tis difficult no longer," cried Griffith; "for here it comes, and in right earnest!"

The rushing sounds of the wind were now, indeed, heard at hand, and the words were hardly past the lips of the young lieutenant, before the vessel bowed down heavily to one side, and then, as she began to move through the water, rose again majestically to her upright position, as if saluting, like a courteous champion, the powerful antagonist with which she was about to contend. Not another minute elapsed, before the ship was throwing the waters aside, with a lively progress, and, obedient to her helm, was brought as near to the desired course as the direction of the wind would allow. The hurry and bustle on the yards gradually subsided, and the men slowly descended to the deck, all straining their eyes to pierce the gloom in which they were enveloped, and some shaking their heads in melancholy doubt, afraid to express the apprehensions they really entertained. All on board anxiously awaited for the fury of the gale; for there were none so ignorant or inexperienced in that gallant frigate, as not to know, that as yet, they only felt the infant efforts of the wind. Each moment, however, it increased in power, though so gradual was the alteration, that the relieved mariners began to believe that all their gloomy forebodings were not to be realized. During this short interval of uncertainty, no other sounds were heard than the whistling of the breeze, as it passed quickly through the mass of rigging that belonged to the vessel, and the dashing of the spray, that began to fly from her bows, like the foam of a cataract.

"It blows fresh," cried Griffith, who was the first to speak in that moment of doubt and anxiety; "but it is no more than a capful of wind, after all. Give us elbow-room, and the right canvas, Mr. Pilot, and I'll handle the ship like a gentlemen's yacht, in this breeze."

"Will she stay, think ye, under this sail?" said the low voice of the stranger.

"She will do all that man, in reason, can ask of wood and iron," returned the lieutenant; "but the vessel don't float the ocean that will tack under double-reefed topsails alone against a heavy sea. Help her with the courses, pilot, and you shall see her come round like a dancing-master."

"Let us feel the strength of the gale first," returned the man who was called Mr. Gray, moving from the side of Griffith to the weather gangway of the vessel, where he stood in silence, looking ahead of the ship, with an air of singular coolness and abstraction.

All the lanterns had been extinguished on the deck of the frigate, when her anchor was secured, and as the first mist of the gale had passed over, it was succeeded by a faint light that was a good deal aided by the glittering foam of the waters, which now broke in white curls around the vessel in every direction. The land could be faintly discerned, rising like a heavy bank of black fog, above the margin of the waters, and was only distinguishable from the heavens by its deeper gloom and obscurity. The last rope was coiled, and deposited in its proper place, by the seamen, and for several minutes the stillness of death pervaded the crowded decks. It was evident to every one that their ship was dashing at a prodigious rate through the waves; and as she was approaching, with such velocity, the quarter of the bay where the shoals and dangers were known to be situated, nothing but the habits of the most exact discipline could suppress the uneasiness of the officers and men within their own bosoms. At length the voice of Captain Munson was heard, calling to the pilot.

"Shall I send a hand into the chains, Mr. Gray," he said, "and try our water?"

Although this question was asked aloud, and the interest it excited drew many of the officers and men around him, in eager impatience for his answer, it was unheeded by the man to whom it was addressed. His head rested on his hand, as he leaned over the hammock-cloths of the vessel, and his whole air was that of one whose thoughts wandered from the pressing necessity of their situation. Griffith was among those who had approached the pilot, and after waiting a moment, from respect, to hear the answer to his commander's question, he presumed on his own rank, and leaving the circle that stood at a little distance, stepped to the side of the mysterious guardian of their lives.

"Captain Munson desires to know whether you wish a cast of the lead?" said the young officer, with a little impatience of manner. No immediate answer was made to this repetition of the question, and Griffith laid his hand unceremoniously on the shoulder of the other, with an intent to rouse him, before he made another application for a reply, but the convulsive start of the pilot held him silent in amazement.

"Fall back there," said the lieutenant, sternly, to the men, who were closing around them in a compact circle; "away with you to your stations, and see all clear for stays." The dense mass of heads dissolved, at this order, like the water of one of the waves commingling with the ocean, and the lieutenant and his companion were left by themselves.

"This is not a time for musing, Mr. Gray," continued Griffith—"remember our compact, and look to your charge—is it not time to put the vessel in stays?—of what are you dreaming?"

The pilot laid his hand on the extended arm of the lieutenant, and grasped it with a convulsive pressure, as he answered—

"'Tis a dream of reality. You are young, Mr. Griffith, nor am I past the noon of life; but should you live fifty years longer, you never can see and experience what I have encountered in my little period of three-and-thirty years!"

A good deal astonished at this burst of feeling, so singular at such a moment, the young sailor was at a loss for a reply; but as his duty was uppermost in his thoughts, he still dwelt on the theme that most interested him.

"I hope much of your experience has been on this coast, for the ship travels lively," he said, "and the daylight showed us so much to dread that we do not feel over-valiant in the dark. How much longer shall we stand on upon this tack?"

The pilot turned slowly from the side of the vessel, and walked toward the commander of the frigate, as he replied, in a tone that seemed deeply agitated by his melancholy reflections—

"You have your wish, then; much, very much, of my early life was passed on this dreaded coast. What to you is all darkness and gloom, to me is as light as if a noon-day sun shone upon it. But tack your ship, sir; tack your ship; I would see how she works before we reach the point where she *must* behave well, or we perish."

Griffith gazed after him in wonder, while the pilot slowly paced the quarter-deck, and then, rousing from his trance, gave forth the cheering order that called each man to his station, to perform the desired evolution. The confident assurances which the young officer had given to the pilot respecting the qualities of his vessel, and his own ability to manage her, were fully realized by the result. The helm was no sooner put alee, than the huge ship bore up gallantly against the wind, and dashing directly

The Pilot: Tom Coffin on the wreck of the Ariel

through the waves, threw the foam high into the air, as she looked boldly into the very eye of the wind, and then, yielding gracefully to its power, she fell off on the other track, with her head pointed from those dangerous shoals that she had so recently approached with such terrifying velocity. The heavy yards swung round, as if they had been vanes to indicate the currents of the air, and in a few moments the frigate again moved with stately progress through the water, leaving the rocks and shoals behind her on one side of the bay, but advancing toward those that offered equal danger on the other.

During this time the sea was becoming more agitated, and the violence of the wind was gradually increasing. The latter no longer whistled amid the cordage of the vessel, but it seemed to howl, surlily, as it passed the complicated machinery that the frigate obtruded on its path. An endless succession of white surges rose above the heavy billows, and the very air was glittering with the light that was disengaged from the ocean. The ship yielded, each moment, more and more before the storm, and in less than half an hour from the time that she had lifted her anchor, she was driven along with tremendous fury by the full power of a gale of wind. Still, the hardy and experienced mariners who directed her movements, held her to the course that was necessary to their preservation, and still Griffith gave forth, when directed by their unknown pilot, those orders that turned her in the narrow channel where safety was alone to be found.

So far, the performance of his duty appeared easy to the stranger, and he gave the required directions in those still, calm tones, that formed so remarkable a contrast to the responsibility of his situation. But when the land was becoming dim, in distance as well as darkness, and the agitated sea alone was to be discovered as it swept by them in foam, he broke in upon the monotonous roaring of the tempest with the sounds of his voice, seeming to shake off his apathy, and rouse himself to the occasion.

"Now is the time to watch her closely, Mr. Griffith," he cried; "here we get the true tide and the real danger. Place the best quartermaster of your ship in those chains, and let an officer stand by him and see that he gives us the right water."

"I will take that office on myself," said the captain; "pass a light into the weather main-chains."

"Stand by your braces!" exclaimed the pilot, with startling quickness. "Heave away that lead!"

These preparations taught the crew to expect the crisis, and every officer and man stood in fearful silence, at his assigned station, awaiting the issue of the trial. Even the quartermaster at the gun gave out his orders to the men at the wheel in deeper and hoarser tones than usual, as if anxious not to disturb the quiet and order of the vessel.

While this deep expectation pervaded the frigate, the piercing cry of the leadsman, as he called "by the mark seven," rose above the tempest, crossed over the decks, and appeared to pass away to leeward, borne on the blast like the warnings of some water-spirit.

"'Tis well," returned the pilot, calmly; "try it again."

The short pause was succeeded by another cry, "and a half-five!"

"She shoals! she shoals!" exclaimed Griffith; "keep her a good full."

"Aye! you must hold the vessel in command, now," said the pilot, with those cool tones that are most appalling in critical moments, because they seem to denote most preparation and care.

The third call of "by the deep four!" was followed by a prompt direction from the stranger to tack.

Griffith seemed to emulate the coolness of the pilot, in issuing the necessary orders to execute this manœuvre.

The vessel rose slowly from the inclined position into which she had been forced by the tempest, and the sails were shaking violently, as if to release themselves from their confinement, while the ship stemmed the billows, when the well-known voice of the sailing-master was heard shouting from the forecastle—

"Breakers! breakers, dead ahead!"

This appalling sound seemed yet to be lingering about the ship, when a second voice cried—

"Breakers on our lee-bow!"

"We are in a bite of the shoals, Mr. Gray," cried the commander. "She loses her way; perhaps an anchor might hold her."

"Clear away that best bower," shouted Griffith, through his trumpet.

"Hold on!" cried the pilot, in a voice that reached the very hearts of all who heard him; "hold on every thing."

The young man turned fiercely to the daring stranger, who thus defied the discipline of his vessel, and at once demanded—

"Who is it that dares to countermand my orders? is it not enough that you run the ship into danger, but you must interfere to keep her there! If another word—"

"Peace, Mr. Griffith," interrupted the captain, bending from the rigging, his gray locks blowing about in the wind, and adding a look of wildness to the haggard care that he exhibited by the light of his lantern; "yield the trumpet to Mr. Gray—he alone can save us."

Griffith threw his speaking-trumpet on the deck, and as he walked proudly away, muttered, in bitterness of feeling—

"Then all is lost, indeed, and among the rest, the foolish hopes with which I visited this coast."

There was, however, no time for reply; the ship had been rapidly running into the wind, and as the efforts of the crew were paralyzed by the contradictory orders they had heard, she gradually lost her way, and in a few seconds all her sails were taken aback.

Before the crew understood their situation, the pilot had applied the trumpet to his mouth, and in a voice that rose above the tempest, he thundered forth his orders. Each command was given distinctly, and with a precision that showed him to be master of his profession. The helm was kept fast, the head yards swung up heavily against the wind, and the vessel was soon whirling round on her heel, with a retrograde movement.

Griffith was too much of a seaman not to perceive that the pilot had seized, with a perception almost intuitive, the only method that promised to extricate the vessel from her situation. He was young, impetuous, and proud—but he was also generous. Forgetting his resentment and his mortification, he rushed forward among the men, and, by his presence and example, added certainty to the experiment. The ship fell off slowly before the gale, and bowed her yards nearly to the water, as she felt the blast pouring its fury on her broadside, while the surly waves beat violently against her stern, as if in reproach at departing from her usual manner of moving.

The voice of the pilot, however, was still heard, steady and calm, and yet so clear and high as to reach every ear; and the obedient seamen whirled the yards at his bidding, in despite of the tempest, as if they handled the toys of their childhood. When the ship had fallen off dead before the wind, her head sails were shaken, her after-yards trimmed, and her helm shifted, before she had time to run upon the danger that had threatened, as well to leeward as to windward. The beautiful fabric, obedient to her government, threw her bows up gracefully toward the wind again, and as her sails were trimmed, moved out from among the dangerous shoals, in which she had been embayed, as steadily and swiftly as she had approached them.

A moment of breathless astonishment succeeded the accomplishment of this nice manœuvre, but there was no time for the usual expressions of surprise. The stranger still held the trumpet, and continued to lift his voice amid the howlings of the blast, whenever prudence or skill directed any change in the management of the ship. For an hour longer, there was a fearful struggle for their preservation, the channel becoming, at each step, more complicated, and the shoals thickening around the mariners on every side. The lead was cast rapidly, and the quick eye of the pilot seemed to pierce the darkness with a keenness of vision that exceeded human power. It was apparent to all in the vessel, that they were under the guidance of one who understood the navigation thoroughly, and their exertions kept pace with their reviving confidence. Again and again, the frigate appeared to be rushing blindly on shoals, where the sea was covered with foam, and where destruction would have been as sudden as it was certain, when the clear voice of the stranger was heard warning them of the danger, and inciting them to their duty. The vessel was implicitly yielded to his government, and during those anxious moments when she was dashing the waters aside, throwing the spray over her enormous yards, each ear would listen eagerly for those sounds that had obtained a command over the crew, that can only be acquired, under such circumstances, by great steadiness and consummate skill. The ship was recovering from the inaction of changing her course, in one of those critical tacks that she had made so often, when the pilot, for the first time, addressed the commander of the frigate, who still continued to superintend the all-important duty of the leadsman.

"Now is the pinch," he said, "and if the ship behaves well, we are safe—but if otherwise, all we have yet done will be useless."

The veteran seaman whom he addressed left the chains, at this portentous notice, and calling to his first-lieutenant, required of the stranger an explanation of his warning.

"See you yon light on the southern headland?" returned the pilot; "you may know it from the star near it—by its sinking, at times, in the ocean. Now observe the hom-moc, a little north of it, looking like a shadow in the horizon—'tis a hill far inland. If we keep that light open from the hill, we shall do well—but if not, we surely go to pieces."

"Let us tack again!" exclaimed the lieutenant.

The pilot shook his head, as he replied—

"There is no more tacking or box-hauling to be done to-night. We have barely room to pass out of the shoals on this course, and if we can weather the 'Devil's-Grip,' we clear their outermost point—but if not, as I said before, there is but an alternative."

"If we had beaten out the way we entered!" exclaimed Griffith, "we should have done well."

"Say also, if the tide would have let us do so," returned the pilot, calmly. "Gentlemen, we must be prompt; we have but a mile to go, and the ship appears to fly. That topsail is not enough to keep her up to the wind; we want both jib and mainsail."

"'Tis a perilous thing to loosen canvas in such a tempest!" observed the doubtful captain.

"It must be done," returned the collected stranger; we perish without it—see! the light already touches the edge of the hom-moc; the sea casts us to leeward!"

"It shall be done!" cried Griffith, seizing the trumpet from the hand of the pilot.

The orders of the lieutenant were executed almost as soon as issued, and every thing being ready, the enormous folds of the mainsail were trusted, loose, to the blast. There was an instant when the result was doubtful; the tremendous threshing of the heavy sail seeming to bid defiance to all restraint, shaking the ship to her centre; but art and strength prevailed, and gradually the canvas was distended, and bellying as it filled, was drawn down to its usual place by the power of a hundred men. The vessel yielded to this immense addition of force, and bowed before it, like a reed bending to a breeze. But the success of the measure was announced by a joyful cry from the stranger, that seemed to burst from his inmost soul.

"She feels it! she springs her luff!—observe," he said, "the light opens from the hom-moc already; if she will only bear her canvas, we shall go clear."

A report like that of a cannon interrupted his exclamation, and something resembling a white cloud was seen drifting before the wind from the head of the ship, till it was driven into the gloom far to leeward.

"'Tis the jib, blown from the bolt-ropes," said the commander of the frigate. "This is no time to spread light duck—but the mainsail may stand it yet."

"The sail would laugh at a tornado," returned the lieutenant, "but the mast springs like a piece of steel."

"Silence all!" cried the pilot. "Now, gentlemen, we shall soon know our fate. Let her luff—luff you can!"

This warning effectually closed all discourse, and the hardy mariners, knowing that they had already done all in the power of man to insure their safety, stood in breathless anxiety, awaiting the result. At a short distance ahead of them the whole ocean was white with foam, and the waves, instead of rolling on, in regular succession, appeared to be tossing about in mad gambols. A single streak of dark billows, not half a cable's length in width, could be discerned running into this chaos of water; but it was soon lost to the eye amid the confusion of the disturbed element. Along this narrow path the vessel moved more heavily than before, being brought so near the wind as to keep her sails touching. The pilot silently proceeded to the wheel, and, with his own hands, he undertook the steering of the ship. No noise proceeded from the frigate to interrupt the horrid tumult of the ocean, and she entered the channel among the breakers, with the silence of a desperate calmness. Twenty times, as the foam rolled away to leeward, the crew were on the eve of uttering their joy as they supposed the vessel past the danger; but breaker after breaker would still heave up before them, following each other into the general mass, to check their exultation. Occasionally, the fluttering of the sails would be heard; and when the looks of the startled seamen were turned to the wheel, they beheld the stranger grasping its spokes, with his quick eye glancing from the water to the canvas. At length the ship reached a point, where she appeared to be rushing directly into the jaws of destruction, when, suddenly, her course was changed, and her head receded rapidly from the wind. At the same instant the voice of the pilot was heard shouting—

"Square away the yards!—in mainsail!"

A general burst from the crew echoed, "square away the yards!" and, quick as thought, the frigate was seen gliding along the channel before the wind. The eye had hardly time to dwell on the foam, which seemed like clouds driving in the heavens, and directly the gallant vessel issued from her perils, and rose and fell on the heavy waves of the open sea.

The seamen were yet drawing long breaths, and gazing about them like men re-covered from a trance, when Griffith approached the man who had so successfully conducted them through their perils. The young lieutenant grasped the hand of the other as he said—

"You have this night proved yourself a faithful pilot, and such a seaman as the world cannot equal."

The pressure of the hand was warmly returned by the unknown mariner, who replied—

"I am no stranger to the seas, and I may yet find my grave in them. But you, too, have deceived me; you have acted nobly, young man, and Congress—"

"What of Congress?" asked Griffith, observing him to pause.

"Why, Congress is fortunate if it has many such ships as this," said the stranger, coldly, walking away toward the commander.

Griffith gazed after him, a moment, in surprise; but as his duty required his atten-tion, other thoughts soon engaged his mind.

The vessel was pronounced to be in safety. The gale was heavy and increasing, but there was a clear sea before them, and, as she slowly stretched out into the bosom of the ocean, preparations were made for her security during its continuance. Before midnight every thing was in order. A gun from the Ariel soon announced the safety of the schooner also, which had gone out by another and an easier channel, that the frigate had not dared to attempt; when the commander directed the usual watch to be set, and the remainder of the crew to seek their necessary repose.

Lionel Lincoln: "Ye monsters in the shape of men what is't ye do!" she exclaimed in a voice that rose above the tumult and had the effect to hush every mouth.

V.

LIONEL LINCOLN.

WRITING was no longer an experiment. Three highly successful works, each differing from the other in character, had been given to the country. The plan of a fourth romance was now sketched, and the first chapters of Lionel Lincoln were soon written.

The leading idea of this book has been considered as in itself a mistake; as presenting difficulties which, by their nature, were all but insuperable. It was the wish of the writer to draw, in the character of Lionel Lincoln, the representative of a large and an honorable class of men, intimately connected with the country and its history, by birth and association, but whose political conviction and action were directly opposed to the triumphant party. Thus far there was assuredly nothing impossible in the plan. Majorities give success and its thousand rewards; but they can show no prerogative endowing them with an exclusive claim to the spirit of heroism; on the contrary, the world's story will prove that the proportion of heroic spirits has often been greater among minorities. Neither was there any thing in the position of the character drawn, or in that of the class he represented, incompatible with a strong interest to be thrown about his person. The feeling of loyalty to a sovereign may be not only natural and strong, but highly honorable also in those born subjects to a crown. It was a feeling which had great depth in many of the best American hearts of the period of the Revolution—one which long swayed the thought and action of Washington himself. It was a feeling to which, in its best forms, every generous nature can render justice. And in the hour of struggle allegiance to any legitimate established government is not to be lightly thrown off. The very men who, when the contest of the Revolution had once begun, were foremost as statesmen and soldiers in behalf of America, were those whose course in its earlier stages was most clearly marked with an honorable reluctance to utter violent language—to raise the standard of revolt—to give the signal for strife. Such a character as that of Lionel was, therefore, not only natural, but could be proved to have had actual existence. The struggles which such a man, in a similar position, must necessarily go through in the thrilling scenes of a great political revolution, offered, indeed, all the necessary materials for interest in a work of fiction. We have recently seen a distinguished English writer of the present day taking much the same view of the subject; in his "Virginians" he has attempted to give a picture of both sides of the great struggle, showing twin-brothers taking opposite ground on the question. The error in Mr. Cooper's novel did not, therefore, lie essentially in the conception of the character of his nominal hero. The greatest obstacle was to be found rather in the position of the author himself: his own sympathies were in fact too strongly enlisted in the opposite direction. While the general outline of the sketch was accurate, and capable of being well filled up, in the details of the work he did not render justice to the character he had himself conceived. He became weary of his task; his own interest in what he had intended for the principal figure of the picture flagged, and, as an inevitable consequence, that of the reader was not sufficiently aroused. A writer of colder temperament, of less earnest sincerity of nature, might have executed the same task much more successfully. In reading Lionel Lincoln, we find that the principal personage does not grow upon us; as we proceed in the book we are constantly expecting some new combination of circumstances, some stirring scene, some great event, which shall bring him into higher and clearer relief. Such events occur, such scenes are given in the narrative; but throughout the book, the figure of Lionel never really fills the eye of the reader, never entirely engrosses his attentions and sympathies. We close the tale with the conviction that we have made the acquaintance of an agreeable, gentlemanly, and honorable young officer of the grenadiers, and nothing more. The author himself was dissatisfied with his work. In his own opinion, a tale connected with the wonderful siege of Boston, and the memorable battle of

Bunker Hill, should have presented some more striking character to the reader than that of Lionel Lincoln.

As if to accumulate obstacles for himself, in this book, not content with the embarrassments belonging to the position of the young American officer enlisted on the side of the crown, the author introduced into the tale two additional characters, each in itself full of unusual difficulties. We have good authority, however, for asserting that in both these instances the task was skilfully managed. In Ralph, the father of Major Lincoln, the author has represented an honorable and educated mind, originally strong and sound, now disturbed and clouded by derangement; erratic and infirm, yet dignified, upright, and authoritative, even under the great calamity. In Job Pray, the rude, half-witted Boston boy, the brother of Lionel, he has drawn a nature entirely homely and untutored, but endowed with generous instincts, struggling under the infirmity of partial idiocy. Both sketches assuredly have merit. Our sympathies are awakened in behalf of the deranged father, they are warmly aroused by the half-witted son, while there is nothing forced, no straining at effect, nothing revolting in either. One of the best physicians in the country repeatedly declared that the nice distinctions between the different shades of disordered reason in Ralph and Job, were drawn with truth and skill. In both instances, the feeling of compassion in the reader's mind is blended with respect for a great infirmity of our common nature; any representation of a character of this kind which does not excite the latter feeling becomes indeed quite unjustifiable.

The natural channel in which the author's sympathies were actually flowing, is clearly betrayed in the sketch of Job, who soon becomes a favorite with the reader. His just, yet half-blind indignation against an oppression which had aroused the noblest minds in the country; his prejudices, honest and natural, but violent and vulgar; his instinctive love of country; his affection for his mother; his generous feeling for Lionel; the petty cunning invariably connected with his diseased mind; the little Yankee peculiarities engrafted on his character; the strange blending of courage and cowardice in his infirm nature, make up together a sketch of much truth and merit. The poor half-witted son of Abigail, the tenant of the old warehouse, becomes, in fact, the true hero of the book.

The title-page of the first edition of Lionel Lincoln bore an inscription afterward erased: " A Legend of the Thirteen Republics." At the time of writing the book, the author had planned a series of works of fiction, to be drawn from the early historical sources of the country—the scene of each tale to be laid in one of the thirteen different colonies which formed the Union. His own love of country had nothing of the petty, provincial, puerile view which would confine patriotism to the limits of one's own horizon. He was loyal to the whole country in the highest sense of the words—to the Union, which is the soul of its national existence. It was his wish to contribute something to the local literature of each of the different divisions of the republic. His departure for Europe, which prevented his visiting the more southern states, and collecting local details, interfered with his carrying this plan into execution. No second work of the projected series having been written, the reference to the Thirteen Legends was removed from the later editions.

The sketch of the battle of Bunker Hill included in this novel, was carefully written. Every effort to preserve accuracy was made. The principal historical authorities, the state papers, official reports, etc., etc., were studied. A journey to Boston was made for the purpose of going over the ground in person. Even almanacs, and records of the weather, were consulted, to insure greater accuracy in detail. The account of the battle is given as a selection from " Lionel Lincoln."

N. ORR. CO.

THE BATTLE OF BUNKER HILL.

WHEN the heavy sleep of morning fell upon his senses, visions of the past and future mingled with wild confusion in the dreams of the youthful soldier. The form of his father stood before him, as he had known it in his childhood, fair in the proportions and vigor of manhood, regarding him with those eyes of benignant but melancholy affection, which characterized their expression after he had become the sole joy of his widowed parent. While his heart was warming at the sight, the figure melted away, and was succeeded by fantastic phantoms, which appeared to dance among the graves on Copp's, led along in those gambols, which partook of the ghastly horrors of the dead, by Job Pray, who glided among the tombs like a being of another world. Sudden and loud thunder then burst upon them, and the shadows fled into their secret places, from whence he could see, ever and anon, glassy eyes and spectral faces, peering out upon him, as if conscious of the power they possessed to chill the blood of the living. His visions now became painfully distinct, and his sleep was oppressed with their vividness, when his senses burst their unnatural bonds, and he awoke. The air of morning was breathing through his open curtains, and the light of day had already shed itself upon the dusky roofs of the town. Lionel arose from his bed, and had paced his chamber several times, in a vain effort to shake off the images that had haunted his slumbers, when the sounds which broke upon the stillness of the air, became too plain to be longer mistaken by a practised ear.

"Ha!" he muttered to himself, "I have been dreaming but by halves—these are the sounds of no fancied tempest, but cannon, speaking most plainly to the soldier!"

He opened his window, and looked out upon the surrounding scene. The roar of artillery was now quick and heavy, and Lionel bent his eyes about him to discover the cause of this unusual occurrence. It had been the policy of Gage to await the arrival of his reinforcements, before he struck a blow which was intended to be decisive; and the Americans were well known to be too scantily supplied with the munitions of war, to waste a single charge of powder in any of the vain attacks of modern sieges. A knowledge of these facts gave an additional interest to the curiosity with which Major Lincoln endeavored to penetrate the mystery of so singular a disturbance. Window after window in the adjacent buildings soon exhibited, like his own, its wondering and alarmed spectator. Here and there a half-dressed soldier, or a busy townsman, was seen hurrying along the silent streets, with steps that denoted the eagerness of his curiosity. Women began to rush wildly from their dwellings, and then, as the sounds broke on their ears with tenfold heaviness in the open air, they shrunk back into their habitations in pallid dismay. Lionel called to three or four of the men, as they hurried by; but, turning their eyes wildly toward his window, they passed on without answering, as if the emergency were too pressing to admit of speech. Finding his repeated inquiries fruitless, he hastily dressed himself and descended to the street. As he left his own door, a half-clad artillerist hurried past him, adjusting his garments with one hand, and bearing in the other some of the lesser implements of the particular corps in which he served.

"What means the firing, sergeant?" demanded Lionel, "and whither do you hasten with those fusees?"

"The rebels, your honor, the rebels!" returned the soldier, looking back to speak, without ceasing his speed; "and I go to my guns!"

"The rebels!" repeated Lionel—"what can we have to fear from a mob of countrymen, in such a position—that fellow has slept from his post, and apprehensions for himself mingle with this zeal for his king!"

The townspeople now began to pour from their dwellings in scores; and Lionel imitated their example, and took his course toward the adjacent height of Beacon Hill. He toiled his way up the steep ascent, in company with twenty more, without exchanging a syllable with men who appeared as much astonished as himself at this early interruption of their slumbers, and in a few minutes he stood on the little grassy platform, surrounded by a hundred interested gazers. The sun had just lifted the thin veil of mist from the bosom of the waters, and the eye was permitted to range over a wide field beneath the light vapor. Several vessels were moored in the channels of the Charles and Mystick, to cover the northern approaches to the place; and as he beheld the column of white smoke that was wreathing about the masts of a frigate among them, Lionel was no longer at a loss to comprehend whence the firing proceeded. While he was yet gazing, uncertain of the reasons which demanded this show of war, immense fields of smoke burst from the side of a ship of the line, who also opened her deep-mouthed cannon, and presently her example was followed by several floating batteries, and lighter vessels, until the wide amphitheatre of hills that encircled Boston was filled with the echoes of a hundred pieces of artillery.

"What can it mean, sir?" exclaimed a young officer of his own regiment, addressing Major Lincoln—"the sailors are in downright earnest, and they scale their guns with shot, I know, by the rattling of the reports!"

"I can boast of a vision no better than your own," returned Lionel; "for no enemy can I see. As the guns seem pointed at the opposite peninsula, it is probable a party of the Americans are attempting to destroy the grass which lies newly mown in the meadows."

The young officer was in the act of assenting to this conjecture, when a voice was heard above their heads, shouting—

"There goes a gun from Copp's! They needn't think to frighten the people with their rake-helly noises; let them blaze away till the dead get out of their graves—the Bay-men will keep the hill!"

Every eye was immediately turned upward, and the wondering and amused spectators discovered Job Pray, seated in the grate of the beacon, his countenance, usually so vacant, gleaming with exultation, while he continued waving his hat high in air, as gun after gun was added to the uproar of the cannonade.

"How now, fellow!" exclaimed Lionel; "what see you? and where are the Bay-men of whom you speak?"

"Where?" returned the simpleton, clapping his hands with childish delight—"why, where they came at dark midnight, and where they'll stand at open noon-day! The Bay-men can look into the windows of old Funnel at last, and now let the reg'lars come on, and they'll teach the godless murderers the law!"

Lionel, a little irritated with the bold language of Job, called to him in an angry voice—

"Come down from that perch, fellow, and explain yourself, or this grenadier shall lift you from your seat, and transfer you to the post, for a little of that wholesome correction which you need."

"You promised that the grannies should never flog Job ag'in," said the changeling, crouching down in the grate, whence he looked out at his threatened chastiser with a lowering and sullen eye—"and Job agreed to run your a'r'nds, and not take any of the king's crowns in pay."

"Come down, then, this instant, and I will remember the compact."

Comforted by this assurance, which was made in a more friendly tone, Job threw himself carelessly from his iron seat, and clinging to the post, he slid swiftly to the earth, where Major Lincoln immediately arrested him by the arm, and demanded—

"Where are those Bay-men, I once more ask?"

"There!" repeated Job, pointing over the low roofs of the town, in the direction of the opposite peninsula. "They dug their cellar on Breed's, and now they are fixing the underpinnin', and next you'll see what a raising they'll invite the people to!"

The instant the spot was named, all those eyes which had hitherto gazed at the vessels themselves, instead of searching for the object of their hostility, were turned on the green eminence which rose a little to the right of the village of Charlestown, and every doubt was at once removed by the discovery. The high, conical summit of Bunker Hill lay naked, and unoccupied, as on the preceding day; but on the extremity of a more humble ridge, which extended within a short distance of the water, a low bank of earth had been thrown up, for purposes which no military eye could mistake. This redoubt, small and inartificial as it was, commanded by its position the whole of the inner harbor of Boston, and even endangered, in some measure, the occupants of the town itself. It was the sudden appearance of this magical mound, as the mists of the morning had dispersed, which roused the slumbering seamen; and it had already become the target of all the guns of the shipping in the bay. Amazement at the temerity of their countrymen held the townsmen silent, while Major Lincoln, and the few officers who stood nigh him, saw, at a glance, that this step on the part of their adversaries would bring the affairs of the leaguer to an instant crisis. In vain they turned their wondering looks on the neighboring eminence, and around the different points of the peninsula, in quest of those places of support with which soldiers generally intrench their defences. The husbandmen opposed to them had seized upon the point best calculated to annoy their foes, without regard to the consequences; and in a few short hours, favored by the mantle of night, had thrown up their work with a dexterity that was only exceeded by their boldness. The truth flashed across the brain of Major Lincoln with his first glance, and he felt his cheeks glow as he remembered the low and indistinct murmurs, which the night air had wafted to his ears, and those inexplicable fancies which had even continued to haunt him till dispersed by truth and the light of day. Motioning to Job to follow, he left the hill with a hurried step, and when they gained the common, he turned, and said, sternly, to his companion—

"Fellow, you have been privy to this midnight work!"

"Job has enough to do in the day, without laboring in the night, when none but the dead are out of their places of rest," returned the lad, with a look of mental imbecility, which immediately disarmed the resentment of the other.

Lionel smiled as he again remembered his own weakness, and repeated to himself—

"The dead! aye, these are the works of the living; and bold men are they who have dared to do the deed. But tell me, Job—for 'tis in vain to attempt deceiving me any longer—what number of Americans did you leave on the hill, when you crossed the Charles to visit the graves on Copp's, the past night?"

"Both hills were crowded," returned the other—"Breed's with the people, and Copp's with the ghosts—Job believes the dead rose to see their children digging so nigh them!"

"'Tis probable," said Lionel, who believed it wisest to humor the wild conceits of the lad, in order to disarm his cunning; "but, though the dead are invisible, the living may be counted."

"Job did count five hundred men marching over the nose of Bunker, by star-light, with their picks and spades; and then he stopped, for he forgot whether seven or eight hundred came next."

"And after you ceased to count, did many others pass?"

"The Bay colony isn't so poorly off for men, that it can't muster a thousand at a raising."

"But you had a master workman on the occasion; was it the wolf-hunter of Connecticut?"

"There is no occasion to go from the province to find a workman to lay out a cellar! —Dickey Gridley is a Boston boy!"

"Ah! he is the chief! we can have nothing to fear then, since the Connecticut woodsman is not at their head!"

"Do you think old Prescott, of Pepperel, will quit the hill while he has a kernel of powder to burn?—no, no, Major Lincoln, Ralph himself an't a stouter warrior; and you can't frighten Ralph!"

"But if they fire their cannon often, their small stock of ammunition will be soon consumed, and then they must unavoidably run."

Job laughed tauntingly, and with an appearance of high scorn, before he answered—

"Yes, if the Bay-men were as dumb as the king's troops, and used such big guns! but the cannon of the colony want but little brimstone, and there's but few of them.— Let the rake-hellies go up to Breed's; the people will teach them the law!"

Lionel had now obtained all he expected to learn from the simpleton, concerning the force and condition of the Americans; and as the moments were too precious to be wasted in vain discourse, he bid the lad repair to his quarters that night, and left him. On entering his own lodgings, Major Lincoln shut himself up in his private apartment, and passed several hours in writing, and examining important papers. One letter, in particular, was written, read, torn, and rewritten, five or six times, until at length he placed his seal, and directed the important paper with a sort of carelessness that denoted his patience was exhausted by repeated trials. These documents were intrusted to Meriton, with orders to deliver them to their several addresses, unless countermanded before the following day; and the young man hastily swallowed a late and light break-fast. While shut up in his closet, Lionel had several times thrown aside his pen to listen, as the hum of the place penetrated to his retirement, and announced the excite-ment and bustle which pervaded the streets of the town. Having at length completed the task he had assigned himself, he caught up his hat, and took his way, with hasty steps, into the centre of the place.

Cannon were rattling over the rough pavements, followed by ammunition wagons, and officers and men of the artillery were seen in swift pursuit of their pieces. Aide-de-camps were riding furiously through the streets, charged with important messages; and here and there an officer might be seen issuing from his quarters, with a countenance in which manly pride struggled powerfully with inward dejection, as he caught the last glance of anguish, which followed his retiring form, from eyes that had been used to meet his own with looks of confidence and love. There was, however, but little time to dwell on these flitting glimpses of domestic woe, amid the general bustle and glitter of the scene. Now and then, the strains of martial music broke up through the wind-ings of the crooked avenues, and detachments of the troops wheeled by, on their way to the appointed place of embarkation. While Lionel stood a moment at the corner of a street, admiring the firm movement of a body of grenadiers, his eye fell on the pow-erful frame and rigid features of M'Fuse, marching at the head of his company with that gravity which regarded the accuracy of the step amongst the important incidents of life. At a short distance from him was Job Pray, timing his paces to the tread of the soldiers, and regarding the gallant show with stupid admiration, while his ear un-consciously drank the inspiring music of their band. As this fine body of men passed on, it was immediately succeeded by a battalion, in which Lionel instantly recognized the facings of his own regiment. The warm-hearted Polwarth led its forward files, and, waving his hand, he cried—

"God bless you, Leo, God bless you—we shall make a fair stand-up fight of this; there is an end of all stag-hunting."

The notes of the horns rose above his voice, and Lionel could do no more than re-turn his cordial salute; when, recalled to his purpose by the sight of his comrades, he turned and pursued his way to the quarters of the commander-in-chief.

The gate of Province-House was thronged with military men; some waiting for admittance, and others entering and departing with the air of those who were charged with the execution of matters of the deepest moment. The name of Major Lincoln was hardly announced before an aide appeared to conduct him into the presence of the governor, with a politeness and haste that several gentlemen, who had been in waiting for hours, deemed in a trifling degree unjust.

Lionel, however, having little to do with murmurs which he did not hear, followed his conductor, and was immediately ushered into the apartment, where a council of war had just closed its deliberations. On the threshold of its door, he was compelled to give way to an officer, who was departing in haste, and whose powerful frame seemed bent a little in the intensity of thought, as his dark, military countenance lighted for an instant with the salutation he returned to the low bow of the young soldier. Around this chief, a group of younger men immediately clustered, and as they departed in company, Lionel was enabled to gather from their conversation, that they took their way for the field of battle. The room was filled with officers of high rank; though here and there was to be seen a man in civil attire, whose disappointed and bitter looks announced him to be one of those mandamus counsellors, whose evil advice had hastened the mischief their wisdom could never repair. From out a small circle of these mortified civilians, the unpretending person of Gage advanced to meet Lionel, forming a marked contrast, by the simplicity of its dress, to the military splendor that was glittering around him.

"In what can I oblige Major Lincoln?" he said, taking the young man by the hand cordially, as if glad to be rid of the troublesome counsellors he had so unceremoniously quitted.

"'Wolfe's own' has just passed me on its way to the boats, and I have ventured to intrude on your excellency to inquire if it were not time its major had resumed his duty."

A shade of thought was seated for a moment on the placid features of the general, and he then answered, with a friendly smile—

"'Twill be no more than an affair of outposts, and must be quickly ended. But should I grant the request of every brave young man whose spirit is up to-day, it might cost his majesty's service the life of some officer that would make the purchase of the pile of earth too dear."

"But may I not be permitted to say, that the family of Lincoln is of the province, and its example should not be lost on such an occasion?"

"The loyalty of the colonies is too well represented here to need the sacrifice," said Gage, glancing his eyes carelessly at the expecting group behind him. "My council have decided on the officers to be employed, and I regret that Major Lincoln's name was omitted, since I know it will give him pain; but valuable lives are not to be lightly and unnecessarily exposed."

Lionel bowed in submission; and, after communicating the little he had gathered from Job Pray, he turned away, and found himself near another officer of high rank, who smiled as he observed his disappointed countenance, and, taking him by the arm, led him from the room, with a freedom suited to his fine figure and easy air.

"Then, like myself, Lincoln, you are not to battle for the king to-day," he said, on gaining the antechamber. "Howe has the luck of the occasion, if there can be luck in so vulgar an affair. But *allons;* accompany me to Copp's, as a spectator, since they deny us parts in the drama; and perhaps we may pick up materials for a pasquinade, though not for an epic."

"Pardon me, General Burgoyne," said Lionel, "if I view the matter with more serious eyes than yourself."

"Ah! I had forgot that you were a follower of Percy in the hunt of Lexington!" interrupted the other; "we will call it a tragedy, then, if it better suits your humor. For myself, Lincoln, I weary of these crooked streets and gloomy houses, and, having some taste for the poetry of nature, would have long since looked out upon the deserted fields of these husbandmen, had the authority, as well as the inclination, rested with me. But Clinton is joining us; he, too, is for Copp's, where we can all take a lesson in arms, by studying the manner in which Howe wields his battalions."

A soldier of middle age now joined them, whose stout frame, while it wanted the grace and ease of the gentleman who still held Lionel by the arm, bore a martial character to which the look of the quiet and domestic Gage was a stranger; and, followed by their several attendants, the whole party immediately left the government-house to take their destined position on the eminence so often mentioned.

As they entered the street, Burgoyne relinquished the arm of his companion, and moved with becoming dignity by the side of his brother general. Lionel gladly availed himself of this alteration to withdraw a little from the group, whose steps he followed at such a distance as permitted him to observe those exhibitions of feeling, on the part of the inhabitants, which the pride of the others induced them to overlook. Pallid and anxious female faces were gleaming out upon them from every window, while the roofs of the houses, and the steeples of the churches, were beginning to throng with more daring and equally interested spectators. The drums no longer rolled along the narrow streets, though, occasionally, the shrill strain of a fife was heard from the water, announcing the movements of the troops to the opposite peninsula. Over all was heard the incessant roaring of the artillery, which, untired, had not ceased to rumble in the air since the appearance of light, until the ear, accustomed to its presence, had learnt to distinguish the lesser sounds we have recorded.

As the party descended into the lower passages of the town, it appeared deserted by every thing having life; the open windows and neglected doors betraying the urgency of the feelings which had called the population to situations more favorable for observing the approaching contest. This appearance of intense curiosity excited the sympathies of even the old and practised soldiers; and, quickening their paces, the whole soon rose from among the gloomy edifices to the open and unobstructed view from the hill.

The whole scene now lay before them. Nearly in their front was the village of Charlestown, with its deserted streets and silent roofs, looking like a place of the dead; or, if the signs of life were visible within its open avenues, 'twas merely some figure moving swiftly in the solitude, like one who hastened to quit the devoted spot. On the opposite point of the south-eastern face of the peninsula, and at the distance of a thousand yards, the ground was already covered by masses of human beings, in scarlet,

Lionel Lincoln: Lionel thought himself a prisoner, as
a man, armed with a long rifle, glided from the wood,
and laid his hand on the rein of his bridle.

with their arms glittering in a noon-day sun. Between the two, though in the more immediate vicinity of the silent town, the rounded ridge, already described, rose abruptly from a flat that was bounded by the water, until, having attained an elevation of some fifty or sixty feet, it swelled gradually to the little crest, where was planted the humble object that had occasioned all this commotion. The meadows, on the right, were still peaceful and smiling, as in the most quiet days of the province, though the excited fancy of Lionel imagined that a sullen stillness lingered about the neglected kilns in their front, and over the whole landscape, that was in gloomy consonance with the approaching scene. Far on the left, across the waters of the Charles, the American camp had poured forth its thousands to the hills; and the whole population of the country, for many miles inland, had gathered to a point to witness a struggle charged with the fate of their nation. Beacon Hill rose from out the appalling silence of the town of Boston, like a pyramid of living faces, with every eye fixed on the fatal point; and men hung along the yards of the shipping, or were suspended on cornices, cupolas, and steeples, in thoughtless security, while every other sense was lost in the absorbing interest of the sight. The vessels of war had hauled deep into the rivers, or, more properly, those narrow arms of the sea which formed the peninsula, and sent their iron missiles with unwearied industry across the low passage, which alone opened the means of communication between the self-devoted yeomen on the hill and their distant countrymen. While battalion landed after battalion on the point, cannon-balls from the battery of Copp's, and the vessels of war, were glancing up the natural glacis that surrounded the redoubt, burying themselves in its earthen parapet, or plunging with violence into the deserted sides of the loftier height which lay a few hundred yards in its rear; and the black and smoking bombs appeared to hover above the spot, as if pausing to select the places in which to plant their deadly combustibles.

Notwithstanding these appalling preparations and ceaseless annoyances, throughout that long and anxious morning, the stout husbandmen on the hill had never ceased their steady efforts to maintain, to the uttermost extremity, the post they had so daringly assumed. In vain the English exhausted every means to disturb their stubborn foes; the pick, the shovel, and the spade, continued to perform their offices; and mound rose after mound, amid the din and danger of the cannonade, steadily, and as well as if the fanciful conceits of Job Pray embraced their real objects, and the laborers were employed in the peaceful pursuits of their ordinary lives. This firmness, however, was not like the proud front, which high training can impart to the most common mind; for, ignorant of the glare of military show—in the simple and rude vestments of their calling—armed with such weapons as they had seized from the hooks above their own mantels—and without even a banner to wave its cheering folds above their heads, they stood, sustained only by the righteousness of their cause, and those deep moral principles which they had received from their fathers, and which they intended this day should show were to be transmitted untarnished to their children. It was afterward known, that they endured their labors and their dangers even in want of that sustenance which is so essential to support animal spirits in moments of calmness and ease; while their enemies, on the point, awaiting the arrival of their latest bands, were securely devouring a meal, which to hundreds among them proved to be their last. The fatal instant now seemed approaching. A general movement was seen among the battalions of the British, who began to spread along the shore, under cover of the brow of the hill—the lingering boats having arrived with the rear of their detachments—and officers hurried from regiment to regiment with the final mandates of their chief. At this moment a body of Americans appeared on the crown of Bunker Hill, and, descending swiftly by the road, disappeared in the meadows to the left of their own redoubt. This band was followed by others, who, like themselves, had broken through the dangers of the narrow pass, by braving the fire of the shipping, and who also hurried to join their comrades on the low land. The British general determined at once to anticipate the arrival of further reinforcements, and gave forth the long-expected order to prepare for the attack.

The Americans had made a show, in the course of that fearful morning, of returning the fire of their enemies, by throwing a few shot from their light field-pieces, as if in mockery of the tremendous cannonade which they sustained. But as the moment of severest trial approached, the same awful stillness, which had settled upon the streets of Charlestown, hovered around the redoubt. On the meadows, to its left, the recently arrived bands hastily threw the rails of two fences into one, and, covering the whole with the mown grass that surrounded them, they posted themselves along the frail defence, which answered no better purpose than to conceal their weakness from their adversaries. Behind this characteristic rampart, several bodies of husbandmen, from the neighboring provinces of New Hampshire and Connecticut, lay on their arms in sullen expectation. Their line extended from the shore to the base of the ridge, where it terminated several hundred feet behind the works; leaving a wide opening in a diagonal direction, between the fence and an earthen breast-work, which ran a short distance down the declivity of the hill, from the north-eastern angle of the redoubt. A few hundred yards in the rear of this rude disposition, the naked crest of Bunker Hill rose unoccupied and undefended; and the streams of the Charles and Mystick, sweeping around its base, approached so near each other as to blend the sounds of their rippling. It was across this low and narrow isthmus, that the royal frigates poured a stream of fire, that never ceased, while around it hovered the numerous parties of the undisciplined Americans, hesitating to attempt the dangerous passage.

In this manner Gage had, in a great degree, surrounded the devoted peninsula with his power; and the bold men, who had so daringly planted themselves under the muzzles of his cannon, were left, as already stated, unsupported, without nourishment, and with weapons from their own gun-hooks, singly to maintain the honor of their nation.

Including men of all ages, and conditions, there might have been two thousand of them; but, as the day advanced, small bodies of their countrymen, taking counsel of their feelings, and animated by the example of the old partisan of the woods, who crossed and recrossed the neck, loudly scoffing at the danger, broke through the fire of the shipping in time to join in the closing and bloody business of the hour.

On the other hand, Howe led more than an equal number of the chosen troops of his prince; and as boats continued to ply between the two peninsulas throughout the afternoon, the relative disparity continued undiminished to the end of the struggle. It was at this point in our narrative that, deeming himself sufficiently strong to force the defences of his despised foes, the arrangements immediately preparatory to such an undertaking were made in full view of the excited spectators. Notwithstanding the security with which the English general marshalled his warriors, he felt that the approaching contest would be a battle of no common incidents. The eyes of tens of thousands were fastened on his movements, and the occasion demanded the richest display of the pageantry of war.

The troops formed with beautiful accuracy, and the columns moved steadily along the shore, and took their assigned stations under cover of the brow of the eminence. Their force was in some measure divided; one moiety attempting the toilsome ascent of the hill, and the other moving along the beach, or in the orchards of the more level ground, toward the husbandmen on the meadows. The latter soon disappeared behind some fruit-trees, and the brick-kilns just mentioned. The advance of the royal columns up the ascent was slow and measured, giving time to their field-guns to add their efforts to the uproar of the cannonade, which broke out with new fury as the battalions prepared to march. When each column arrived at the allotted point, it spread the gallant array of its glittering warriors under a bright sun.

"It is a glorious spectacle," murmured the graceful chieftain by the side of Lionel, keenly alive to all the poetry of his alluring profession; "how exceeding soldier-like! and with what accuracy his 'first-arm ascends the hill,' toward his enemy!"

The intensity of his feelings prevented Major Lincoln from replying, and the other soon forgot that he had spoken, in the overwhelming anxiety of the moment. The advance of the British line, so beautiful and slow, resembled rather the ordered steadiness of a drill, than an approach to a deadly struggle. Their standards fluttered proudly above them; and there were moments when the wild music of their bands was heard rising on the air, and tempering the ruder sounds of the artillery. The young and thoughtless in their ranks turned their faces backward, and smiled exultingly, as they beheld steeples, roofs, masts, and heights, teeming with their thousands of eyes, bent on the show of their bright array. As the British lines moved in open view of the little redoubt, and began slowly to gather around its different faces, gun after gun became silent, and the curious artillerist, or tired seaman, lay extended on his heated piece, gazing in mute wonder at the spectacle. There was just then a minute when the roar of the cannonade seemed passing away like the rumbling of distant thunder.

"They will not fight, Lincoln," said the animated leader at the side of Lionel—"the military front of Howe has chilled the hearts of the knaves, and our victory will be bloodless!"

"We shall see, sir—we shall see!"

The words were barely uttered, when platoon after platoon, among the British delivered its fire, the blaze of musketry flashing swiftly around the brow of the hill, and was immediately followed by heavy volleys that ascended from the orchard. Still no answering sound was heard from the Americans, and the royal troops were soon lost to the eye, as they slowly marched into the white cloud which their own fire had alone created.

"They are cowed, by heavens—the dogs are cowed!" once more cried the gay companion of Lionel, "and Howe is within two hundred feet of them, unharmed!"

At that instant a sheet of flame glanced through the smoke, like lightning playing in a cloud, while at one report a thousand muskets were added to the uproar. It was not altogether fancy which led Lionel to imagine that he saw the smoky canopy of the hill to wave, as if the trained warriors it enveloped faltered before this close and appalling discharge; but, in another instant, the stimulating war-cry, and the loud shouts of the combatants were borne across the strait to his ears even amid the horrid din of the combat. Ten breathless minutes flew by like a moment of time, and the bewildered spectators on Copp's were still gazing intently on the scene, when a voice was raised among them, shouting—

"Hurrah! let the rake-hellies go up to Breed's; the people will teach 'em the law!"

"Throw the rebel scoundrel from the hill! Blow him from the muzzle of a gun!" cried twenty soldiers in a breath.

"Hold!" exclaimed Lionel—"'tis a simpleton, an idiot, a fool!"

But the angry and savage murmurs as quickly subsided, and were lost in other feelings, as the bright red lines of the royal troops were seen issuing from the smoke, waving and recoiling before the still vivid fire of their enemies.

"Ha!" said Burgoyne—"'tis some feint to draw the rebels from their hold!"

"'Tis a palpable and disgraceful retreat!" muttered the stern warrior nigh him, whose truer eye detected at a glance the discomfiture of the assailants.—"'Tis another base retreat before the rebels!"

"Hurrah!" shouted the reckless changeling again; there come the reg'lars out of the orchard too!—see the grannies skulking behind the kilns! Let them go on to Breed's; the people will teach 'em the law!"

No cry of vengeance preceded the act this time, but fifty of the soldiery, rushed as by a common impulse, on their prey. Lionel had not time to utter a word of remonstrance, before Job appeared in the air, borne on the uplifted arms of a dozen men, and at the next instant he was seen rolling down the steep declivity, with a velocity that carried him to the water's edge. Springing to his feet, the undaunted changeling once more waved his hat in triumph, and shouted forth again his offensive challenge. Then turning, he launched his canoe from its hiding place among the adjacent lumber, amid a shower of stones, and glided across the strait; his little bark escaping unnoticed in the crowd of boats that were rowing in all directions. But his progress was watched by the uneasy eye of Lionel, who saw him land and disappear, with hasty steps, in the silent streets of the town.

While this trifling by-play was enacting, the great drama of the day was not at a stand. The smoky veil, which clung around the brow of the eminence, was lifted by the air, and sailed heavily away to the south-west, leaving the scene of the bloody struggle again open to the view. Lionel witnessed the grave and meaning glances which the two lieutenants of the king exchanged as they simultaneously turned their glasses from the fatal spot, and, taking the one proffered by Burgoyne, he read their explanation in the numbers of the dead that lay profusely scattered in front of the redoubt. At this instant, an officer from the field held an earnest communication with the two leaders; when, having delivered his orders, he hastened back to his boat, like one who felt himself employed in matters of life and death.

"It shall be done, sir," repeated Clinton, as the other departed, his own honest brow sternly knit under high martial excitement.—"The artillery have their orders, and the work will be accomplished without delay."

"This, Major Lincoln!" cried his more sophisticated companion, "this is one of the trying duties of the soldier! To fight, to bleed, or even to die, for his prince, is his happy privilege; but it is sometimes his unfortunate lot to become the instrument of vengeance."

Lionel waited but a moment for an explanation—the flaming balls were soon seen taking their wide circuit into the air, and carrying their desolation among the close and inflammable roofs of the opposite town. In a very few minutes, a dense black smoke arose from the deserted buildings, and forked flames played actively along the heated shingles, as though rioting in their unmolested possession of the place. He regarded the gathering destruction in painful silence; and, on bending his looks toward his companions, he fancied, notwithstanding the language of the other, that he read the deepest regret in the averted eye of him who had so unhesitatingly uttered the fatal mandate to destroy.

In scenes like these we are attempting to describe, hours appear to be minutes, and time flies as imperceptibly as life slides from beneath the feet of age. The disordered ranks of the British had been arrested at the base of the hill, and were again forming under the eyes of their leaders, with admirable discipline, and extraordinary care. Fresh battalions, from Boston, marched with high military pride into the line, and every thing betokened that a second assault was at hand. When the moment of stupid amazement, which succeeded the retreat of the royal troops, had passed, the troops and batteries poured out their wrath with tenfold fury on their enemies. Shot were incessantly glancing up the gentle acclivity, madly ploughing across its grassy surface, while black and threatening shells appeared to hover above the work, like the monsters of the air, about to stoop upon their prey.

Still all lay quiet and immovable within the low mounds of earth, as if none there had a stake in the issue of the bloody day. For a few moments only, the tall figure of an aged man was seen slowly moving along the summit of the rampart, calmly regarding the dispositions of the English general in the more distant part of his line, and after exchanging a few words with a gentleman, who joined him in his dangerous look-out, they disappeared together behind the grassy banks. Lionel soon detected the name of Prescott of Pepperel, passing through the crowd in low murmurs, and his glass did not deceive him when he thought, in the smaller one of the two, he had himself descried the graceful person of the unknown leader of the ' caucus.'

All eyes were now watching the advance of the battalions, which once more drew nigh the point of contest. The heads of the columns were already in view of their enemies, when a man was seen swiftly ascending the hill from the burning town: he paused amid the peril, on the natural glacis, and swung his hat triumphantly, and Lionel even fancied he heard the exulting cry, as he recognized the ungainly form of the simpleton, before it plunged into the work.

The right of the British once more disappeared in the orchard, and the columns in front of the redoubt again opened with all the imposing exactness of their high discipline. Their arms were already glittering in a line with the green faces of the mound, and Lionel heard the experienced warrior at his side murmuring to himself—

"Let him hold his fire, and he will go in at the point of the bayonet!"

But the trial was too great for even the practised courage of the royal troops. Volley succeeded volley, and in a few moments they had again curtained their ranks behind the misty screen produced by their own fire. Then came the terrible flash from the redoubt, and the eddying volumes from the adverse hosts rolled into one cloud, enveloping the combatants in its folds, as if to conceal their bloody work from the spectators. Twenty times, in the short space of as many minutes, Major Lincoln fancied he heard the incessant roll of the American musketry die away before the heavy and regular volleys of the troops; and then he thought the sounds of the latter grew more faint, and were given at longer intervals.

The result however, was soon known. The heavy bank of smoke, which now even clung along the ground, was broken in fifty places; and the disordered masses of the British were seen driven before their deliberate foes, in wild confusion. The flashing swords of the officers in vain attempted to arrest the torrent, nor did the fight cease, with many of the regiments, until they had even reached their boats. At this moment a hum was heard in Boston, like a sudden rush of wind, and men gazed in each other's faces with undisguised amazement. Here and there a low sound of exultation escaped some unguarded lip, and many an eye gleamed with a triumph that could no longer be suppressed. Until this moment the feelings of Lionel had vacillated between the pride of country and military spirit; but, losing all other feelings in the latter sensation, he now looked fiercely about him, as if he would seek the man who dare exult in the repulse of his comrades. The poetic chieftain was still at his side, biting his nether lip in vexation; but his more tried companion had suddenly disappeared. Another quick glance fell upon his missing form in the act of entering a boat at the foot of the hill. Quicker than thought, Lionel was on the shore, crying, as he flew to the water's edge—

"Hold! for God's sake, hold! remember the 47th is in the field, and that I am its major!"

"Receive him," said Clinton, with that grim satisfaction, with which men acknowledge a valued friend in moments of great trial; "and then row for your lives, or, what is of more value, for the honor of the British name."

The brain of Lionel whirled as the boat shot along its watery bed, but before it had gained the middle of the stream he had time to consider the whole of the appalling scene. The fire had spread from house to house, and the whole village of Charlestown, with its four hundred buildings, was just bursting into flames. The air seemed filled with whistling balls, as they hurtled above his head, and the black sides of the vessels of war were vomiting their sheets of flame with unwearied industry. Amid this tumult, the English general and his companions sprung to land. The former rushed into the disordered ranks, and, by his presence and voice, recalled the men of one regiment to their duty. But long and loud appeals to their spirit and their ancient fame were necessary, to restore a moiety of their former confidence to men who had been thus rudely repulsed, and who now looked along their thinned and exhausted ranks, missing, in many instances, more than half the well-known countenances of their fellows. In the midst of the faltering troops stood their stern and unbending chief; but of all those gay and gallant youths, who followed in his train as he had departed from Province-House that morning, not one remained, but in his blood. He alone seemed undisturbed in that disordered crowd; and his mandates went forth as usual, calm and determined. At length the panic in some degree subsided, and order was once more restored, as the high-spirited and mortified gentlemen of the detachment regained their lost authority.

The leaders consulted together, apart, and the dispositions were immediately renewed for the assault. Military show was no longer affected, but the soldiers laid down all the useless implements of their trade, and many even cast aside their outer garments, under the warmth of a broiling sun, added to the heat of the conflagration, which began to diffuse itself along the extremity of the peninsula. Fresh companies were placed in the columns, and most of the troops were withdrawn from the meadows, leaving merely a few skirmishers, to amuse the Americans who lay behind the fence. When each disposition was completed, the final signal was given to advance.

Lionel had taken post in his regiment, but marching on the skirt of the column, he commanded a view of most of the scene of battle. In his front moved a battalion, reduced to a handful of men in the previous assaults. Behind these came a party of the marine guards, from the shipping, led by their own veteran major; and next followed the dejected Nesbitt and his corps, among whom Lionel looked in vain for the features of the good-natured Polwarth. Similar columns marched on their right and left, encircling three sides of the redoubt by their battalions.

A few minutes brought him in full view of that humble and unfinished mound of earth, for the possession of which so much blood had that day been spilt in vain. It lay, as before, still as if none breathed within its bosom, though a terrific row of dark tubes were arrayed along its top, following the movements of the approaching columns, as the eyes of the imaginary charmers of our own wilderness are said to watch their victims. As the uproar of the artillery again grew fainter, the crash of falling streets, and the appalling sounds of the conflagration, on their left, became more audible. Immense volumes of black smoke issued from the smouldering ruins, and, bellying outward, fold beyond fold, it overhung the work in a hideous cloud, casting its gloomy shadow across the place of blood.

A strong column was now seen ascending, as if from out the burning town, and the advance of the whole became quick and spirited. A low call ran through the platoons, to note the naked weapons of their adversaries, and it was followed by the cry of "To the bayonet! to the bayonet!"

"Hurrah for the Royal Irish!" shouted M'Fuse, at the head of the dark column from the conflagration.

"Hurrah!" echoed a well-known voice from the silent mound; "let them come on to Breed's; the people will teach 'em the law!"

Men think at such moments with the rapidity of lightning, and Lionel had even fancied his comrades in possession of the work, when the terrible stream of fire flashed in the faces of the men in front.

"Push on with the ——th," cried the veteran major of marines—"push on, or the 18th will get the honor of the day!"

"We cannot," murmured the soldiers of the ——th; "their fire is too heavy!"

"Then break, and let the marines pass through you!"

The feeble battalion melted away, and the warriors of the deep, trained to conflicts of hand to hand, sprang forward, with a loud shout, in their places. The Americans, exhausted of their ammunition, now sunk sullenly back, a few hurling stones at their foes, in desperate indignation. The cannon of the British had been brought to enfilade their short breast-work, which was no longer tenable; and as the columns approached closer to the low rampart, it became a mutual protection to the adverse parties.

"Hurrah for the Royal Irish!" again shouted M'Fuse, rushing up the trifling ascent, which was but of little more than his own height.

"Hurrah!" repeated Pitcairn, waving his sword on another angle of the work— "the day's our own!"

One more sheet of flame issued out of the bosom of the work, and all those brave men, who had emulated the examples of their officers, were swept away, as though a whirlwind had passed along. The grenadier gave his war-cry once more, before he pitched headlong among his enemies; while Pitcairn fell back into the arms of his own child. The cry of "Forward, 47th," rung through their ranks, and in their turn this veteran battalion gallantly mounted the ramparts. In the shallow ditch Lionel passed the expiring marine, and caught the dying and despairing look from his eyes, and in another instant he found himself in the presence of his foes. As company followed company into the defenceless redoubt, the Americans sullenly retired by its rear, keeping the bayonets of the soldiers at bay with clubbed muskets and sinewy arms. When the whole issued upon the open ground, the husbandmen received a close and fatal fire from the battalions, which were now gathering around them on three sides. A scene of wild and savage confusion then succeeded to the order of the fight, and many fatal blows were given and taken, the mêlée rendering the use of fire-arms nearly impossible for several minutes.

Lionel continued in advance, pressing on the footsteps of the retiring foe, stepping over many a lifeless body in his difficult progress. Notwithstanding the hurry, and vast disorder of the fray, his eye fell on the form of the graceful stranger, stretched lifeless on the parched grass, which had greedily drank his blood. Amid the ferocious cries, and fiercer passions of the moment, the young man paused, and glanced his eyes around him, with an expression that said he thought the work of death should cease. At this instant the trappings of his attire caught the glaring eyeballs of a dying yeoman, who exerted his wasting strength to sacrifice one more worthy victim to the manes of his countrymen. The whole of the tumultuous scene vanished from the senses of Lionel at the flash of the musket of this man, and he sunk beneath the feet of the combatants, insensible of further triumph, and of every danger.

The fall of a single officer, in such a contest, was a circumstance not to be regarded; and regiments passed over him without a single man stooping to inquire into his fate. When the Americans had disengaged themselves from the troops, they descended into the little hollow between the two hills, swiftly, and like a disordered crowd, bearing off most of their wounded, and leaving but few prisoners in the hands of their foes. The formation of the ground favored their retreat, as hundreds of bullets whistled harmlessly above their heads; and by the time they gained the acclivity of Bunker, distance was added to their security. Finding the field lost, the men at the fence broke away in a body from their position, and abandoned the meadows; the whole moving in confused masses behind the crest of the adjacent height. The shouting soldiery followed in their footsteps, pouring in fruitless and distant volleys; but on the summit of Bunker their tired platoons were halted, and they beheld the throng move fearlessly through the tremendous fire that enfiladed the low pass, as little injured as though most of them bore charmed lives.

The day was now drawing to a close. With the disappearance of their enemies, the ships and batteries ceased their cannonade; and presently not a musket was heard in that place, where so fierce a contest had so long raged. The troops commenced fortifying the outward eminence, on which they rested, in order to maintain their barren conquest; and nothing further remained for the achievement of the royal lieutenants, but to go and mourn over their victory.

Last of the Mohicans: Placing Alice, then, on the same horse with Cora, he seized the bridle, and commenced his route by plunging deeper into the forest.

VI.

THE MOHICANS.

In the summer of 1825, a travelling party of some half-dozen gentlemen left New York with the intention of making an excursion to Saratoga and Lake George. Of this party Mr. Cooper was one. Several young Englishmen of note were among his companions, all of whom, at a later period, became prominent in public life as members of the British government. Those were happy days for travellers—ere the shrill steam-whistle had been heard, startling the quiet flocks in rural fields; tradition tells us that it was possible at that period to move leisurely, actually to find pleasure in travelling itself, to feel a sense of enjoyment in moving over a road, from one point to another, to see clearly, to breathe freely —a state of things extremely difficult to comprehend, when, captives in a close and crowded car, we are whirling at the will of a desperate locomotive. A day could then be given to a river shore and its varied beauties, to an inland valley and its quiet repose; while, at the present moment, we are condemned to rush blindly, over the same ground, in an atmosphere of smoke and dust, at the speed of a steeple-chase, and with the constraint of a German "Par-force Jagd!" The excursion proved a very pleasant one. Parts of the ground were new to Mr. Cooper, whose eye for natural scenery was delicate and sensitive as that of a poet, while his interest in every thing practical, in all true progress, was as thorough and comprehensive as that of any plodding utilitarian. The conversation of a party of highly-educated young men, with European views of things, naturally gave additional interest to the journey. Mr. Cooper was much struck with a remark on the size of the forest-trees of America, smaller than was anticipated, scarcely equal in size, it was asserted, to those of the older parks, and church-yards and village greens of England.   One is scarcely prepared indeed for this result of civilization; we should rather have believed that the pride of the forests would naturally reveal itself in grander forms within the bounds of the wilderness—that the fostering care of man could do little for the woods.   Such was then, the usual American idea on this subject; but we are beginning, it is hoped, to learn another lesson, to discover that the forests and groves are one of the higher forms of husbandry.   As yet, in America, man has done absolutely nothing to improve, and much to mar, this great gift of Providence.

A conversation occurring at the time, in connection with a very different subject, may be alluded to.   It relates to a point connected with that singular fragment of feudal ages, the framework of English society; to a point of legal precedence in rank, among the English peers—as to which of the House of Peers could claim to be premier baron of England.   Mr. Cooper, unless the writer's memory is deceived, asserted that it was Howard, Duke of Norfolk, as Baron Fitzalan, who held this rank.   Another peer was named by the gentleman with whom he was conversing; each was confident as to his own view, and a wager was laid on the subject.   Returning to New York, inquiry proved that the nobleman named by Mr. Cooper actually held the rank of premier baron of England, and the author received, as a memento of the discussion, a seal with a baron's coronet for the device, and for inscription, the old Scottish proverb, "He that will to Cupar, maun to Cupar!"   Some years earlier Mr. Cooper had amused himself with a course of reading in English biography and heraldry, which gave him confidence in the correctness of the opinion he had expressed.

The party moved slowly up the Hudson, halting in the Highlands at West Point; thence to Catskill, which Mr. Cooper had already seen with delight, a few years earlier, as Natty can testify:

" 'It must have been a sight of melancholy pleasure, indeed,' said Edwards, while his eye roved along the shores and over the hills, where the clearings, groaning with the golden corn, were cheering the forests with the signs of life, 'to have roamed over these mountains, and along this sheet of beautiful water, without a living soul to speak to, or to thwart your humor.'

" 'Haven't I said it was a cheerful!' said Leather-Stocking.   'Yes, yes—when the trees begun to be kivered with the leaves, and the ice was out of the lake, it was a second paradise.   I have travelled the woods for fifty-three years, and have made them my home for more than forty, and I can say that I have met but one place that was more to my liking; and that was only to eyesight, and not for hunting or fishing.'

" 'And where was that?' asked Edwards.

" 'Where! why up on the Catskills. I used often to go up into the mountains after wolves' skins, and bears; once they bought me to get them a stuffed painter; and so I often went. There's a place in them hills that I used to climb to when I wanted to see the carryings-on of the world, that would well pay any man for a barked shin or a torn moccasin. You know the Catskills, lad, for you must have seen them on your left, as you followed the river up from York, looking as blue as a piece of clear sky, and holding the clouds on their tops, as the smoke curls over the head of an Indian chief at a council-fire. Well, there's the High-peak and the Round-top, which lay back, like a father and mother among their children, seeing they are far above all the other hills. But the place I mean is next to the river, where one of the ridges juts out a little from the rest, and where the rocks fall for the best part of a thousand feet, so much up and down, that a man standing on their edges is fool enough to think he can jump from top to bottom.'

" 'What see you when you get there?' asked Edwards.

" 'Creation!' said Natty, dropping the end of his rod into the water, and sweeping one hand around him in a circle—" all creation, lad. I was on that hill when Vaughan burnt 'Sopus, in the last war, and I seen the vessels come out of the Highlands as plain as I can see that lime-scow rowing into the Susque-hanna, though one was twenty times further from me than the other. The river was in sight for seventy miles, under my feet, looking like a curled shaving, though it was eight long miles to its banks. I saw the hills in the Hampshire grants, the high lands of the river, and all that God had done or man could do, as far as eye could reach—you know that the Indians named me for my sight, lad—and from the flat on the top of that mountain, I have often found the place where Albany stands; and as for 'Sopus! the day the royal troops burnt the town, the smoke seemed so nigh, that I thought I could hear the screeches of the women.'

" 'It must have been worth the toil, to meet with such a glorious view!'

" 'If being the best part of a mile in the air, and having men's farms and housen at your feet, with rivers looking like ribbons, and mountains bigger than the 'Vision,' seeming to be haystacks of green grass under you, gives any satis-faction to a man, I can recommend the spot. When I first come into the woods to live, I used to have weak spells, and I felt lonesome; and then I would go into the Catskills and spend a few days on that hill, to look at the ways of man; but it's now many a year since I felt any such longings, and I'm getting too old for them rugged rocks. But there's a place, a short two miles back of that very hill, that in late times I relished better than the mountain ; for it was more kivered with the trees, and more nateral.'

"'And where was that?' inquired Edwards, whose curiosity was strongly excited by the simple description of the hunter.

"'Why, there's a fall in the hills, where the water of two little ponds that lie near each other breaks out of their bounds, and runs over the rocks into the valley. The stream is, maybe, such a one as would turn a mill, if so useless a thing was wanted in the wilderness. But the hand that made that 'Leap' never made a mill! There the water comes crooking and winding among the rocks, first so slow that a trout could swim in it, and then starting and running just like any creater that wanted to make a far spring, till it gets to where the mountain divides, like the cleft hoof of a deer, leaving a deep hollow for the brook to tumble into. The first pitch is nigh two hundred feet, and the water looks like flakes of driven snow, afore it touches the bottom ; and there the stream gathers itself together again for a new start, and maybe flutters over fifty feet of flat-rock, before it falls for another hundred, when it jumps about from shelf to shelf, first turning this-away, and then turning that-away, striving to get out of the hollow, till it finally comes to the plain.'

"'I have never heard of this spot before!' exclaimed Edwards ; 'it is not mentioned in the books.'

"'I never read a book in my life,' said Leather-Stocking ; 'and how should a man who has lived in towns and schools know any thing about the wonders of the woods! No, no, lad ; there has that little stream of water been playing among them hills, since He made the world, and not a dozen white men have ever laid eyes on it. The rock sweeps like mason-work, in a half-round, on both sides of the fall, and shelves over the bottom for fifty feet ; so that when I've been sitting at the foot of the first pitch, and my hounds have run into the caverns behind the sheet of water, they've looked no bigger than so many rabbits. To my judgment, lad, it's the best piece of work that I've met with in the woods ; and none know how often the hand of God is seen in a wilderness but them that rove it for a man's life.'

"'What becomes of the water?—in which direction does it run? Is it a tributary of the Delaware?'

"'Anan!' said Natty.

"'Does the water run into the Delaware?'

"'No, no ; it's a drop for the old Hudson ; and a merry time it has till it gets down off the mountain. I've sat on the shelving rock many a long hour, boy, and watched the bubbles as they shot by me, and thought how long it would be

before that very water, which seemed made for the wilderness, would be under
the bottom of a vessel, and tossing in the salt sea. It is a spot to make a man
solemnize. You can see right down into the valley that lies to the east of the
High-Peak, where, in the fall of the year, thousands of acres of woods are before
your eyes, in the deep hollow, and along the side of the mountain, painted like
ten thousand rainbows, by no hand of man, but with the ordering of God's
providence.'

 " ' Why, you are eloquent, Leather-Stocking,' exclaimed the youth.

 " ' Anan !' repeated Natty.

 " ' The recollection of the sight has warmed your blood, old man.' "

Farther up the river, the poor deluded Shakers were visited, and beheld with
compassion in their beautiful valley and neat village at Lebanon. Good dinners
were eaten at hospitable tables in Albany. The Cohoes, formerly a favorite spot
with the writer, were seen and still admired, in spite of the busy mills springing
up on their banks. The gentlemen mingled awhile with the gay throng at Saratoga and Ballston. Thence they passed to Lake George and Glenn's Falls. There
the ground was quite new to the American as well as to the European members
of the party. With Lake George, still so freshly wild in its wooded heights, its
untilled islands, its crystal waters, its silent shores, the author was greatly charmed.
After lingering awhile on its banks with delight, the party retraced their steps,
pausing, like others, at Glenn's Falls. The hand of man had already been busy
here, turning the power of the stream to account for industrial purposes, but there

was far more of natural beauty still clinging about the spot than at the present hour, and the singular character of the dark and silent caverns in the heart of the troubled stream was then very impressive. The travellers were much struck with those dark and sombre rocks, and the flood falling in fantastic wreaths of foam about them. While in the caverns, one of the gentlemen of the party observed to Mr. Cooper that here was the very scene for a romance. Some pleasantry passed between them on the subject, and the writer promised his companion, that a book should actually be written in which these caves should hold an important place; and the idea of a romance, essentially Indian in character, then first suggested itself to his mind. The gentleman to whom the promise was given has since been prime minister of England. Before leaving the falls, the ground was examined closely, with a view to accurate description at a later hour. The actual natural features of the spot were combined in imagination with those which had been partially defaced by man: the ancient forests were again restored, the first rude and unfinished steps of early civilization disappeared, and the waters fell once more, as they had fallen for thousands of forgotten years, in full, natural torrents, unchecked by any barrier raised by human labor. In the tale which was soon after written, the reader, with a beautiful touch of poetical instinct, is led to those wild caverns, through the unbroken forest, in company with the backwoodsman and the savage, in a moment of peril, and in the dark hours of night. Natty's picture of the spot, given to his wondering companions, seeking shelter within the caves, of which they had still but a vague impression, is offered to the reader.

"When the voice of Hawk-eye ceased, the roar of the cataract sounded like the roar of distant thunder.

"'Are we quite safe in this cavern?' demanded Heyward. 'Is there no danger of surprise? A single armed man, at its entrance, would hold us at his mercy.'

"A spectral-looking figure stalked from out the darkness behind the scout, and, seizing a blazing brand, held it toward the further extremity of their place of retreat. Alice uttered a faint shriek, and even Cora rose to her feet, as this appalling object moved into the light; but a single word from Heyward calmed them, with the assurance it was only their attendant. Chingachgook, who, lifting another blanket, discovered that the cavern had two outlets. Then, holding the brand, he crossed a deep, narrow chasm in the rocks, which ran at right angles with the passage they were in, but which, unlike that, was open to the heavens, entering another cave, which answered to the description of the first, in every essential particular.

" 'Such old foxes as Chingachgook and myself are not often caught in a burrow with one hole,' said Hawk-eye, laughing; 'you can easily see the cunning of the place—the rock is black limestone, which every body knows is soft; it makes no uncomfortable pillow, where brush and pine-wood are scarce; well, the fall was once a few yards below us, and, I dare to say, was, in its time, as regular and handsome a sheet of water as any along the Hudson. But old age is a great injury to good looks, as these sweet young ladies have yet to learn. The place is sadly changed! Those rocks are full of cracks, and in some places they are softer than in other some, and the water has worked out deep hollows for itself, until it has fallen back, aye, some hundred feet, breaking here, and wearing there, until the falls have neither shape nor consistency.'

" 'In what part of them are we?' asked Heyward.

" 'Why, we are nigh the spot that Providence first placed them at, but where, it seems, they were too rebellious to stay. The rock proved softer on each side of us, and so they left the centre of the river bare and dry, first working out these two little holes for us to hide in.'

" 'We are, then, on an island?'

" 'Aye! There are falls on two sides of us, and the river above and below! If you had daylight, it would be worth the trouble to step up on the height of this rock, and look at the pervarcity of the water. It falls by no rule at all; sometimes it leaps; sometimes it tumbles; there it tumbles, here it shoots; in one place 'tis white as snow, and in another 'tis green as grass; hereabouts, it pitches into deep hollows, that rumble and quake the 'arth; and there-away, it ripples and sings like a brook, fashioning whirlpools and gulleys in the old stone, as if 'twas no harder than trodden clay. The whole design of the river seems disconcerted. First it runs smoothly, as if meaning to go down the descent as things were ordered; then it angles about and faces the shore; nor are there places wanting where it looks backward, as if unwilling to leave the wilderness and mingle with the salt! Aye, lady, the fine cobweb-looking cloth you wear at your throat is coarse and like a fish-net to little spots I can show you where the river fabricates all sorts of images, as if, having broken loose from order, it would try its hand at every thing. And yet, what does it amount to! After the water has been suffered to have its will, for a time, like a headstrong man, it is gathered together by the hand that made it, and a few rods below you may see it all flowing on steadily toward the sea, as was preordained from the first foundation of the 'arth!' "

Returning home, the book was immediately commenced. It was very rapidly written, and some three or four months from the time its first pages were composed, the last chapter was finished. Planned beneath the summer leaves, those

leaves had scarcely fallen when the story was told, and Natty and Chingachgook
were left in the wilderness, beside the rude grave of Uncas. It was with some
hesitation that the writer attempted, what has always been considered as a dangerous experiment, the introduction for a second time of a prominent and successful character already familiar to the reader, in an earlier book. It was very seldom,
however, that he now consulted with any friend but one, regarding the work in
hand; and the affectionate counsellor at his side, well aware that the consciousness of power might, in itself, render practicable a task in which so much interest
was shown, advised his carrying out the plan. The step was taken, and Natty
and Chingachgook were once more brought before the reader; but at a period
supposed to be earlier in their own career than that of the Pioneers, and beneath
the shadow of the unbroken forest.

Although the book was very rapidly written, yet during its progress—soon
after commencing it, indeed—the writer was seized with a serious illness. Naturally of a very sound and vigorous constitution, he had scarcely known until lately
what a day's physical ailing was. But a year or two earlier, while returning from
a visit to Bedford, the carriage he was driving broke down at one of the villages
on the Sound, and, always glad of an excuse for being afloat, he took passage for
New York in a sloop. The wind began to fail; he was anxious to reach home,
and, in order to make the utmost of the tide, he took the helm, steering the little
craft himself through Hell-Gate; the day was extremely sultry, and exposure to
the intense heat brought on a sudden and severe attack of fever, which in its first
hours partook something of the character of a stroke of the sun. And now, in
the autumn of 1825, exposure again brought on the same disease. During the
height of the attack, his mind was filled with images connected with the book
recently begun. One afternoon, suddenly rousing himself, he called for pen and
paper; but, too ill to use them himself, he requested Mrs. Cooper, watching
anxiously at his side, to write to his dictation. Most reluctantly, and in fear of
delirium, the request was complied with, and solely with a view of relieving his

mind from temporary excitement. A page of notes was rapidly dictated, and written out; to his alarmed nurse they appeared the wild incoherent fancies of delirium, with which the names of Natty, Chingachgook, and Cora, already familiar to her, were blended. But in truth there was no delirium; a clear and vivid picture of the struggle between Magua and Chingachgook filled his mind at the moment, and only a few weeks later the chapter—the twelfth of the book —was actually written from that rude sketch. And this proved to be one of the very few instances in which preliminary notes relating to a work in hand were thrown on paper. At the same period he was visited by his old college tutor and kind friend, Professor Silliman, who left the house with some serious fears as to the result of the attack. By the mercy of Providence, however, he soon recovered from all immediate danger; though for several years he suffered from the consequences of the disease by a form of nervous dyspepsia, previously unknown to him.

Early in the winter of 1826, "The Last of the Mohicans" was published, by Messrs. Carey & Lea, of Philadelphia. Its success was greater than that of any previous book from the same pen. The freshness of the subject gave it a singular charm, while the rapid succession of spirited incident, entirely original in character, and the powerful interest infused into the whole work, commanded attention in a very unusual degree. Natty was greeted anew with delight; there could be no doubt as to the success of the experiment of presenting him a second time to the reader. The character was sketched even more forcibly, though with less of poetical light, perhaps, than in the first book. It was the difference between vigorous manhood and venerable age. And instead of the single Indian, in the person of Chingachgook, warrior after warrior appears, until the scene is filled with numerous war-parties, and the villages of contending tribes. The writer had been at pains to obtain accurate details regarding Indian life and character, although the sources of information open to him at that day were very few indeed, compared with those which he might have commanded at the present hour; the earlier writers on those subjects, Heckwelder, Charlevoix, Penn, Smith, Elliot, Colden, were studied. The narratives of Lang, of Lewis and Clarke, of Mackenzie, were examined. His own opportunities of intercourse with the red man had been few; occasionally some small party of the Oneidas, or other representatives of the Five Nations, had crossed his path in the valley of the Susquehanna, or on the shores of Lake Ontario, where he served when a midshipman in the navy. And more recently, since the idea of introducing these wild people into his books had occurred to him, he had been at no little pains to seize every opportunity offered for observation. Fortunately for his purpose, deputations to Washington from the Western tribes, were quite frequent at that moment; he visited these different parties, as they passed through Albany and New York, following them in several instances to Washington for the purpose of closer observation, and with a view also to gathering information from the officers and interpreters who accompanied them.   From these sources he drew the details of his pictures in "The Mohicans."

In Europe the book produced quite a startling effect; the freshness of the subject, in the sense of fiction, naturally adding greatly to the vivid interest of the narrative.   As yet, there had been but one American work of the imagination in which the red man was introduced with any prominence: "Edgar Huntley," by Brockden Brown, a writer of undoubted talent, but scarcely known in England. While alluding to his work, it may be well to remark that Mr. Cooper had not read "Edgar Huntley" since his own boyhood, when his writing an Indian romance himself would have seemed an event wildly improbable.   Of the books of Brockden Brown, "Weiland" had made the deepest impression on his mind. "The Mohicans" would assuredly have been precisely the book it now is had "Edgar Huntley" never been written.   "The Atala" of M. de Chateaubriand he never read; it was precisely the kind of book in which he would never have felt the least interest, quite too far removed from the realities of life for him to read more than a page or two.   To the particular merits of that kind of book he was perhaps scarcely capable of doing justice; he would have lacked the patience to look for them amid pages so little in harmony with his own nature.   In reading "The Mohicans" for revision, a few years before his death, he observed, with a smile, that the book must needs have some interest for the reader, since it could amuse even the writer, who had in a great measure forgotten the details of his own work.   He saw the defects of the book, however, more plainly perhaps than his readers.   There were some faults of plot, and other errors of detail which did not satisfy him.   One defect of the book must strike those who knew him as singularly inconsistent with his own character.   Munro, as a father placed in most painful circumstances, becomes a mere cipher, not only in the earlier scenes, but later, when we are following with the deepest anxiety the movements of Natty, and Uncas, and Heyward, intent on the rescue of the sisters; while the scout, and the lover, and the young warrior, command our eager attention at every step, we actually forget the presence of the parent who accompanies the party.   Never surely was there a father whose love for his children was of a deeper, purer, stronger nature than his own; never was there one whose daily life and manner were more demonstrative of the feeling; the weakness of Munro's character on this particular point, as drawn in "The Mohicans," becomes therefore the more remarkable. On the other hand, may we not assert that Magua, the subtle, treacherous, revengeful warrior, is one of the most skilfully drawn of his Indian sketches—a creature as thoroughly savage as any that ever roamed over the same ground, in real existence.

The name of Horican given to the lake was in one sense an application of his own; it was quite as legitimate, however, as that given to the Cayuga and the Oneida and the Seneca, farther toward the setting sun. We give the author's remarks on this subject:

"There is one point on which we wish to say a word. Hawk-eye calls the Lac du St. Sacrement, the 'Horican.' As we believe this to be an appropriation of the name that has its origin with ourselves, the time has arrived, perhaps, when the fact should be frankly admitted. While writing this book, it occurred to us that the French name of this lake was too complicated, the American too commonplace, and the Indian too unpronounceable, for either to be used familiarly in a work of fiction. Looking over an ancient map, it was ascertained that a tribe of Indians, called 'les Horicans' by the French, existed in the neighborhood of this beautiful sheet of water. As every word uttered by Natty was not to be understood as rigid truth, we took the liberty of putting 'the Horican' into his mouth, as the substitute for 'Lake George.' The name has appeared to find favor, and, all things considered, it may possibly be quite as well to let it stand, instead of going back to the House of Hanover for the appellation of our finest sheet of water."

"The Mohicans" is one of those books to which no single extract can do full justice, since it is the rapid succession of original incident, the spirit and poetical movement of the whole work which make its great merit. The canoe chase on the Horican with the Longue Carabine in the foreground, is given as a picture from its pages.

CANOE CHASE ON THE HORICAN.

THE heavens were still studded with stars, when Hawk-eye came to arouse the sleepers. Casting aside their cloaks, Munro and Heyward were on their feet, while the woodsman was still making his low calls at the entrance of the rude shelter where they had passed the night. When they issued from beneath its concealment, they found the scout awaiting their appearance nigh by, and the only salutation between them was the significant gesture for silence, made by their sagacious leader.

"Think over your prayers," he whispered, as they approached him; "for he to whom you make them knows all tongues; that of the heart as well as those of the mouth. But speak not a syllable; it is rare for a white voice to pitch itself properly in the woods, as we have seen by the example of that miserable devil, the singer. Come," he continued, turning toward a curtain of the works; "let us get into the ditch on this side, and, be regardful to step on the stones and fragments of wood as you go."

His companions complied, though to one of them the reasons of all this extraordinary precaution were yet a mystery. When they were in the low cavity that surrounded the earthen fort on three of its sides, they found the passage nearly choked by the ruins. With care and patience, however, they succeeded in clambering after the scout, until they reached the sandy shore of the Horican.

"That's a trail that nothing but a nose can follow," said the satisfied scout, looking back along their difficult way; "grass is a treacherous carpet for a flying party to tread on, but wood and stone take no print from a moccasin. Had you worn your armed boots, there might, indeed, have been something to fear! but with the deer-skin suitably prepared, a man may trust himself, generally, on rocks with safety. Shove in

Last of the Mohicans: "Then you must have lost your
eyesight afore losing your way, for the road across the
portage is cut to a good two rods, and is as grand a
path I calculate, as any that runs into London, or
even before the palace of the king himself."

the canoe nigher to the land, Uncas; this sand will take a stamp as easily as the butter of the Dutchers on the Mohawk. Softly, lad, softly; it must not touch the beach, or the knaves will know by what road we have left the place."

The young man observed the precaution; and the scout, laying a board from the ruins to the canoe, made a sign for the two officers to enter. When this was done, every thing was studiously restored to its former disorder; and then Hawk-eye succeeded in reaching his little birchen vessel, without leaving behind him any of those marks which he appeared so much to dread. Heyward was silent until the Indians had cautiously paddled the canoe some distance from the fort, and within the broad and dark shadow that fell from the eastern mountains on the glassy surface of the lake; then he demanded—

"What need have we for this stolen and hurried departure?"

"If the blood of an Oneida could stain such a sheet of pure water as this we float on," returned the scout, "your two eyes would answer your own question. Have you forgotten the skulking reptyle that Uncas slew?"

"By no means. But he was said to be alone, and dead men give no cause for fear!"

"Aye, he was alone in his deviltry! but an Indian, whose tribe counts so many warriors, need seldom fear his blood will run out, without the death-shriek coming speedily from some of his enemies."

"But our presence—the authority of Colonel Munro would prove a sufficient protection against the anger of our allies, especially in a case where the wretch so well merited his fate. I trust in Heaven you have not deviated a single foot from the direct line of our course, with so slight a reason."

"Do you think the bullet of that varlet's rifle would have turned aside, though his sacred majesty the king had stood in its path!" returned the stubborn scout. "Why did not the grand Frencher, he who is captain-general of the Canadas, bury the tomahawks of the Hurons, if a word from a white man can work so strongly on the natur of an Indian?"

The reply of Heyward was interrupted by a deep and heavy groan from Munro; but after he had paused a moment, in deference to the sorrow of his aged friend, he resumed the subject.

"The Marquis of Montcalm can only settle that error with his God," said the young man solemnly.

"Aye, aye, now there is reason in your words, for they are bottomed on religion and honesty. There is a vast difference between throwing a regiment of white coats atwixt the tribes and the prisoners, and coaxing an angry savage to forget he carries a knife and a rifle, with words that must begin with calling him 'your son.' No, no," continued the scout, looking back at the dim shore of William Henry which now appeared to be fast receding, and laughing in his own silent but heartfelt manner; "I have put a trail of water atween us; and unless the imps can make friends with the fishes, and hear who has paddled across their basin this fine morning, we shall throw the length of the Horican behind us before they have made up their minds which path to take."

"With foes in front, and foes in our rear, our journey is like to be one of danger!"

"Danger!" repeated Hawk-eye, calmly; "no, not absolutely in danger; for, with vigilant ears and quick eyes, we can manage to keep a few hours ahead of the knaves; or, if we must try the rifle, there are three of us who understand its gifts as well as any you can name on the borders. No, not of danger; but that we shall have what you may call a brisk push of it, is probable; and it may happen, a brush, a skrimmage, or some such divarsion, but always where covers are good, and ammunition abundant."

It is possible that Heyward's estimate of danger, distinguished as he was for spirit, differed in some degree from that of the scout, for, instead of replying, he now sat in silence, while the canoe glided over several miles of water. Just as the day dawned they entered the narrows of the lake, and stole swiftly and cautiously among their numberless little islands. It was by this road that Montcalm had retired with his army, and the adventurers knew not but he had left some of his Indians in ambush, to protect the rear of his forces, and collect the stragglers. They therefore approached the passage with the customary silence of their guarded habits.

Chingachgook laid aside his paddle, while Uncas and the scout urged the light vessel through the crooked and intricate channels, where every foot that they advanced exposed them to the danger of some sudden rising on their progress. The eyes of the Sagamore moved warily from islet to islet, and copse to copse, as the canoe proceeded; and when a clear sheet of water permitted, his keen vision was bent along the bald rocks and impending forests that frowned upon the narrow strait.

Heyward, who was a doubly-interested spectator, as well from the beauties of the place as from the apprehension natural to his situation, was just believing that he had permitted the latter to be excited without sufficient reason, when the paddles ceased moving, in obedience to a signal from Chingachgook.

"Hugh!" exclaimed Uncas, nearly at the moment that the light tap his father had made on the side of the canoe, notified them of the vicinity of danger.

"What now?" asked the scout; "the lake is as smooth as if the winds had never blown, and I can see along its sheet for miles; there is not so much as the black head of a loon dotting the water!"

The Indian gravely raised his paddle, and pointed in the direction in which his own steady look was riveted. Duncan's eyes followed the motion. A few rods in their front lay another of the low wooded islets, but it appeared as calm and peaceful as if its solitude had never been disturbed by the foot of man.

"I see nothing," he said, "but land and water; and a lovely scene it is!"

"Hist!" interrupted the scout. "Aye, Sagamore, there is always a reason for what you do! 'Tis but a shade, and yet it is not natural. You see the mist, major, that is rising above the island; you can't call it a fog, for it is more like a streak of thin cloud"—

"It is vapor from the water!"

"That a child could tell. But what is the edging of blacker smoke, that hangs along its lower side, and which you may trace down into the thicket of hazel? 'Tis from a fire; but one that, in my judgment, has been suffered to burn low."

"Let us, then, push for the place, and relieve our doubts," said the impatient Duncan; "the party must be small that can lie on such a bit of land."

"If you judge of Indian cunning by the rules you find in books, or by white sagacity, they will lead you astray, if not to your death," returned Hawk-eye, examining the signs of the place with that acuteness which distinguished him. "If I may be permitted to speak in this matter, it will be to say, that we have but two things to choose between: the one is, to return, and give up all thoughts of following the Hurons"—

"Never!" exclaimed Heyward, in a voice far too loud for their circumstances.

"Well, well," continued Hawk-eye, making a hasty sign to repress his ardor; "I am much of your mind myself; though I thought it becoming my experience to tell the whole. We must, then, make a push, and if the Indians or Frenchers are in the narrows, run the gauntlet through these toppling mountains. Is there reason in my words, Sagamore?"

The Indian made no other answer than by dropping his paddle into the water, and urging forward the canoe. As he held the office of directing its course, his resolution was sufficiently indicated by the movement. The whole party now plied their paddles vigorously, and in a very few moments they had reached a point whence they might command an entire view of the northern shore of the island, the side that had hitherto been concealed.

"There they are, by all the truth of signs!" whispered the scout; "two canoes and a smoke! The knaves haven't yet got their eyes out of the mist, or we should hear the accursed whoop. Together, friends—we are leaving them, and are already nearly out of whistle of a bullet."

The well known crack of a rifle, whose ball came skipping along the placid surface of the strait, and a shrill yell from the island, interrupted his speech, and announced that their passage was discovered. In another instant several savages were seen rushing into the canoes, which were soon dancing over the water, in swift pursuit. These fearful precursors of a coming struggle produced no change in the countenances and movements of his three guides, so far as Duncan could discover, except that the strokes of their paddles were longer and more in unison, and caused the little bark to spring forward like a creature possessing life and volition.

"Hold them there, Sagamore," said Hawk-Eye, looking coolly backward over his left shoulder, while he still plied his paddle; "keep them just there. Them Hurons have never a piece in their nation that will execute at this distance; but 'killdeer' has a barrel on which a man may safely calculate."

The scout having ascertained that the Mohicans were sufficient of themselves to maintain the requisite distance, deliberately laid aside his paddle, and raised the fatal rifle. Three several times he brought the piece to his shoulder, and when his companions were expecting its report, he as often lowered it, to request the Indians would permit their enemies to approach a little nigher. At length, his accurate and fastidious eye seemed satisfied, and throwing out his left arm on the barrel, he was slowly elevating the muzzle, when an exclamation from Uncas, who sat in the bow, once more caused him to suspend the shot.

"What now, lad?" demanded Hawk-eye; "you saved a Huron from the death-shriek by that word; have you reason for what you do?"

Uncas pointed toward the rocky shore, a little in their front, whence another war-canoe was darting directly across their course. It was too obvious, now, that their situation was imminently perilous, to need the aid of language to confirm it. The scout laid aside his rifle, and resumed the paddle, while Chingachgook inclined the bows of the canoe a little toward the western shore, in order to increase the distance between them and this new enemy. In the mean time, they were reminded of the presence of those who pressed upon their rear, by wild and exulting shouts. The stirring scene awakened even Munro from the dull apathy into which he was plunged by the weight of his misfortunes.

"Let us make for the rocks on the main," he said, with the firm mien of a tried soldier, "and give battle to the savages. God forbid that I, or those attached to me and mine, should ever trust again to the faith of any servant of the Louises!"

"He who wishes to prosper in Indian warfare," returned the busy scout, "must not be too proud to learn from the wit of a native. Lay her more along the land, Sagamore; we are doubling on the varlets, and perhaps they may try to strike our trail on the long calculation."

Hawk-eye was not mistaken; for, when the Hurons found their course was likely to throw them behind their chase, they rendered it less direct, until, by gradually bearing more and more obliquely, the two canoes were, ere long, gliding on parallel lines, within two hundred yards of each other. It now became entirely a trial of speed. So rapid was the progress of the light vessels, that the lake curled in their front in miniature waves, and their motion became undulating by its own velocity. It was, perhaps, owing to this circumstance, in addition to the necessity of keeping every hand employed at the paddles, that the Hurons had not immediate recourse to their fire-arms. The exertions of the fugitives were too severe to continue long, and the pursuers had the advantage of numbers. Duncan observed, with uneasiness, that the scout began to look anxiously about him, as if searching for some further means of assisting their flight.

"Edge her a little more from the sun, Sagamore," said the stubborn woodsman; "I see the knaves are sparing a man to the rifle. A single broken bone might lose us our scalps. Edge more from the sun, and we will put the island between us."

The expedient was not without its use. A long, low island lay at a little distance before them, and as they closed with it the chasing canoe was compelled to take a side opposite to that on which the pursued passed. The scout and his companions did not neglect this advantage, but the instant they were hid from observation by the bushes they redoubled efforts that before had seemed prodigious. The two canoes came round the last low point like two coursers at the top of their speed, the fugitives taking the lead. This change had brought them nigher to each other, however, while it altered their relative positions.

"You showed knowledge in the shaping of birchen bark, Uncas, when you chose this from among the Huron canoes," said the scout, smiling, apparently, more in satisfaction at their superiority in the race than from that prospect of final escape which now began to open a little upon them. "The imps have put all their strength again at the paddles, and we are to struggle for our scalps with bits of flattened wood, instead of clouded barrels and true eyes! A long stroke and together, friends."

"They are preparing for a shot," said Heyward; "and as we are in a line with them it can scarcely fail."

"Get you then into the bottom of the canoe," returned the scout; "you and the colonel; it will be so much taken from the size of the mark."

Heyward smiled as he answered—

"It would be but an ill example for the highest in rank to dodge, while the warriors were under fire!"

"Lord! Lord! that is now a white man's courage!" exclaimed the scout; "and like too many of his notions, not to be maintained by reason. Do you think the Sagamore, or Uncas, or even I, who am a man without a cross, would deliberate about finding a cover in a skrimmage, when an open body would do no good! For what have the Frenchers reared up their Quebec, if fighting is always to be done in the clearings?"

"All that you say is very true, my friend," replied Heyward; "still our customs must prevent us from doing as you wish."

A volley from the Hurons interrupted the discourse, and, as the bullets whistled about them, Duncan saw the head of Uncas turned, looking back at himself and Munro. Notwithstanding the nearness of the enemy, and his own great personal danger, the countenance of the young warrior expressed no other emotion, as the former was compelled to think, than amazement at finding men willing to encounter so useless an exposure. Chingachgook was probably better acquainted with the notions of white men, for he did not even cast a glance aside from the riveted look his eye maintained on the object by which he governed their course. A ball soon struck the light and polished paddle from the hands of the chief, and drove it through the air far in advance. A shout arose from the Hurons, who seized the opportunity to fire another volley. Uncas described an arc in the water with his own blade, and as the canoe passed swiftly on, Chingachgook recovered his paddle, and flourishing it on high, he gave the warwhoop of the Mohicans, and then lent his own strength and skill again to the important task.

The clamorous sounds of "le Gros Serpent," "la Longue Carabine," "le Cerf Agile," burst at once from the canoes behind, and seemed to give new zeal to the pursuers. The scout seized "kill-deer in his left hand, and elevating it above his head, he shook it in triumph at his enemies. The savages answered the insult with a yell, and immediately another volley succeeded. The bullets pattered along the lake, and one even pierced the bark of their little vessel. No perceptible emotion could be discovered in the Mohicans during this critical moment, their rigid features expressing neither hope nor alarm; but the scout again turned his head, and laughing in his own silent manner, he said to Heyward—

"The knaves love to hear the sounds of their pieces; but the eye is not to be found among the Mingoes that can calculate a true range in a dancing canoe! You see the dumb devils have taken off a man to charge, and by the smallest measurement that can be allowed, we move three feet to their two!"

Duncan, who was not altogether as easy under this nice estimate of distances as his companions, was glad to find, however, that owing to their superior dexterity, and the diversion among their enemies, they were very sensibly obtaining the advantage. The Hurons soon fired again, and a bullet struck the blade of Hawk-eye's paddle without injury.

"That will do," said the scout, examining the slight indentation with a curious eye; "it would not have cut the skin of an infant, much less of men, who, like us, have been blown upon by the heavens in their anger. Now, major, if you will try to use this piece of flattened wood, I'll let 'kill-deer' take a part in the conversation."

Heyward seized the paddle, and applied himself to the work with an eagerness that supplied the place of skill, while Hawk-eye was engaged in inspecting the priming of his rifle. The latter then took a swift aim, and fired. The Huron in the bows of the leading canoe had risen with a similar object, and he now fell backward, suffering his gun to escape from his hands into the water. In an instant, however, he recovered his feet, though his gestures were wild and bewildered. At the same moment his companions suspended their efforts, and the chasing canoes clustered together, and became stationary. Chingachgook and Uncas profited by the interval to regain their wind, though Duncan continued to work with the most persevering industry. The father and son now cast calm but inquiring glances at each other, to learn if either had sustained any injury by the fire; for both well knew that no cry or exclamation would, in such a moment of necessity, have been permitted to betray the accident. A few large drops of blood were trickling down the shoulder of the Sagamore, who, when he perceived that the eyes of Uncas dwelt too long on the sight, raised some water in the hollow of his hand, and washing off the stain, was content to manifest, in this simple manner, the slightness of the injury.

"Softly, softly, major," said the scout, who by this time had reloaded his rifle; "we are a little too far already for a rifle to put forth its beauties, and you see yonder imps are holding a council. Let them come up within striking distance—my eye may well be trusted in such a matter—and I will trail the varlets the length of the Horican, guaranteeing that not a shot of theirs shall, at the worst, more than break the skin, while 'kill-deer' shall touch the life twice in three times."

"We forget our errand," returned the diligent Duncan. "For God's sake, let us profit by this advantage, and increase our distance from the enemy."

"Give me my children," said Munro, hoarsely; "trifle no longer with a father's agony, but restore me my babes!"

Long and habitual deference to the mandates of his superiors, had taught the scout the virtue of obedience. Throwing a last and lingering glance at the distant canoes, he laid aside his rifle, and, relieving the wearied Duncan, resumed the paddle, which he wielded with sinews that never tired. His efforts were seconded by those of the Mohicans, and a very few minutes served to place such a sheet of water between them and their enemies, that Heyward once more breathed freely.

The lake now began to expand, and their route lay along a wide reach, that was lined, as before, by high and ragged mountains. But the islands were few, and easily avoided. The strokes of the paddles grew more measured and regular, while they who plied them continued their labor, after the close and deadly chase from which they had just relieved themselves, with as much coolness as though their speed had been tried in sport, rather than under such pressing, nay, almost desperate, circumstances.

Instead of following the western shore, whither their errand led them, the wary Mohican inclined his course more toward those hills, behind which Montcalm was known to have led his army into the formidable fortress of Ticonderoga. As the Hurons, to every appearance, had abandoned the pursuit, there was no apparent reason for this excess of caution. It was, however, maintained for hours, until they had reached a bay, nigh the northern termination of the lake. Here the canoe was driven upon the beach, and the whole party landed. Hawk-eye and Heyward ascended an adjacent bluff, where the former, after considering the expanse of water beneath him, attentively, for many minutes, pointed out to the latter a small object, hovering under a headland, at the distance of several miles.

"Do you see it?" demanded the scout. "Now, what would you account that spot, were you left alone to white experience to find your way through this wilderness?"

"But for its distance and its magnitude, I should suppose it a bird. Can it be a living object?"

"'Tis a canoe of good birchen bark, and paddled by fierce and crafty Mingoes! Though Providence has lent to those who inhabit the woods eyes that would be needless to men in the settlements, where there are inventions to assist the sight, yet no human organs can see all the dangers which at this moment circumvent it. These varlets pretend to be bent chiefly on their sun-down meal, but the moment it is dark, they will be on our trail, as true as hounds on the scent. We must throw them off, or our pursuit of le Renard Subtil may be given up. These lakes are useful at times, especially when the game takes the water," continued the scout, gazing about him with a countenance of concern, "but they give no cover, except it be to the fishes. God knows what the country would be, if the settlements should ever spread far from the two rivers. Both hunting and war would lose their beauty."

"Let us not delay a moment, without some good and obvious cause."

"I little like that smoke, which you may see worming up along the rock above the canoe," interrupted the abstracted scout. "My life on it, other eyes than ours see it, and know its meaning! Well, words will not mend the matter, and it is time that we were doing."

Hawk-eye moved away from the look-out, and descended, musing profoundly, to the shore. He communicated the result of his observations to his companions in Delaware, and a short and earnest consultation succeeded. When it terminated, the there instantly set about executing their new resolutions.

The canoe was lifted from the water, and borne on the shoulders of the party. They proceeded into the wood, making as broad and obvious a trail as possible. They soon reached a watercourse, which they crossed, and continued onward, until they came to an extensive and naked rock. At this point, where their footsteps might be expected to be no longer visible, they retraced their route to the brook, walking backward, with the utmost care. They now followed the bed of the little stream to the lake, into which they immediately launched their canoe again. A low point concealed them from the headland, and the margin of the lake was fringed for some distance with dense and overhanging bushes. Under the cover of these natural advantages, they toiled their way with patient industry, until the scout pronounced that he believed it would be safe once more to land.

The halt continued until evening rendered objects indistinct and uncertain to the eye. Then they resumed their route, and, favored by the darkness, pushed silently and vigorously toward the western shore. Although the rugged outline of mountain, to which they were steering, presented no distinctive marks to the eyes of Duncan, the

Mohican entered the little haven he had selected with the confidence and accuracy of an experienced pilot.

The boat was again lifted and borne into the woods, where it was carefully concealed under a pile of brush. The adventurers assumed their arms and packs, and the scout announced to Munro and Heyward, that he and the Indians were at last in readiness to proceed.

VII.

THE PRAIRIE.

ERE "The Mohicans" was published, a second romance of Indian adventure had been already planned. But the scene was changed. The ground was no longer overshadowed by the boundless forest and timbered heights; the limpid lakes, the falling streams of the eastern valleys, were no longer accessories in the picture. In the course of his inquiries regarding the habits and character of the red man, while writing "The Mohicans," Mr. Cooper was thrown repeatedly into temporary associations with parties of warriors from the tribes beyond the Mississippi, on their way to smoke the calumet at the council halls in Washington. He was much interested by some of the chiefs—the anecdotes of their different deeds of wild prowess, told by the interpreters; of their singular fortitude and powers of physical endurance; of their wily cunning and fierce passions; the vein of poetry and laconic eloquence, if the expression may be used, marking their brief speeches; their natural dignity of manner and grace of gesture, blended with their strongly-marked savage mien and accoutrements, struck him very forcibly. Tales of great buffalo hunts; of battles between the mounted tribes, of vast fires sweeping over these boundless plains, were listened to with the vivid interest and sympathy and searching inquiry always aroused in him by narratives of adventure. The result was a determination to attempt a second Indian book, whose scenes should be laid on the wild Western plains, among the mounted tribes beyond the Mississippi.

The prairies he had never seen. His travels westward had not extended farther than Buffalo and Niagara, where he had gone on duty, when serving in the navy. And at the moment of planning the book, he had not leisure for an excursion beyond the Mississippi, much as he wished to see that singular region. The necessary information could, therefore, be drawn from books and conversation only. But the eye of genius has a living lens of its own, peculiar to itself, endowing it with an insight which penetrates far below the surface of things, which seizes objects though veiled by the intervening cloud, which is capable of clear perception far beyond the common horizon; give it but a vague outline, let it but fix its vision on some distant point, and ere long great facts appear, strong and distinct in all the force of their reality, while lesser details of poetical grace and natural feeling come to light, and live and glow like the flowers beneath the sunbeam. With Shakespeare it looks toward Italy, and he who had never trod other than his native soil, brings all Venice, and Verona, and "Padova la dotta" to the shores of England, and throws the softness of the Italian moon over the nearest lawn. With the author of "Waverley" it looks into the scroll of History, and the page becomes illuminated with all the quaint pageantry of mediæval Time, in life-like glow and movement. It turns, with the poet of "Childe Harold," toward the Russian steppe, and the wild troop of untamed horse comes rushing in savage fury toward the terrified reader.

The sketches of Indian character, as drawn by the writer of "The Mohicans" and "The Prairie," have been declared too poetical, too much idealized. To a certain degree this criticism may be just. His was a mind naturally attracted by the noblest elements in every subject; he had little sympathy with the petty—he took no pleasure in dwelling on the perverted deformities of our common nature. His best characters—those which are the most complete, the most highly-finished, which take the strongest hold of the reader's mind—were usually cast in a noble mould. It was natural that this should be so; never was there a pen held by a writer of works of the imagination more frankly honest, more simply sincere, more invariably guided by the real feeling of the author, than his own. He wrote from the heart. It was no cold, factitious head-work with him. His own personal views were always elevated; to this fact his whole life bears testimony—a testimony which assumes its strongest character to those who knew most intimately the habitual daily course of that life. Writing, with him, was simply the outpouring of his own nature, the expression of his own inmost train of thought, the current of real feeling in his own breast. Every character at all a favorite with him, he instinctively idealized—he gave it something of the glow ever warm at his own heart's core. It was, therefore, quite a matter of course that in drawing Indian character he should dwell on the better traits of the picture, rather than on the coarser and more revolting though more common points. Like

West, he could see the Apollo in the young Mohican.   He chose to draw from a
Tamemund, a Powhattan, a Metacom.   To-day we are apt to forget that such men
have existed ; we stumble over a drunken Oneida, or Chippewa, lying in our
path, and conceive ourselves entitled to lower the whole race, in its past independent existence, to the condition of the fallen wretch before us, degraded by
vices, thrust upon him by the white man.   With Uncas, with the Pawnee Loup,
the author may have shown us the red man in a highly poetical light ; and yet
in each case the picture is in itself so beautiful, that which of us shall deliberately
say he could wish the outline less noble, the coloring less pure !

The idea of a narrative connected with the great Prairies being conceived,
the figure of Natty once more rose before the writer.   Again there was a moment
of hesitation ; would the public tolerate the introduction of the same character
for a third time ; would it be possible to carry the old hunter, in extreme age,
through a train of freshly novel incident without impairing the native dignity,
the simple beauty of the conception ?   The doubt lasted but a moment ; the
affection, if one may so term it, of the writer for this creation of his mind,
blended with the consciousness of the ability to carry out the idea, decided the
question ; and with the first pages of the narrative the old man is revealed, standing in the solitude of the silent plain :

" The sun had fallen below the crest of the nearest wave of the prairie, leaving the usual rich and glowing train on its track.   In the centre of this flood of
fiery light, a human form appeared, drawn against the gilded background, as
distinctly, and, seemingly as palpable, as though it would come within the grasp
of any extended hand.   The figure was colossal ; the attitude musing and melancholy, and the situation directly in the route of the travellers.   But, imbedded as
it was in its setting of garish light, it was impossible to distinguish more concerning its proportions or character.

" The effect of such a spectacle was instantaneous and powerful.   The man in
front of the emigrants came to a stand, and remained gazing at the mysterious
object with a dull interest, that soon quickened into a species of superstitious awe.
His sons, so soon as the first emotions of surprise had a little abated, drew slowly
around him, and, as they who governed the teams gradually followed their
example, the whole party was soon condensed in one silent and wondering
group.   Notwithstanding the impression of a supernatural agency was very general among the travellers, the ticking of gun-locks was heard and one or two
of the bolder of the youths cast their rifles forward, in guarded readiness for
any service.

" ' Send the boys off to the right,' exclaimed the resolute wife and mother, in

J. Hamilton pinx.   D. H. Cushman Sculpt.

The Prairie: Appearance of the Trapper to the Emigrants

a sharp, dissonant voice; 'I warrant me, Asa or Abner will give some account of the creatur !'

" 'It may be well enough to try the rifle,' muttered a dull-looking man, whose features, both in outline and expression, bore no small resemblance to the first speaker, and who loosened the stock of his piece and brought it dexterously to the front, while delivering this decided opinion; 'the Pawnee Loups are said to be hunting by hundreds in the plains; if so, they'll never miss a single man from their tribe.'

" 'Stay !' exclaimed a soft-toned but fearfully-alarmed female voice, which was easily to be traced to the trembling lips of the younger of the two women; 'we are not all together; it may be a friend !'

" 'Who is scouting now ?' demanded the father, scanning, at the same time, the cluster of his stout sons with a displeased and sullen eye. 'Put by the piece, put by the piece ;' he continued, diverting the other's aim, with the finger of a giant, and with the air of one it might be dangerous to deny. 'My job is not yet ended ; let us finish the little that remains in peace.'

" The man who had manifested so hostile an intention appeared to understand the other's allusion, and suffered himself to be diverted from his object. The sons turned their inquiring looks on the girl who had so eagerly spoken, to require an explanation ; but, as if content with the respite she had obtained for the stranger, she had already sunk back in her seat, and now chose to affect a maidenly silence.

" In the mean time, the hues of the heavens had often changed. In place of the brightness which had dazzled the eye, a gray and more sober light had succeeded, and as the setting lost its brilliancy, the proportions of the fanciful form became less exaggerated, and finally quite distinct. Ashamed to hesitate, now that the truth was no longer doubtful, the leader of the party resumed his journey, using the precaution, as he ascended the slight acclivity, to release his own rifle from the strap, and to cast it into a situation more convenient for sudden use.

" There was little apparent necessity, however, for such watchfulness. From the moment when it had thus unaccountably appeared, as it were, between the heavens and the earth, the stranger's figure had neither moved nor given the smallest evidence of hostility. Had he harbored any such evil intention, the individual who now came plainly into view seemed but little qualified to execute them.

" A frame that had endured the hardships of more than eighty seasons was not qualified to awaken apprehension in the breast of one as powerful as the emigrant.   Notwithstanding his years, and his look of emaciation if not of suffering, there was that about this solitary being, however, which said that time, and not disease, had laid his hand too heavily on him.   His form had withered, but it was not wasted.   The sinews and muscles, which had once denoted great strength, though shrunken, were still visible; and his whole figure had attained an appearance of induration, which, if it were not for the well-known frailty of humanity, would have seemed to bid defiance to the further approaches of decay. His dress was chiefly of skins, worn with the hair to the weather; a pouch and horn were suspended from his shoulders; and he leaned on a rifle of uncommon length, but which, like its owner, exhibited the wear of long and hard service.

  "As the party drew nigher to this solitary being, and came within a distance to be heard, a low growl issued from the grass at his feet, and then a tall, gaunt, toothless hound arose lazily from his lair, and shaking himself, made some show of resisting the nearer approach of the travellers.

  "'Down, Hector, down,' said his master, in a voice that was a little tremulous and hollow with age.   'What have ye to do, pup, with men who journey on their lawful callings?'

  "'Stranger,·if you ar' much acquainted in this country,' said the leader of the emigrants, 'can you tell a traveller where he may find necessaries for the night.'

  "'Is the land filled on the other side of the Big River?' demanded the old man, solemnly, and without appearing to hearken to the other's question; 'or why do I see a sight I had never thought to behold again!'

  "'Why, there is country left, it is true, for such as have money, and ar' not particular in the choice,' returned the emigrant; 'but to my taste, it is getting crowdy.   What may a man call the distance from this place to the nighest point on the main river.'

  "'A hunted deer could not cool his sides in the Mississippi, without travelling a long five hundred miles.'

  "'And in what way may you name the district, hereaway?'

  "'By what name,' returned the old man, pointing significantly upward, 'would you call the spot where you see yonder cloud?'

  "The emigrant looked at the other, like one who did not comprehend his meaning, and who half suspected he was trifled with, but he contented himself by saying—

  "'You ar' but a new inhabitant, like myself, I reckon, stranger, otherwise you wouldn't be backward in helping a traveller to some advice; which costs but little, seeing it is only a gift in words.'

" 'It is not a gift, but a debt that the old owe to the young. What would you wish to know ?'

" 'Where I may 'camp for the night. I'm no great difficulty-maker, as to bed and board, but, all old journeyers, like myself, know the virtue of sweet water, and a good browse for the cattle.'

" ' Come, then, with me, and you shall be master of both ; and little more is it that I can offer on this hungry prairie.'

" As the old man was speaking, he raised his heavy rifle to his shoulder, with a facility a little remarkable for his years and appearance, and without further words led the way over the acclivity into the adjacent bottom."

"The Prairie" was commenced in New York, in the winter of 1826. The author was at that time suffering from the consequences of the attack of fever, which for several years affected his health quite seriously. He was anxious to finish his work, however, at an early day. The profits of his pen had of late years become of importance to him ; the settlement of his father's estate, under very unfavorable circumstances, had made great and unforeseen changes in his fortune. The prospect of an ample inheritance had passed away. He was now a poor man. There were debts to be discharged—debts brought upon him by no extravagance of his own, but through the misconduct of others for whom he had assumed responsibilities. To discharge these debts became of course his first object. And to effect this purpose, he attempted writing at a moment when enfeebled by the effects of fever. To keep up his strength for the task, he tried a stimulant; he took coffee before writing; and this was the only occasion on which he ever resorted to any thing of the kind for the same purpose. Through life his manner of living was generous, but clearly temperate. Wine he drank daily, but at dinner only, and then always moderately. Rarely, indeed, did he take a single glass at any other hour, excepting at an occasional supper-party. Opium never entered his lips. Even the habit of smoking was never formed. Those few cups of coffee, while writing "The Prairie,' are believed to have been the only instance in which a stimulant of any kind was resorted to, while writing; the effect on his nerves was not good, and the coffee was given up after a short time.

In the summer of 1826, having honorably discharged the debts alluded to, he sailed for Europe, carrying his wife and children with him, and provided with the means of support for one year in advance. The last chapters of "The Prairie" were written in the third story of the old Hotel de Jumièges, in the Faubourg St. Germain, a building which is now occupied by the nuns of the adjoining convent of St. Maur.

A few passages from letters of the author belonging to this period are inserted here. The first shows us a French landscape as seen by him. The second relates to an interview between Sir Walter Scott and Mr. Cooper, the former having visited France at this moment with the view of collecting materials for the "Life of Napoleon," which he was then writing.

A FRENCH LANDSCAPE.

"After amusing ourselves with the spectacle of the diligence, we found the scenery too beautiful to re-enter the carriage immediately, and we walked to the top of the mountain. The view from the summit was truly admirable. The Seine comes winding its way through a broad, rich valley, from the southward, having just before run east, and a league or two beyond, due west, our own Susquehanna being scarcely less crooked. The stream was not broad, but its numerous isles, willowy banks, and verdant meadows, formed a line for the eye to follow. Rouen, in the distance, with its ebony towers, fantastic roofs, and straggling suburbs, lines its shores, at a curvature where the stream swept away west again, bearing craft of the sea on its bosom. Those dark old towers have a sombre, mysterious air, which harmonizes admirably with the recollections that crowd the mind at such a moment! Scarce an isolated dwelling was to be seen, but the dense population is compressed into villages and *bourgs*, that dot the view, looking brown, and teeming like the nests of wasps. Some of these places still have remains of walls, and most of them are so compact and well-defined that they appear more like vast castles than like the open villages of England or

America. All are gray, sombre, and absolutely without glare, rising from the background of pale verdure, to many appropriate *bas-reliefs*.

"The road was strewed with peasants of both sexes, wending their way homeward from the market of Rouen. One tawny woman, with no other protection for her head than a high, but perfectly clean cap, was going past us, driving an ass, with the panniers loaded with manure. We were about six miles from the town, and the poor beast, after staggering some eight or ten miles to the market in the morning, was staggering back with this heavy freight at even. I asked the woman, who, under the circumstances, could not but be a resident of one of the neighboring villages, the name of a considerable *bourg*, that lay about gun-shot distant in plain view, on the other side of the river. 'Monsieur je ne saurais vous dire, parceque, voyez-vous, je ne suis pas de ce pays là.' I once inquired of a servant-girl at a French inn, who might be the owner of a *château* near by, the gate of which was within a hundred feet of the house we were in. She was unable to say, urging as an apology, that she had only been six weeks in her present place! This too, was in a small country hamlet. . . . The road for the rest of the afternoon, led us over hills and plains, from one reach of the river to another, for we crossed the latter repeatedly before reaching Paris. The appearance of the country was extraordinary to our eyes. Isolated houses were rare, but villages dotted the whole expanse. No obtrusive colors, but the eye had frequently to search against the hill-side, or in the valley, and first, detecting a mass, it gradually took in the picturesque angles, roofs, towers and walls of the little *bourg*. Not a fence or visible boundary of any sort, to mark the limits of possession. Not a hoof in the fields grazing, and occasionally a sweep of mountain land which resembled a pattern card, with its stripes of green and yellow, and other hues, the narrow fields of the rural proprietors. The play of light and shade on these gay upland patches, though not strictly in conformity with the laws of taste, was certainly attractive. When they fell entirely into shadow, the harvest being over, and their gaudy colors lessened, they resembled the melancholy and wasted vestiges of a festival. At Louviers we dined, and there we found a new object of wonder in the church. It was of the Gothic of the *bourg*, less elaborated and more rudely wrought than that of the larger towns, but quaint, and, the population considered, vast. Ugly dragons thrust out their grinning heads at us from the buttresses. The most agreeable monstrosities imaginable, were crawling along the gray old stones. After passing this place, the scenery lost a good deal of the pastoral appearance, which renders Normandy rather remarkable in France, and took still more of the starch pattern-card look just mentioned. Still it was sombre, the villages were to be detached by the eye from their setting of fields,

and here and there, one of those 'silent fingers pointing to the skies,' raised itself
into the air like a needle, to prick the consciences of the thoughtless. The dusky
hues of all the villages, contrasted oddly, and not unpleasantly, with the carnival
colors of the grains."

*   *   *   *   *   *   *

INTERVIEW WITH SIR WALTER SCOTT.

" It might have been ten days after the arrival of Sir Walter Scott, that I had
ordered a carriage one morning, with the intention of driving over to the other
side of the river, and had got as far as the lower flight of steps on my way to the
door, when another coach drove into the court. It was raining, and as my own
carriage moved off to make room for the new-comer, I stopped on the stairs until
it should return. The carriage-steps rattled, and presently a large, heavy-moulded
man appeared in the door of the hotel. He was gray, and limped a little, walking
with a cane. We passed each other on the stairs, bowing, as a matter of course.
I had got to the door, and was about to enter the carriage, when it flashed on my
mind that the visit might be to myself. I had not the slightest suspicion who the
visitor was, though I fancied both the face and form were known to me.

" The stranger went up the large stone steps slowly, leaning with one hand
on the iron railing, and, with the other on his cane. He was on the first landing,
as I stopped, and, turning toward the next flight, our eyes met. The idea I might
be the person he wanted, seemed then to strike him for the first time : 'Est-ce
Monsieur—que j'ai l'honneur de voir ?' he asked, in French, and with but an indifferent accent. 'Monsieur, je m'appelle ——Eh-bien, donc, je suis Walter Scott.'

"I ran up the landing, shook him by the hand, which he stood holding out to
me cordially, and expressed my sense of the honor he was conferring. He told
me, in substance, that the Princesse ——— had been as good as her word, and,
having succeeded herself in getting hold of him, she had good-naturedly given
him my address. By way of cutting short all ceremony, he had driven from his
hotel to my lodgings. All this time he was speaking French, while my answers
and remarks were in English, suddenly recollecting himself, he said, ' Well, here
have I been *parlez-vousing* to you in a way to surprise you, no doubt ; but these
Frenchmen have got my tongue so set to their lingo, that I have half forgotten my
own language.' As we proceeded up the next flight of stairs, he accepted my
arm, and continued the conversation in English, walking with more difficulty than
I had expected to see.

*   *   *   *   *   *   *   *

" There would be an impropriety in my relating all that passed in this inter-

The Prairie: A series of masterly and rapid evolutions
with the horses now commenced. The wheelings, the
charges, the advances and the circuitous retreats,
were like the flights of circling swallows.

view ; but we talked over a matter of business, and then the conversation was more general. You will remember that Sir Walter was still the *Unknown*—he did not avow himself for several months after—and that he was believed to be in Paris in search of facts for the ' Life of Napoleon.' Notwithstanding the former circumstance, he spoke of his works with great frankness and simplicity, and without the parade of asking any promises of secrecy. In short, as he commenced in this style, his authorship was alluded to by us both just as if it had never been called in question. He asked me if I had a copy of the —————— by me, and on my confessing I did not own a single volume of any thing I had written, he laughed, and said he believed that most authors had the same feeling on the subject; as for himself, he cared not if he never saw a Waverley novel again as long as he lived. Curious to know whether a writer as great and as practised as he, felt the occasional despondency which invariably attends all my own little efforts of this nature, I remarked that I found the mere composition of a tale a source of pleasure, so much so that I always invented twice as much as was committed to paper, in my walks, or in bed, and in my own judgment much the best parts of the composition never saw the light; for what was written was usually written at set hours, and was a good deal a matter of chance, and that going over and over the same subject in proofs disgusted me so thoroughly with the book, that I supposed every one else would be disposed to view it in the same light. To this he answered that he was spared much of the labor of proof-reading, Scotland, he presumed, being better off than America in this respect; but still he said he ' would as soon see his dinner again after a hearty meal as to read one of his own tales, when he was fairly rid of it.'

" He sat with me nearly an hour, and he manifested, during the time the conversation was not tied down to business, a strong propensity to humor. Having occasion to mention our common publisher in Paris, he quaintly termed him, with a sort of malicious fun, ' Our Gosling'—his name was Gorselin—adding he hoped he at least ' laid golden eggs.'

" I hoped he had found the facilities he desired, in obtaining facts for the forthcoming history. He rather hesitated about admitting this. ' One can hear as much as he pleases in the way of anecdote,' he said, ' but then, as a gentleman, he is not always sure how much of it he can, with propriety, relate in a book; beside'—throwing all his latent humor into the expression of his small gray eyes —' one may even doubt how much of what he hears is fit for history on another account.' He paused, and his face assumed an exquisite air of confiding simplicity, as he continued with perfect *bonne foi*, and strong Scotch feeling, ' I have been to see my countryman M'Donald, and I rather think that will be about as much as I can do here, now.' This was uttered with so much *naïveté* that I could hardly believe it was the same man, who, a moment before, had shown so much shrewd distrust of oral relations of facts.

"I inquired when we might expect the work. 'Some time in the course of the winter,' he replied, 'though it is likely to prove larger than I at first intended. We have got several volumes printed, but I find I must add to the matter considerably, in order to dispose of the subject. I thought I should get rid of it in seven volumes, which are already written, but it will reach, I think, to nine.' 'If you have still two to write, I shall not expect to see the book before spring.' 'You may : let me once get back to Abbotsford, and I'll soon knock off these two fellows.' To this I had nothing to say, although I thought such a *tour de force* in writing might better suit invention than history.

"When he rose to go, I begged him to step into the *salon*, that I might have the gratification of introducing my wife to him. To this he very good-naturedly assented, and entering the room, after presenting Mrs. —— and my nephew W——, he took a seat. He sat some little time, and his fit of pleasantry returned, for he illustrated his discourse by one or two apt anecdotes, related with a slightly Scottish accent, which he seemed to drop and assume at will. Mrs. —— observed to him that the *bergère* in which he was seated had been twice honored that morning, for General Lafayette had not left it more than half an hour. Sir Walter looked surprised at this, and said, inquiringly, 'I thought he had gone to America to pass the rest of his days?' On my explaining the true state of the case, he merely observed, 'He is a great man;' and yet I thought the remark was made coldly, or in complaisance to us.

"When Sir Walter left us, it was settled that I was to breakfast with him the following day but one. I was punctual, of course, and found him in a new silk *douillette* that he had just purchased, trying, 'as hard as he could,' as he pleasantly observed, 'to make a Frenchman of himself'—an undertaking as little likely to be successful, I should think, in the case of his Scottish exterior and Scottish interior too, as any experiment well could be. There were two or three visitors present, beside Miss Ann Scott, his daughter, who was his companion on the journey. He was just answering an invitation from the Princess —— to an evening party, as I entered. 'Here,' said he, 'you are a friend of the lady, and *parlez-vous* so much better than I: can you tell me whether this is for *Jundi*, or *Lundi*, or *Mardi*, or whether it means no day at all?' I told him the day of the week intended. 'You get notes occasionally from the lady, or you could not read her scrawl so readily!' 'She is very kind to us, and we often have occasion to read her writing.' 'Well, it is worth a very good dinner to get through a page of it.' 'I take my revenge in kind; I fancy she has the worst of it!' 'I don't know, after all, that she will get much the better of me, with this *plume d'auberge.*' He was quite right, for, although Sir Walter writes a smooth, even hand, and one that appears rather well than otherwise on a page, it is one of the most difficult to decipher I have ever met with; the i's, u's, m's, n's, a's, e's, l's, and r's, for want of dots, crossings, and being fully rounded, looking all alike, and rendering the reading slow and difficult, without great familiarity with his mode of handling the pen; at least I have found it so.

"He had sealed the note, and was about writing the direction, when he seemed at a loss: 'How do you address this lady—as "Her Highness?"' I was much surprised at this question from him, for it denoted a want of familiarity with the world, that one would not have expected in a man who had been so very much and so long courted by the great. But, after all, his life has been very provincial, though, as his daughter remarked in the course of the morning, they had no occasion to quit Scotland to see all the world, all the world coming to see Scotland.

"The next morning he was with me again, for near an hour, and we completed our little affair. After this we had a conversation on the law of copyrights in the two countries, which, as we possess a common language, is a subject of great national interest. I understood him to say that he had a double right in England to his works; one under a statute, and the other growing out of common law. Any one, publishing a book, let it be written by whom it might, in England, duly complying with the law, can secure the right, whereas none but a citizen can do the same in America. I regret to say that I misled him on the subject of our copyright law, which, after all, is not so much more illiberal than that of England, as I had thought it.

"I told Sir Walter Scott that, in order to secure a copyright in America, it was necessary the book should never have been published *anywhere else.* This was said under the popular notion of the matter; or that which is entertained among the booksellers. Reflection and examination have since convinced me of my error: the publication alluded to in the law can only mean publication in America; for, as the object of doing certain acts previously to publication is merely to forewarn the American public that the right is reserved, there can be no motive for having reference to any other publication. It is, moreover, in conformity with the spirit of all laws to limit the meaning of their phrases by their proper jurisdiction. Let us suppose a case. An American writes a book; he sends a copy to England, where it is published in March; complying with the terms of our own copyright law, as to the entries and notices, the same work is published here in April. Now will it be pretended that his right is lost, always providing that his own is the first *American* publication? I do not see how it can be so, by either the letter or the spirit of the law. The intention is to encourage the citizen to write, and to give him a first property in the fruits of his labor; and the precautionary provisions of the law are merely to prevent others from being injured for want of proper information. It is of no moment to either of these objects that the author of a work has already reaped emolument in a foreign country: the principle is to encourage literature by giving it all the advantages it can obtain.

"If these views are correct, why may not an English writer secure a right in this country, by selling it in season to a citizen here? An equitable bond might not, probably would not, be sufficient; but a *bona fide* transfer for a valuable consideration, I begin to think, would. It seems to me that all the misconception which has existed on this point has arisen from supposing that the term publication refers to other than a publication in the country. But, when one remembers how rare it is to get lawyers to agree on a question like this, it becomes a layman to advance his opinion with great humility. I suppose, after all, a good way of getting an accurate notion of the meaning of the law would be to toss a dollar into the air, and cry 'heads,' or 'tails!' Sir Walter Scott seemed fully aware of the great circulation of his books in America, as well as how much he lost by not being able to secure a copyright. Still he admitted they produced him something. Our conversation on this subject terminated by a frank offer, on his part, of aiding me with the publishers of his own country—an offer twice renewed, after intervals of several years; but, although grateful for the kindness, I was not so circumstanced as to be able to profit by it.

"He did not appear to me to be pleased with Paris. His notions of the French were pretty accurate, though clearly not free from the old-fashioned prejudices. 'After all,' he remarked, 'I am a true Scot, never, except on this occasion, and the short visit I made to Paris in 1815, having been out of my own country, unless to visit England, and I have even done very little of the latter.' I understood him to say he had never been in Ireland at all.

"I met him once more in the evening, at the hotel of the Princess ——. The party had been got together in a hurry, and was not large. Our hostess contrived to assemble some exceedingly clever people, however, among whom were one or two women, already historical, and whom I had fancied long since dead. All the female part of the company, with the silent delicacy that the French so well understand, appeared with ribbons, hats, or ornaments of some sort or other, of a Scottish stamp. Indeed, almost the only woman in the room who did not appear as a Caledonian was Miss Scott. She was in half-mourning, and, with her black eyes and jet-black hair, might very well have passed for a Frenchwoman, but for a slight peculiarity about the cheek-bones. She looked exceedingly well, and was much admired. Having two or three more places to go to, they staid but an hour. As a matter of course, all the Frenchwomen were exceedingly *empressées* in their manner to the Great Unknown; and as there were three or four who were very exaggerated on the score of romance, he was quite lucky if he escaped some absurdities. Nothing could be more patient than his manner under it all; but as soon as he very well could, he got into a corner where I went to speak to him. He said, laughingly, that he spoke French with so much difficulty, he was embarrassed to answer the compliments. 'I am as good a lion as need be, allowing my mane to be stroked as familiarly as they please, but I can't growl for them in French. How is it with you?' Disclaiming the necessity of being either a good or a bad lion, being very little troubled in that way, for his amusement, I related to him an anecdote. Pointing out to him a Comtesse de ———, who was present, I told him I had met this lady once a week for several months, and at every *soirée* she invariably sailed up to me to say: 'Oh Monsieur, quels livres!—vos charmans livres—que vos livres sont charmans!' and I had just made up my mind that she was, at least, a woman of taste, when she approached me with the utmost *sang froid*, and cried, 'Bon soir, monsieur ———; je viens d'acheter tous vos livres, et je compte profiter de la première occasion pour les lire!'

"I took leave of him in the ante-chamber, as he went away, for he was to quit Paris the following evening.

"Sir Walter Scott's person and manner have been so often described, that you will not ask much of me in this way, especially as I saw so little of him. His frame is large and muscular, his walk difficult, in appearance, though he boasted himself a vigorous mountaineer, and his action in general measured and heavy. His features and countenance were very Scottish, with the short thick nose, heavy lips, and massive cheeks. The superior or intellectual part of his head was neither deep nor broad, but perhaps the reverse, though singularly high. Indeed, it is quite uncommon to see a skull so round and tower-like in the formation, though I have met with them in individuals not at all distinguished for talents. I do not think a casual observer would find any thing unusual in the exterior of Sir Walter Scott, beyond his physical force, which is great, without being at all extraordinary. His eye, however, is certainly remarkable. Gray, small, and without lustre, in his graver moments it appears to look inward, instead of regarding external objects, in a way, though the expression more or less belongs to abstraction, that I have never seen equalled. His smile is good-natured and social; and when he is in the mood, as happened to be the fact so often in our brief intercourse as to lead me to think it characteristic of the man, his eye would lighten with a great deal of latent fun. He spoke more freely of his private affairs than I had reason to expect, though our business introduced the subject naturally; and, at such times, I thought the expression changed to a sort of melancholy resolution that was not wanting in sublimity.

"The manner of Sir Walter Scott is that of a man accustomed to see much of the world without being exactly a man of the world himself. He has, evidently, great social tact, perfect self-possession, is quiet, absolutely without pretension, and has much dignity; and yet it struck me that he wanted the ease and *aplomb* of one accustomed to live with his equals. The fact of his being a lion may produce some such effect; but I am mistaken if it be not more the influence of early habits and opinions, than of any thing else.

"Scott has been so much the mark of society, that it has evidently changed his natural manner, which is far less restrained than it is his habit to be in the world. I do not mean by this the mere restraint of decorum, but a drilled simplicity or demureness, like that of girls who are curbed in their tendency to fun and light-heartedness, by the dread of observation. I have seldom known a man of his years whose manner was so different in a *tête-à-tête*, and in the presence of a third person. In Edinburgh, the circle must be small, and he, probably, knows every one. If strangers do go there, they do not go all at once, and, of course, the old faces form the great majority, so that he finds himself always on familiar ground. I can readily imagine that in Auld Reekie, and among the right set, warmed, perhaps, by a glass of mountain-dew, Sir Walter Scott, in his peculiar way, is one of the pleasantest companions the world holds.

The principal subject of the conversation between Sir Walter Scott and Mr. Cooper, may be stated to have related to the pecuniary affairs of the author of "Waverley," as regarded his interests in America. Mr. Cooper was most warmly and sincerely engaged in forwarding those interests. He wrote private letters, articles for papers and periodicals, and other public appeals, with this view. It was his hope that something nearer to a just compensation for the fruits of his labors than he had yet received, might be given to the veteran writer, struggling under adversity. He believed that a man whose works—purely original, the off-spring of his own individual mind and labor, were providing sources of livelihood to ten thousand printers, and increase of wealth to a hundred booksellers, had every right to look for a respectable portion of the receipts of his works, from a people speaking the same language, and every reading household of whom had those works passing through their hands. For a time the American author was quite sanguine of the result. This hope was destined to be disappointed. Publics, whether under Crown or Congress, are not often generous; simply just they are, perhaps, never.

"The Prairie" was published by Messrs. Cary and Lea, of Philadelphia, in the autumn of 1826. It was read with less eagerness than the "Last of the Mohicans," by the public generally; but a position higher than that of any previous work of the same writer was conceded to it by the better class of critics. In France, it was very greatly admired. At a later day, when revising his works for a final edition, the writer expressed much regret that he had not confined the characters to those naturally connected with the ground, the rude backwoodsman and his family group, with the Pawnees and Dacotahs, all moving about Natty as a common centre. The introduction of Iñez and Middleton, he declared a great blemish. The book was a favorite with himself; it gave him pleasure to have written it, and yet he seldom thought with much interest of his own works after they had once passed from his portfolio. This was especially the case during the first fifteen or twenty years of his professional career, when he seems very rarely to have looked back to his own writings, and still more rarely to have opened one.

THE THICKET ON THE PRAIRIE.

THE mustering of the borderers on the following morning was silent, sullen, and gloomy. The repast of the hour was wanting in the inharmonious accompaniment with which Esther ordinarily enlivened their meals; for the effects of the powerful opiate the Doctor had administered, still muddled her usually quick intellects. The young men brooded over the absence of their elder brother, and the brows of Ishmael himself were sternly knit, as he cast his scowling eyes from one to the other, like a man who was preparing to meet and to repel an expected assault on his authority. In the midst of this family distrust, Ellen and her midnight confederate, the naturalist, took their usual places among the children, without awakening suspicion or exciting comment. The only apparent fruits of the adventure in which they had been engaged, were occasional upliftings of the eyes, on the part of the Doctor, which were mistaken by the observers for some of his scientific contemplations of the heavens, but which, in reality, were no other than furtive glances at the fluttering walls of the proscribed tent.

At length the squatter, who had waited in vain for some more decided manifestation of the expected rising among his sons, resolved to make a demonstration of his own intentions.

"Asa shall account to me for this undutiful conduct!" he coolly observed. "Here has the livelong night gone by, and he outlying on the prairie, when his hand and his rifle might both have been wanted in a brush with the Siouxes, for any right he had to know the contrary."

"Spare your breath, good man," retorted his wife; "be saving of your breath; for you may have to call long enough for the boy before he will answer!"

"It ar' a fact, that some men be so womanish, as to let the young master the old!

J. Hamilton pinx.{.}

A. Kyles Sculp.{.}

The Prairie: An Incident on the Prairie

But you, old Esther, should know better than to think such will ever be the nature of things in the family of Ishmael Bush."

"Ah! you are a hectorer with the boys, when need calls! I know it well, Ishmael; and one of your sons have you driven from you, by your temper; and that, too, at a time when he is most wanted."

"Father," said Abner, whose sluggish nature had gradually been stimulating itself to the exertion of taking so bold a stand, "the boys and I have pretty generally concluded to go out on the search of Asa. We are disagreeable about his 'camping on the prairie, instead of coming in to his own bed, as we all know he would like to do—"

"Pshaw!" muttered Abiram; "the boy has killed a buck; or perhaps a buffalo; and he is sleeping by the carcass to keep off the wolves, till day; we shall soon see him, or hear him bawling for help to bring in his load."

"'Tis little help that a son of mine will call for to shoulder a buck or to quarter your wild beef!" returned the mother. "And you, Abiram, to say such an uncertain thing! you, who said yourself that the redskins had been prowling around this place no later than the yesterday—"

"I!" exclaimed her brother, hastily, as if anxious to retract an error; "I said it then, and I say it now; and so you will find it to be. The Tetons are in our neighborhood, and happy will it prove for the boy if he is well shut of them."

"It seems to me," said Dr. Battius, speaking with the sort of deliberation and dignity one is apt to use after having thoroughly ripened his opinions by sufficient reflection, "it seems to me, a man but little skilled in the signs and tokens of Indian warfare, especially as practised in these remote plains, but one who, I may say without vanity, has some insight into the mysteries of nature—it seems, then, to me, thus humbly qualified, that when doubts exist in a matter of such moment, it would always be the wisest course to appease them."

"No more of your doctoring for me!" cried the grum Esther; "no more of your quiddities in a healthy family, say I! Here was I doing well, only a little out of sorts with over-instructing the young, and you dosed me with a drug that still hangs about my tongue, like a pound weight on a humming-bird's wing!"

"Is the medicine out?" dryly demanded Ishmael; "it must be a rare doser that, if it gives a heavy feel to the tongue of old Esther!"

"Friend," continued the Doctor, waving his hand for the angry wife to maintain the peace; "that it cannot perform all that is said of it, the very charge of good Mrs. Bush is a sufficient proof. But to speak of the absent Asa. There is doubt as to his fate, and there is a proposition to solve it. Now, in the natural sciences, truth is always a desideratum; and I confess it would seem to be equally so in the present case, which may be called a vacuum where, according to the laws of physic, there should exist some pretty palpable proofs of materiality."

"Don't mind him, don't mind him," cried Esther, observing that the rest of his auditors listened with an attention which might proceed equally from acquiescence in his proposal or ignorance of its meaning. "There is a drug in every word he utters."

"Dr. Battius wishes to say," Ellen modestly interposed, "that as some of us think Asa is in danger, and some think otherwise, the whole family might pass an hour or two in looking for him."

"Does he?" interrupted the woman; "then Dr. Battius has more sense in him than I believed! He is right, Ishmael; and what he says, shall be done. I will shoulder a rifle myself; and woe betide the redskin that crosses my path! I have pulled a trigger before to-day; aye, and heard an Indian yell, too, to my sorrow."

The spirit of Esther diffused itself, like the stimulus which attends a victorious war-cry, among her indolent sons. They arose in a body, and declared their determination to second so bold a resolution. Ishmael prudently yielded to an impulse he could not resist, and in a few minutes the woman appeared, shouldering her arms, prepared to lead forth, in person, such of her descendants as chose to follow in her train.

"Let them stay with the children that please," she said; "and them follow me, who ar' not chicken-hearted!"

"Abiram, it will not do to leave the huts without some guard," Ishmael whispered, glancing his eye upward.

The man whom he addressed started, and betrayed extraordinary eagerness in his reply.

"I will tarry and watch the camp."

A dozen voices were instantly raised in objections to this proposal. He was wanted to point out the places where the hostile tracks had been seen, and his termagant sister openly scouted at the idea, as unworthy of his manhood. The reluctant Abiram was compelled to yield, and Ishmael made a new disposition for the defence of the place; which was admitted, by every one, to be all-important to their security and comfort.

He offered the post of commandant to Dr. Battius, who, however, peremptorily and somewhat haughtily declined the doubtful honor; exchanging looks of singular intelligence with Ellen as he did so. In this dilemma the squatter was obliged to constitute the girl herself castellan; taking care, however, in deputing this important trust, to omit no words of caution and instruction. When this preliminary point was settled, the young men proceeded to arrange certain means of defence, and signals of alarm, that were adapted to the weakness and character of the garrison. Several masses of rock were drawn to the edge of the upper level, and so placed as to leave it at the discretion of the feeble Ellen and her associates, to cast them or not, as they might choose, on the heads of any invaders—who would, of necessity, be obliged to mount the eminence by the difficult and narrow passage already so often mentioned. In addition to this formidable obstruction, the barriers were strengthened and rendered nearly impassable. Smaller missiles, that might be hurled by the hands of even the younger children, but which would prove, from the elevation of the place, exceedingly dangerous, were provided in profusion. A pile of dried leaves and splinters were placed, as a beacon, on the upper rock, and then, even in the jealous judgment of the squatter, the post was deemed competent to maintain a creditable siege.

The moment the rock was thought to be in a state of sufficient security, the party who composed what might be called the sortie, sallied forth on their anxious expedition. The advance was led by Esther in person, who, attired in a dress half masculine, and bearing a weapon like the rest, seemed no unfit leader for the group of wildly-clad frontier-men that followed leisurely in her rear.

"Now, Abiram!" cried the Amazon, in a voice that was cracked and harsh, for the simple reason of being used too often in a strained and unnatural key. "Now, Abiram, run with your nose low; show yourself a hound of the true breed, and do some credit to your training. You it was that saw the prints of the Indian moccasin, and it behoves you to let others be as wise as yourself. Come; come to the front, man, and give us a bold lead."

The brother, who appeared at all times to stand in salutary awe of his sister's authority, complied; though it was with a reluctance so evident, as to excite sneers even among the unobservant and indolent sons of the squatter. Ishmael himself moved among his tall children, like one who expected nothing from the search, and who was indifferent alike to its success or failure. In this manner the party proceeded until their distant fortress had sunk so low, as to present an object no larger nor more distinct than a hazy point, on the margin of the prairie. Hitherto their progress had been silent and somewhat rapid, for as swell after swell was mounted and passed, without varying, or discovering a living object to enliven the monotony of the view, even the tongue of Esther was hushed in increasing anxiety. Here, however, Ishmael chose to pause, and casting the butt of his rifle from his shoulder to the ground, observed—

"This is enough. Buffalo signs and deer signs ar' plenty; but where ar' the Indian footsteps that you have seen, Abiram?"

"Still farther to the west," returned the other, pointing in the direction he named. "This was the spot where I struck the track of the buck I killed; it was after I took the deer, that I fell upon the Teton trail."

"And a bloody piece of work you made of it, man!" cried the squatter, pointing tauntingly to the soiled garments of his kinsman, and then directing the attention of the spectators to his own, by the way of a triumphant contrast. "Here have I cut the throat of two lively does, and a scampering fawn, without spot or stain; while you, blundering dog as you ar', you have made as much work for Eester and her girls, as though butchering was your regular calling. Come, boys; I say it is enough. I am too old not to know the signs of the frontiers, and no Indian has been here, since the last fall of water. Follow me; and I will make a turn that shall give us at least the beef of a fallow cow for our trouble."

"Follow *me!*" echoed Esther, stepping undauntedly forward. "I am leader to-day, and I *will* be followed. For who so proper, let me know, as a mother to head a search for her lost child?"

Ishmael regarded his intractable mate with a smile of indulgent pity. Observing that she had already struck out a path for herself, different both from that of Abiram and the one he had seen fit to choose, and being unwilling to draw the cord of authority too tight just at that moment, he again sullenly submitted to her will. But Dr. Battius, who had hitherto been a silent and thoughtful attendant on the woman, now saw fit to raise his feeble voice in the way of remonstrance.

"I agree with thy partner in life, worthy and gentle Mrs. Bush," he said, "in believing that some *ignis fatuus* of the imagination has deceived Abiram, in the signs or symptoms of which he has spoken."

"Symptoms, yourself!" interrupted the termagant. "This is no time for bookish words, nor is this a place to stop and swallow medicines. If you are a-leg-weary, say so, as a plain-speaking man should; then seat yourself on the prairie, like a hound that is foot-sore, and take your natural rest."

"I accord in the opinion," the naturalist calmly replied, complying literally with the opinion of the deriding Esther, by taking his seat, very coolly, by the side of an indigenous shrub; the examination of which he commenced, on the instant, in order that science might not lose any of its just and important dues. "I honor your excellent advice, Mistress Esther, as you may perceive. Go thou in quest of thy offspring; while I tarry here in pursuit of that which is better, viz., an insight into the arcana of nature's volume."

The woman answered with a hollow, unnatural, and scornful laugh, and even her heavy sons, as they slowly passed the seat of the already abstracted naturalist, did not disdain to manifest their contempt in significant smiles. In a few minutes the train had mounted the nearest eminence, and, as it turned the rounded acclivity, the doctor was left to pursue his profitable investigations in entire solitude.

Another half-hour passed, during which Esther continued to advance on her seemingly fruitless search. Her pauses, however, were becoming frequent, and her looks wandering and uncertain, when footsteps were heard clattering through the bottom, and at the next instant a buck was seen to bound up the ascent, and to dart from before their eyes, in the direction of the naturalist. So sudden and unlooked-for had been the passage of the animal, and so much had he been favored by the shape of the ground, that before any one of the foresters had time to bring his rifle to his shoulder, it was already far beyond the range of a bullet.

"Look out for the wolf!" shouted Abner, shaking his head in vexation, at being a single moment too late. "A wolf's skin will be no bad gift in a winter's night; aye, yonder the hungry devil comes!"

"Hold!" cried Ishmael, knocking up the levelled weapon of his too eager son.

" 'Tis not a wolf; but a hound of thorough blood and bottom. Ha! we have hunters nigh: there ar' two of them!"

He was still speaking when the animals in question came leaping on the track of the deer, striving with noble ardor to outdo each other. One was an aged dog, whose strength seemed to be sustained purely by his generous emulation, and the other a pup, that gambolled even while he pressed most warmly on the chase. They both ran, however, with clean and powerful leaps, carrying their noses high, like animals of the most keen and subtle scent. They had passed; and in another minute they would have been running open-mouthed with the deer in view, had not the younger dog suddenly bounded from the course and uttered a cry of surprise. His aged companion stopped also, and returned panting and exhausted to the place where the other was whirling around in swift and apparently in mad evolutions, circling the spot in his own footsteps, and continuing his outcry in a short, snappish barking. But, when the elder hound had reached the spot, he seated himself, and lifting his nose high into the air, he raised a long, loud, and wailing howl.

"It must be a strong scent," said Abner, who had been, with the rest of the family, an admiring observer of the movements of the dogs, "that can break off two such creatures so suddenly from their trail!"

"Murder them!" cried Abiram; "I'll swear to the old hound; 'tis the dog of the trapper, whom we now know to be our mortal enemy."

Though the brother of Esther gave such hostile advice, he appeared in no way ready to put it into execution himself. The surprise which had taken possession of the whole party, exhibited itself in his own vacant, wondering stare, as strongly as in any of the admiring visages by whom he was surrounded. His denunciation, therefore, notwithstanding its dire import, was disregarded; and the dogs were left to obey the impulses of their mysterious instinct, without let or hindrance.

It was long before any of the spectators broke the silence; but the squatter at length so far recollected his authority as to take on himself the right to control the movements of his children.

"Come away, boys; come away, and leave the hounds to sing their tunes for their own amusement," Ishmael said, in his coldest manner. "I scorn to take the life of a beast because its master has pitch'd himself too nigh my clearing; come away, boys; come away; we have enough of our own work before us, without turning aside to do that of the whole neighborhood."

"Come *not* away!" cried Esther, in tones that sounded like the admonitions of some sibyl. "I say, come *not* away, my children. There is a meaning and a warning in this; and as I am a woman and a mother, will I know the truth of it all!"

So saying, the awakened wife of the squatter brandished her weapon, with an air that was not without its wild and secret influence, and led the way toward the spot where the dogs still remained, filling the air with their long-drawn and piteous complaints. The whole party followed in her steps, some too indolent to oppose, others obedient to her will, and all more or less excited by the uncommon character of the scene.

"Tell me, you, Abner—Abiram—Ishmael!" the woman cried, standing over a spot where the earth was trampled and beaten, and plainly sprinkled with blood—" tell me, you who ar' hunters! what sort of animal has here met his death? Speak! Ye ar' men, and used to the signs of the plains, all of ye; is it the blood of wolf or panther?"

"A buffalo—and a noble and powerful creatur' has it been!" returned the squatter, who looked down calmly on the fatal signs which so strangely affected his wife. "Here are the marks of the spot where he has struck his hoofs into the earth, in the death-struggle; and yonder he has plunged and torn the ground with his horns. Aye, a buffalo bull of wonderful strength and courage has he been!"

"And who has slain him?" continued Esther. "Man! where, then, are the offals? Wolves!—they devour not the hide! Tell me, ye men and hunters, is this the blood of a beast?"

"The creatur' has plunged over the hillock," said Abner, who had proceeded a short distance beyond the rest of the party. "Ah! there you will find it, in yon swale of alders. Look! a thousand carrion birds ar' hovering, this very moment, above the carcass."

"The animal has still life in him," returned the squatter, "or the buzzards would settle upon their prey! By the action of the dogs it must be something ravenous; I reckon it is the white bear from the upper falls. They are said to cling desperately to life!"

"Aye, let us go back," said Abiram; "there may be danger, and there can be no good, in attacking a ravenous beast. Remember, Ishmael, 'twill be a risky job, and one of small profit!"

The young men smiled at this new proof of the well-known pusillanimity of their too sensitive uncle. The oldest even proceeded so far as to express his contempt, by bluntly saying—

"It will do to cage with the other animal we carry; then we may go back double-handed into the settlements, and set up for showmen around the court-houses and gaols of Kentucky."

The dark, threatening frown which gathered on the brow of his father, admonished the young man to forbear. Exchanging looks that were half rebellious, with his brethren, he saw fit to be silent. But instead of observing the caution recommended by Abiram, they proceeded in a body, until they again came to a halt within a few yards of the matted cover of the thicket.

The scene had now, indeed, become wild and striking enough to have produced a powerful effect on minds better prepared than those of the unnurtured family of the squatter, to resist the impressions of such an exciting spectacle. The heavens were as usual at the season, covered with dark, driving clouds, beneath which interminable flocks of aquatic birds were again on the wing, holding their toilsome and heavy way toward the distant waters of the south. The wind had risen, and was once more sweeping over the prairie in gusts, which it was often vain to oppose; and then again the blasts would seem to mount into the upper air, as if to sport with the drifting vapor, whirling and rolling vast masses of the dusky and ragged volumes over each other, in a terrific and yet grand disorder. Above the little brake, the flocks of birds still held their flight, circling with heavy wings about the spot, struggling at times against the torrent of wind, and then, favored by their position and height, making bold swoops upon the thicket, away from which, however, they never failed to sail, screaming in terror, as if apprised, either by sight or instinct, that the hour of their voracious dominion had not yet fully arrived.

Ishmael stood for many minutes, with his wife and children clustered together, in an amazement, with which awe was singularly mingled, gazing in death-like stillness on the imposing sight. The voice of Esther at length broke the charm, and reminded the spectators of the necessity of resolving their doubts in some manner more worthy of their manhood, than by a dull and inactive observation.

"Call in the dogs," she said; "call in the hounds and put them into the thicket; there ar' men enough of ye, if ye have not lost the spirit with which I know ye were born, to tame the tempers of all the bears west of the big river. Call in the dogs, I say, you Enoch! Abner! Gabriel! has wonder made ye deaf as well as dumb?"

One of the young men complied; and having succeeded in detaching the hounds from the place, around which, until then, they had not ceased to hover, he led them down to the margin of the thicket.

"Put them in, boy; put them in," continued the woman; "and you, Ishmael and Abiram, if any thing wicked or hurtful comes forth, show them the use of your rifles, like frontier-men. If ye ar' wanting in spirit, before the eyes of my children will I put ye both to shame!"

The youths, who, until now, had detained the hounds, let slip the thongs of skin, by which they had been held, and urged them to the attack by their voices. But it would seem that the elder dog was restrained by some extraordinary sensation, or that he was much too experienced to attempt the rash adventure. After proceeding a few yards to the very verge of the brake, he made a sudden pause, and stood trembling in all his aged limbs, apparently as unable to recede as to advance. The encouraging calls of the young men were disregarded, or only answered by a low and plaintive whining. For a minute the pup also was similarly affected; but less sage, or more easily excited, he was induced at length to leap forward, and finally to dash into the cover. An alarmed and startling howl was heard, and, at the next minute, he broke out of the thicket, and commenced circling the spot, in the same wild and unsteady manner as before.

"Have I a man among my children?" demanded the aroused Esther. "Give me a truer piece than a childish shot-gun, and I will show you what the courage of a frontier-woman can do."

"Stay, mother," exclaimed Abner and Enoch; "if you *will* see the creatur', let *us* drive it into view."

This was quite as much as the youths were accustomed to utter, even on more important occasions; but having thus given a pledge of their intentions, they were far from being backward in redeeming it. Preparing their arms with the utmost care, they advanced with steadiness to the brake. Nerves less often tried than those of the young borderers might easily have shrunk before the dangers of so uncertain an undertaking. As they proceeded, the howls of the dogs became more shrill and plaintive. The vultures and buzzards settled so low as to flap the bushes with their heavy wings, and the wind came hoarsely sweeping along the naked prairie, as if the spirits of the air had also descended to witness the approaching development.

There was a breathless moment, when the blood of the usually undaunted Esther flowed backward to her heart, as she saw her sons push aside the matted branches of thicket, and bury themselves in its labyrinth. A deep and solemn pause succeeded. Then arose two loud and piercing cries, in quick succession, which were followed by a quiet still more awful and appalling.

"Come back, come back, my children," cried the woman, the feelings of a mother getting the entire ascendency in her bosom.

But her voice was hushed, and every faculty seemed frozen with horror, as at that instant the bushes once more parted, and the two adventurers reappeared, pale, and nearly insensible themselves, and laid at her feet the stiff and motionless body of the lost Asa, with the marks of a violent death but too plainly stamped on every pallid lineament.

The dogs uttered a long and closing howl, and then breaking off together, they disappeared on the forsaken trail of the deer. The flight of birds wheeled upward into the heavens, filling the air with their complaints at having been robbed of a victim, which, frightful and disgusting as it was, still bore too much of the impression of humanity to become the prey of their obscene appetites.

"Stand back! stand off, the whole of ye!" said Esther hoarsely, to the crowd, which pressed too closely on the corpse; "I am his mother, and my right is better than that of ye all! Who has done this? Tell me, Ishmael, Abiram, Abner? open your mouths and your hearts, and let God's truth, and no other, issue from them. Who has done this bloody deed?"

Her husband made no reply, but stood, leaning on his rifle, looking sadly, but with an unaltered eye, at the mangled remains of his son. Not so the mother; she threw herself on the earth, and receiving the cold and ghastly head of the dead man into her lap, she sat many minutes contemplating those muscular features, on which the death-agony was still horridly impressed, in a silence even more expressive than any language of lamentation could possibly have proved.

The voice of the woman was literally frozen in grief. In vain Ishmael attempted a few words of rude consolation; she neither listened nor answered. Her sons gathered about her in a circle, and expressed, after their uncouth manner, their sympathy in her sorrow, as well as their sense of their own loss, but she motioned them away, impatiently, with her hand. At times her fingers played in the matted hair of the dead, and at others they lightly attempted to smooth the painfully expressive muscles of its ghastly visage, as the hand of the mother is often seen to linger fondly about the features of her sleeping child. Then starting from their revolting office, her hands would flutter around her, and seem to seek some fruitless remedy against the violent blow, which had thus suddenly destroyed the child in whom she had not only placed her greatest hopes, but so much of her maternal pride. It was while engaged in the latter incomprehensible manner, that the lethargic Abner turned aside, and swallowing the unwonted emotions which were rising in his own throat, he observed—

"Mother means that we should look for the signs, that we may know in what manner Asa has come by his end."

"We owe it to the accursed Siouxes!" answered Ishmael; "twice have they put me deeply in their debt! The third time, the score shall be cleared!"

But, as if not content with this plausible explanation, and, perhaps secretly glad to avert their eyes from a spectacle which awakened such extraordinary and unusual sensations in their sluggish bosoms, the sons of the squatter turned away in a body from their mother and the corpse, and proceeded to make the inquiries which they fancied the former had so repeatedly demanded. Ishmael made no objections; but, though he accompanied his children while they proceeded in the investigation, it was more with the appearance of complying with their wishes, at a time when resistance might not be seemly, than with any visible interest in the result. As the borderers, notwithstanding their usual dulness, were well instructed in most things connected with their habits of life, an inquiry, the success of which depended so much on signs and evidences that bore so strong a resemblance to a forest trail, was likely to be conducted with skill and acuteness. Accordingly, they proceeded to the melancholy task with great readiness and intelligence.

Abner and Enoch agreed in their accounts as to the position in which they had found the body. It was seated nearly upright, the back supported by a mass of matted brush, and one hand still grasping a broken twig of the alders. It was most probably owing to the former circumstance that the body had escaped the rapacity of the carrion birds, which had been seen hovering above the thicket, and the latter proved that life had not yet entirely abandoned the hapless victim when he entered the brake. The opinion now became general that the youth had received his death-wound in the open prairie, and had dragged his enfeebled form into the cover of the thicket for the purpose of concealment. A trail through the bushes confirmed this opinion. It also appeared, on examination, that a desperate struggle had taken place on the very margin of the thicket. This was sufficiently apparent by the trodden branches, the deep impressions on the moist ground, and the lavish flow of blood.

"He has been shot in the open ground, and come here for a cover," said Abiram; "these marks would clearly prove it. The boy has been set upon by the savages in a body, and has fou't like a hero as he was, until they have mastered his strength, and then drawn him to the bushes."

To this probable opinion there was now but one dissenting voice—that of the slow-minded Ishmael, who demanded that the corpse itself should be examined in order to a more accurate knowledge of its injuries. On examination, it appeared that a rifle-bullet had passed directly through the body of the deceased, entering beneath one of his brawny shoulders, and making its exit by the breast. It required some knowledge in gunshot wounds to decide this delicate point, but the experience of the borderers was quite equal to the scrutiny; and a smile of wild, and certainly of singular satisfaction, passed among the sons of Ishmael when Abner confidently announced that the enemies of Asa had assailed him in the rear.

"It must be so," said the gloomy but attentive squatter. "He was of too good a stock and too well trained, knowingly to turn the weak side to man or beast! Remember, boys, that while the front of manhood is to your enemy, let him be who or what he may, you ar' safe from cowardly surprise. Why, Eester, woman! you ar' getting beside yourself; with picking at the hair and the garments of the child! Little good can you do him now, old girl."

"See!" interrupted Enoch, extricating from the fragments of cloth the morsel of lead which had prostrated the strength of one so powerful, "here is the very bullet."

Ishmael took it in his hand, and eyed it long and closely.

"There's no mistake," at length he muttered through his compressed teeth. "It is from the pouch of that accursed trapper. Like many of the hunters, he has a mark in his mould, in order to know the work his rifle performs; and here you see it plainly —six little holes, laid crossways."

"I'll swear to it!" cried Abiram, triumphantly. "He show'd me his private mark, himself, and boasted of the number of deer he had laid upon the prairies with these very bullets! Now, Ishmael, will you believe me when I tell you the old knave is a spy of the redskins!"

The lead passed from the hand of one to that of another; and unfortunately for the reputation of the old man, several among them remembered also to have seen the aforesaid private bullet-marks, during the curious examination which all had made of his accoutrements. In addition to this wound, however, were many others of a less dangerous nature, all of which were supposed to confirm the supposed guilt of the trapper.

The Prairie: "The tick of the lock is as well known to the knaves as the blast of a trumpet to a soldier! lay down the piece – lay down the piece."

The traces of many different struggles were to be seen, between the spot where the first blood was spilt and the thicket, to which it was now generally believed Asa had retreated as a place of refuge. These were interpreted into so many proofs of the weakness of the murderer, who would have sooner dispatched his victim, had not even the dying strength of the youth rendered him formidable to the infirmities of one so old. The danger of drawing some others of the hunters to the spot, by repeated firing, was deemed a sufficient reason for not again resorting to the rifle, after it had performed the important duty of disabling the victim. The weapon of the dead man was not to be found, and had doubtless, together with many other less valuable and lighter articles, that he was accustomed to carry about his person, become a prize to his destroyer.

But what, in addition to the tell-tale bullet, appeared to fix the ruthless deed with peculiar certainty on the trapper, was the accumulated evidence furnished by the trail; which proved, notwithstanding his deadly hurt, that the wounded man had still been able to make a long and desperate resistance to the subsequent efforts of his murderer. Ishmael seemed to press this proof with a singular mixture of sorrow and pride— sorrow, at the loss of a son, whom in their moments of amity he highly valued; and pride, at the courage and power he had manifested to his last and weakest breath.

"He died as a son of mine should die," said the squatter, gleaning a hollow consolation from so unnatural an exultation; "a dread to his enemy to the last, and without help from the law! Come, children; we have first the grave to make, and then to hunt his murderer."

The sons of the squatter set about their melancholy office in silence and in sadness. An excavation was made in the hard earth, at a great expense of toil and time, and the body was wrapped in such spare vestments as could be collected among the laborers. When these arrangements were completed, Ishmael approached the seemingly unconscious Esther, and announced his intention to inter the dead. She heard him, and quietly relinquished her grasp of the corpse, rising in silence to follow it to its narrow resting-place. Here she seated herself again at the head of the grave, watching each movement of the youths with eager and jealous eyes. When a sufficiency of earth was laid upon the senseless clay of Asa, to protect it from injury, Enoch and Abner entered the cavity, and trod it into a solid mass by the weight of their huge frames, with an appearance of a strange, not to say savage, mixture of care and indifference. This well-known precaution was adopted to prevent the speedy exhumation of the body by some of the carnivorous beasts of the prairie, whose instinct was sure to guide them to the spot. Even the rapacious birds appeared to comprehend the nature of the ceremony, for, mysteriously apprised that the miserable victim was now about to be abandoned by the human race, they once more began to make their airy circuits above the place, screaming as if to frighten the kinsmen from their labor of caution and love.

Ishmael stood, with folded arms, steadily watching the manner in which this necessary duty was performed, and when the whole was completed, he lifted his cap to his sons, to thank them for their services, with a dignity that would have become one much better nurtured. Throughout the whole of a ceremony which is ever solemn and admonitory, the squatter had maintained a grave and serious deportment. His vast features were visibly stamped with an expression of deep concern; but at no time did they falter, until he turned his back, as he believed forever, on the grave of his first-born. Nature was then stirring powerfully within him, and the muscles of his stern visage began to work perceptibly. His children fastened their eyes on his, as if to seek a direction to the strange emotions which were moving their own heavy natures, when the struggle in the bosom of the squatter suddenly ceased, and, taking his wife by the arm, he raised her to her feet as though she had been an infant, saying, in a voice that was perfectly steady, though a nice observer would have discovered that it was kinder than usual—

"Eester, we have now done all that man and woman can do. We raised the boy, and made him such as few others were like, on the frontiers of America; and we have given him a grave. Let us go."

The woman turned her eyes slowly from the fresh earth, and laying her hands on the shoulders of her husband, stood looking him anxiously in the eyes for many moments, before she uttered in a voice, deep, frightful, and nearly choked—

"Ishmael! Ishmael! you parted from the boy in your wrath!"

"May the Lord pardon his sins freely as I have forgiven his worst misdeeds," calmly returned the squatter; "woman, go you back to the rock, and read in your Bible; a chapter in that book always does you good. You *can* read, Eester; which is a privilege I never did enjoy."

"Yes, yes," muttered the woman, yielding to his strength, and suffering herself to be led, though with powerful reluctance, from the spot, "I *can* read; and how have I used the knowledge! But he, Ishmael, he has not the sin of wasted l'arning to answer for. We have spared him *that*, at least! whether it be in mercy or in cruelty, I know not."

Her husband made no reply, but continued steadily to lead her in the direction of their temporary abode. When they reached the summit of the swell of land, which they knew was the last spot from which the situation of the grave of Asa could be seen, they all turned, as by common concurrence, to take a farewell view of the place. The little mound itself was not visible; but it was frightfully indicated by the flock of screaming birds which hovered above it. In the opposite direction, a low, blue hillock, in the skirts of the horizon, pointed out the place where Esther had left the rest of her young, and served as an attraction to draw her reluctant steps from the last abode of her eldest son. Nature quickened in the bosom of the mother at the sight, and she finally yielded the rights of the dead to the more urgent claims of the living.

The foregoing occurrences had struck a spark from the stern tempers of a set of beings so singularly moulded in the habits of their uncultivated lives, which served to keep alive among them the dying embers of family affection. United to their parents by ties no stronger than those which use had created, there had been great danger, as Ishmael had foreseen, that the overloaded hive would quickly swarm, and leave him saddled with the difficulties of a young and helpless brood, unsupported by the exertions of those whom he had already brought to a state of maturity. The spirit of insubordination, which emanated from the unfortunate Asa, had spread among his juniors, and the squatter had been made painfully to remember the time when, in the wantonness of his youth and vigor, he had, reversing the order of the brutes, cast off his own aged and failing parents, to enter into the world unshackled and free. But the danger had now abated, for a time at least; and if his authority was not restored with all its former influence, it was visibly admitted to exist, and to maintain its ascendency a little longer.

It is true that his slow-minded sons, even while they submitted to the impressions of the recent event, had glimmerings of terrible distrust, as to the manner in which their elder brother had met with his death. There were faint and indistinct images in the minds of two or three of the oldest, which portrayed the father himself as ready to imitate the example of Abraham, without the justification of the sacred authority which commanded the holy man to attempt the revolting office. But then, these images were so transient and so much obscured in intellectual mists, as to leave no very strong impressions, and the tendency of the whole transaction, as we have already said, was rather to strengthen than to weaken the authority of Ishmael.

In this disposition of mind, the party continued their route toward the place whence they had that morning issued on a search which had been crowned with so melancholy a success. The long and fruitless march which they had made under the direction of Abiram, the discovery of the body and its subsequent interment, had so far consumed the day, that by the time their steps were retraced across the broad tract of waste which lay between the grave of Asa and the rock, the sun had fallen far below his meridian altitude. The hill had gradually risen as they approached, like some tower emerging from the bosom of the sea, and when within a mile, the minuter objects that crowned its height came dimly into view.

"It will be a sad meeting for the girls!" said Ishmael, who, from time to time, did not cease to utter something which he intended should be consolatory to the bruised spirit of his stricken partner. "Asa was much regarded by all the young; and seldom failed to bring in from his hunts something that they loved."

"He did—he did," murmured Esther; "the boy was the pride of the family. My other children are as nothing to him!"

"Say not so, good woman," returned the father, glancing his eye a little proudly at the athletic train which followed, at no great distance, in the rear. "Say not so, old

Eester; for few fathers and mothers have greater reason to be boastful than ourselves.

"Thankful, thankful," muttered the humbled woman; "ye mean thankful, Ishmael!"

"Then thankful let it be, if you like the word better, my good girl—but what has become of Nelly and the young! The child has forgotten the charge I gave her, and has not only suffered the children to sleep, but, I warrant you, is dreaming of the fields of Tennessee at this very moment. The mind of your niece is mainly fixed on the settlements, I reckon."

"Aye, she is not for us; I said it, and thought it, when I took her, because death had stripped her of all other friends. Death is a sad worker in the bosom of families, Ishmael! Asa had a kind feeling to the child, and they might have come one day into our places, had things been so ordered."

"Nay, she is not gifted for a frontier wife, if this is the manner she is to keep house while the husband is on the hunt. Abner, let off your rifle, that they may know we ar' coming. I fear Nelly and the young ar' asleep."

The young man complied with an alacrity that manifested how gladly he would see the rounded, active figure of Ellen, enlivening the ragged summit of the rock. But the report was succeeded neither by signal nor answer of any sort. For a moment the whole party stood in suspense, awaiting the result, and then a simultaneous impulse caused the whole to let off their pieces at the same instant, producing a noise which might not fail to reach the ears of all within so short a distance.

"Ah! there they come at last!" cried Abiram, who was usually among the first to seize on any circumstance which promised relief from disagreeable apprehensions.

"It is a petticoat fluttering on the line," said Esther; "I put it there myself."

"You ar' right; but now she comes; the jade has been taking her comfort in the tent!"

"It is not so, said Ishmael, whose usually inflexible features were beginning to manifest the uneasiness he violently felt. "It is the tent itself blowing about loosely in the wind. They have loosened the bottom, like silly children as they ar', and unless care is had, the whole will come down!"

The words were scarcely uttered before a hoarse, rushing blast of wind swept by the spot where they stood, raising the dust into little eddies, in its progress; and then, as if guided by a master hand, it quitted the earth, and mounted in its progress to the precise spot on which all eyes were just then riveted. The loosened linen felt its influence, and tottered; but regained its poise, and, for a moment, it became tranquil. The cloud of leaves next played in circling revolutions around the place, and then descended with the velocity of a swooping hawk, and sailed away into the prairie in long straight lines, like a flight of swallows resting on their expanded wings. They were followed for some distance by the snow-white tent, which, however, soon fell behind the rock, leaving its highest peak as naked as when it lay in the entire solitude of the desert.

"The murderers have been here!" moaned Esther. "My babes! my babes!"

For a moment even Ishmael faltered before the weight of such an unexpected blow. But shaking himself, like an awakened lion, he sprang forward, and pushing aside the impediments of the barrier, as though they had been feathers, he rushed up the ascent with an impetuosity which proved how formidable a sluggish nature may become when thoroughly aroused.

VIII

THE RED ROVER.

SINGULARLY different from "The Prairie" was the book now planned. A brilliant romance of the sea followed the wild movement of Pawnee and Dahcotah over the great plains; a character as widely opposite as possible from the beautiful picture of the trapper, in his serene and sylvan old age, becomes the principal figure in the new work. A nature quick in intellect, endowed with great force of will, possessing every advantage of social position and culture in early life, but wildly passionate and wayward, is represented as having, in an evil hour, while smarting under some act of official injustice, violently thrown off all social restraint, and cast itself loose on the stormy tide of life, an outlaw in spirit, a corsair in deed. This figure appears for a few brief weeks of its wayward course before the reader. He comes in the height of a career, successful in so far as evil may claim reality of success—having achieved ruthless fame, and power, and treasure, in the dark field of violence; a few weeks pass over; a short but most eventful drama is enacted on the bosom of the deep, within the narrow bounds of two ships. The rover is brought once more into contact with pure influences, from which he had long utterly estranged himself. The voice of a sister falls upon his ear—an elder sister, one who had been more than a companion; one who, beyond a sister's affection, had given something of a mother's deep love, and anxious tenderness, and compassionate sympathy to the wayward youth at her side. Old memories awaken; home feeling revives; conscience is powerfully aroused. The passionate spirit, in the very hour of its greatest triumph, bows in penitence. The rover surrenders his captives; his wild

The Red Rover: "Our work is done! He that strikes
another blow makes an enemy of me."

crew is disbanded; with his own hand he fires the beautiful and victorious craft which had long been the scourge of the seas. He disappears. Half a lifetime passes away in obscurity. Again he crosses his sister's threshold to die, having been victorious in honorable conflict under the flag freshly unfurled to the western breezes by the young republic. A character like that of the rover was exceedingly difficult to draw. To represent a man who had so recklessly outlawed himself, to give him the ungovernable, passionate nature which could alone throw him into such a course, to make no attempt at veiling the dark coloring of that career of violence, and yet to avoid all revolting detail, and to throw about the individual just such a degree of lingering intellectual and moral light as to awaken our sympathies, and to render final penitence and submission to just restraints probable—this was assuredly no easy task. Many similar characters have been drawn, some by the hands of masters; is there one in English literature, whether in prose or in verse, more clearly conceived, more skilfully carried out? The principle on which the contrition of the rover is founded is one entirely true to reality. We see it constantly in the quiet course of daily life. There are few men, probably, among those blessed with pure home influences in boyhood, over whose hearts those influences do not retain a secret, latent power, even in the dark period of a career of sin. The feeling may be feeble in degree, it may be unacknowledged by the heart in which it still lives, it may be silenced by pride, it may be stifled by evil passion, chilled by the cold sneer of the world, polluted by corrupt example, perverted by sophism, entangled within the thousand petty webs of a miserable selfishness—but rarely indeed—nay, perhaps never—does it become utterly and irretrievably extinct so long as that heart beats. Again and again, in the course of life, it moves in the secret depths of the soul—it whispers to conscience, it appeals to reason. Belonging in its essence to eternal Truth, like truth, it is undying in spirit. The ultimate fate of the individual, the final coloring which his life is to receive, must ever depend on the response given to such appeals. With many men in this condition, as years move onward, time discovers, one by one, all that is false and treacherous in the thousand alluring deceits of crime, and vice, and sin. Their souls open anew to the blessed influences of Holy Truth. With many men this renovation is effected slowly indeed, often almost imperceptibly; step by step they regain something of the lost ground, something of those treasures which prodigal manhood has trifled away—the humility, the simplicity, the faith, the love of their childhood. But there are others for whom a few brief days—nay, some signal hour—shall accomplish the same great work; the scales of error are torn from their eyes, the pure light of Heaven shines once more upon the darkened mind, and warms anew

into a better life that chilled and hardened soul.   A singular incident, bearing
this moral, offering as it were an illustration of the narrative we are now looking
over, has been placed on authentic record by a great and truthful writer.   Un-
happily, the book is not within reach ; a version necessarily imperfect must be
accepted for the original words.

On the shores of southern Florida, and among the rocky islets or "keys" of
the Gulf of Mexico, there is a rare and a beautiful bird, to which the name of the
Zenaida Dove has been given by Prince Charles Bonaparte, the ornithologist.
This creature is very beautiful in its delicate form and plumage ; its general coloring is of a warm and rosy gray, varying in lighter or deeper shades, and barred
with brown and white on back and wing, while its breast bears a shield of pure
and vivid blue, bordered with gold, and its cheeks are marked with spots of deep
ultramarine.   Legs and feet are of a deep rose-color, and the nails black.   Harmless and innocent, like others of its tribe, this little creature flits to and fro, in
small family groups, over the rocky islets, and along the warm, sandy beaches of
the Gulf—" Tampa's desert strand."

"On that lone shore loud moans the sea."

There are certain rocky keys where it loves especially to alight, attracted by the
springs which here and there gush up pure and fresh among the coral rocks.   The
low note of this little creature is more than usually sweet, pure, and mournful
in its tone.   But the doves are not the only visitors of those rare springs.   A few
years since, pirates haunted the same spots, seeking, like the birds, water from
those natural fountains.   It chanced one day, that a party of those fierce outlaws
came to a desolate key to fill their water-casks, ere sailing on some fresh cruise
of violence.   A little flock of the rosy-gray doves—and their flocks are ever few
and rare—were flitting and cooing in peace about the rocky basin when these
wretched men appeared ; in affright they took wing and flew away.   The casks
were filled, and the fierce crew rowed their boat off to the guilty craft lying at
anchor in the distance.   For some reason unexplained, however, one of the band
remained awhile on the island, alone.   He threw himself, in a quiet evening hour,
on the rocks near the spring, looking over the broad sea, where here and there a
low solitary islet rose from the deep, while the vessel with which his own fate had
long been connected, lay idle in the offing.   Presently the little doves, seeing all
quiet again, returned to their favorite spring, flitting to and fro in peace, uttering
to each other their low, gentle notes, so caressing, and so plaintive.   It may have
been that in the wild scenes of his dark career, the wretched man had never
known the silent force of solitude.   He was now gradually overpowered by its

influences, pressing upon heart and mind; he felt himself to be alone with his Maker and his conscience. The works of the Holy One surrounded him—the pure heavens hanging over his head, the sea stretching in silent grandeur far beyond the horizon; one object, alone, connected with man, lay within range of his eye—the guilty craft, which, like an evil phantom, lay in the offing, brooding sin. A fearful consciousness of guilt came over the wretched man. Curse, and ribald jest, and brutal threat, and shriek of death, had long been sounds most familiar. And now those little doves came hovering about him, uttering their guileless notes of tenderness and innocence. Far away, in his native woods, within sight of father's roof, he had often listened in boyhood to other doves, whose notes, like these, were pure and sweet. Home memories, long banished from his breast, returned. The image of his mother stood before him. Those little doves, still uttering their low, pure, inoffensive note, seemed like the far-off echoes of every sacred word of devout faith, of pure precept, of generous feeling, which in happier years had reached his ear. His heart was utterly subdued. The stern pride of manhood, and the callous pride of sin, gave way. A powerful tide of contrition swept away all evil barriers. Bitter tears of penitence fell upon the stone on which his head rested. It was the turning point of life. He arose from the rock resolved to retrace his steps—to return to better things. The resolution was adhered to. He broke away from his wicked courses, thrust temptation aside, returned to his native soil to lead a life of penitence and honest toil. Years later, a stranger came to his cabin, in the wild forests of the southern country—a man venerable in mien, shrewd and kindly in countenance—wandering through the woods on pleasant errands of his own; the birds of the region were his object. The inmate of the cabin had much to tell on this subject; gradually, as the two were thrown together in the solitude of the forest, the heart of the penitent opened to his companion. He avowed that he loved the birds of heaven; he had cause to love them—the doves especially; they had been as friends to him; they had been with him, they had spoken to his heart, in the most solemn hour of life! Then came that singular confession. The traveller was Audubon, the great ornithologist, who has left on record in his works the striking incident. In olden time, what a beautiful ballad would have been written on such a theme: fresh and free as the breeze of the forest, sweet and plaintive as the note of the dove!

"The Red Rover" is most completely a book of the sea—as much so as "The Mohicans" is a tale of the forest. The whole drama is almost entirely enacted on the ocean. The curtain rises in port; but the varied scenes, so full of nautical interest, and succeeding each other in startling rapidity, are wholly unfolded on the bosom of the deep. It is believed that there is scarcely another book in

English literature so essentially marine in spirit.   It is like some material picture
of the sea, drawn by a master hand, where the eye looks abroad over the rolling
waves, where it glances at the sea-bird fluttering amid the spray, and then rests
upon the gallant ship, with swelling canvas, bending before the breeze, until the
land behind us, and the soil beneath our own feet, are forgotten.   In the Rover,
the different views of the ocean, in majestic movement, are very noble, while the
two vessels which carry the heart of the narrative with them come and go with
wonderful power and grace, guided by the hand of one who was both pilot and
poet in his own nature.   The love story, as usual in the novel of that period, and
that particular class, is insignificant, though "Gertrude" is certainly very pretty
and proper, which is much more than one would venture to aver of many heroines
of the present hour.   In reality, however, our worthy friends Dick Fid, that
arrant old foretopman, and his comrade, Negro S'ip, are the true lovers of the
narrative; and most worthy and most real they are—the last, indeed, is a noble
creature, a hero under the skin of Congo.   As for Wilder, the author professed
to owe him an apology for having thrown a sufficiently clever fellow, and an
honorable man no doubt, into a position slightly equivocal; he declared himself,
however, very much indebted to a friendly critic who saw much to admire in the
course pursued by the young lieutenant—this *crachat* of the obliging reviewer
relieving the author's mind, as he avowed, of a great weight of responsibility on
that particular point!

The book was very rapidly written, within some three or four months, during
the summer of 1827.   The writer was then living in the small village of St.
Ouen, near Paris, occupying a pleasant country house on the banks of the Seine,

adjoining a small château where Madame de Staël had passed much of her time, at the period when M. Neckar was in power. The village itself had little indeed to recommend it, being insignificant in every way, but the house was one the writer much enjoyed, from its spacious rooms, beautiful garden and shrubbery, all shut in within gray walls fourteen feet in height, a little blooming paradise in itself, like so many similar gardens on the outskirts of the ancient cities of Europe. A broad terrace lay at the end of the garden, overhanging the river, which in itself could boast of little beauty, broad and brown, seldom enlivened even by a sail-boat; a wide extent of beautiful plain lay beyond, bounded by fine bold hills, teeming with gray villages and hamlets. A pleasant summer-house, or *pavillon*, stood at one extremity of the terrace, and here many pages of "The Red Rover" were written. A few passages from letters of this period are given:

"One of our great amusements is to watch the *living* life on the river; there is no *still* life in France. All the washerwomen of the village assemble, three days in the week, beneath our terrace, and a merrier set of *grisettes* is not to be found in the neighborhood of Paris. They chatter, and joke, and splash, and scream from morning to night, lightening the toil by never-ceasing good humor. Occasionally an enormous scow-like barge is hauled up, against the current, by stout horses, loaded to the water's edge, or one without freight comes dropping down the stream, nearly filling the whole river as it floats broad-side to. There are three or four islands opposite, and now and then a small boat is seen paddling among them. We have even tried *punting* ourselves, but the amusement was soon exhausted. Not long since I passed half an hour on the terrace, an amused witness of the perils of a voyage across the Seine in a *punt*. The adventurers were a *bourgeois*, his wife, sister, and child. Honest Pierre, the waterman, had conditioned to take the whole party to the island opposite, and to return them safe to the main for the modicum of five sous. The old fox invariably charged me a franc for the same service. There was much demurring and many doubts, about encountering the risks; and more than once the women would have receded had not the man treated the matter as a trifle. He affirmed '*parole d'honneur*' that his father had crossed the Loire a dozen times, and no harm had come of it! This encouraged them, and with many petty screams they finally embarked. The punt was a narrow scow that a ton weight would not have disturbed, the river was so low and sluggish that it might have two-thirds of the distance, and the width was not three hundred feet. Pierre protested that the danger was certainly not worth mentioning, and away he went, as philosophical in appearance as his punt. The voyage was made in safety; but the bows of the boat had touched the shore on its return before the passengers ventured to smile. The excursion, like most travelling, was likely to be most productive of happiness by the recollections. But the women were no sooner landed, than that rash adventurer, the husband, brother, and father, seized an oar, and began to ply it with all his force. He wished to be able to tell his *confreres* of the Rue Montmartre how a punt might be rowed. Pierre had landed gallantly to assist the ladies, and the boat, relieved of its weight, slowly yielded to the impulse of the oar, and inclined its bows from the land. 'Oh, Edouard! mon mari! mon frère!—que fais-tu?' exclaimed the ladies. 'Ce n'est rien,' returned the man, puffing, and giving another lusty sweep, by which he succeeded in forcing the punt fully twenty feet from the shore. 'Edouard, cher Edouard!' 'Laissez moi m'amuser!—je m'amuse! je m'amuse!' cried the husband in a tone of indignant remonstrance. But Edouard, a light, sleek little *épicier*, of about five-and-thirty, had never heard that an oar on each side was necessary in a boat, and the harder he pulled the less likely was he to regain the shore. Of this he now began to be convinced, as he whirled more into the centre of the current; his efforts became really frantic; his imagination probably painting the perils of a distant voyage in an unknown bark, to an unknown land, and all without food or compass! The women screamed. The louder they cried, the more strenuously he persevered, plying vigorously with both arms his single oar, and crying, 'Laissez moi m'amuser! je m'amuse! je m'amuse!' By this time the perspiration was streaming from his face. I called to the imperturbable Pierre, who stood in silent admiration of his punt playing such antics, and desired him to tell the man to put his oar on the bottom, and push his boat ashore. 'Oui, monsieur!' said the rogue, with a leer, for he remembered the francs, and we soon had our adventurer safe on *terra firma* again. Then began the tender expostulations, the affectionate reproaches, and the kind injunctions for the truant to remember that he was a husband and a father. Edouard, secretly cursing the punt and all rivers in his heart, made light of the matter, however, protesting to the last that he had been amusing himself.

"We have had a *fête*, too; for every village in the vicinity of Paris has its *fête*. The square was filled with whirligigs and flying horses, and all the ingenious contrivances of the French to make and to spend a sous pleasantly. There was service in the parish church, at which our neighbors sang in a style fit for St. Peter's; and the villagers danced quadrilles on the green, with an air that would be thought fine in many a country drawing-room. I enjoy all this greatly. We have also visited Enghien and Montmorenci. The latter, as you know already, stands on the side of a low mountain, in plain view of Paris. It is a town of some size, with very uneven streets, some of them being actually sharp acclivities, and a Gothic church that is seen from afar, and that is well worth viewing near by. These quaint edifices afford us deep delight by their antiquity, architecture, size, and pious histories. What matters it to us, how much or how little superstition may blend with the rites, when we know and feel that we are standing in a nave that has echoed with orisons to God for a thousand years? This of Montmorenci is not quite so old, however, having been partially rebuilt some three centuries since. Dulaure, a severe judge of aristocracy, denounces the pretensions of the Montmorencis, to be the *premiers barons chrétiens;* affirming that they were neither the first barons nor the first Christians, by a great many. He says that the extravagant title has most probably been a war-cry in the time of the crusaders. According to his account of the family, it originated, about the year 1008, in a certain Burchard, who, proving a bad neighbor to the Abbey of St. Denis, the vassals of which he was in the habit of robbing, besides now and then despoiling a monk, the king caused his fortress in the Isle St. Denis to be razed; after which, by a treaty, he was put in possession of the mountain hard by, with permission to erect another hold, near a fountain, at a place called in the charters Montmorenciacum. Hence the name and the family. This writer thinks that the first castle must have been built of wood! We took a road that led us up to a bluff on the mountain, behind the town, where we obtained a new and very peculiar view of Paris and its environs. The French towns have no straggling suburbs. A few wine-houses, to save the *octroi*, are built near the gates, compactly, as in the town itself, and there the buildings cease as suddenly as if pared down by the knife. The fields touch the walls in many places; between St. Ouen and the *guingettes* at the Barrière de Clichy, a distance of two miles, there is but one solitary building. A wide plain separates Paris on this side from the mountains, and of course our view extended across it. The number of villages was absolutely astounding. Although I did not attempt counting them, I should think not fewer than a hundred were in sight, all gray, picturesque, and clustering round the high nave, and high church-tower, like chickens gathering beneath the wing. The day was clouded, and the hamlets rose from their beds of verdure, sombre but distinct, with their faces of wall now in subdued light, and now quite shaded, resembling the glorious *darks* of Rembrandt's pictures.

"I am often in the saddle since our removal to St. Ouen. I first commenced exploring in the cabriolet, with my wife for a companion, during which time, several pretty drives, of whose existence one journeying along the great roads would form no idea, were discovered. At last, as these became exhausted, I mounted, and pricked into the fields. The result has been a better knowledge of the details of ordinary rural life, in this country, than a stranger would get by a residence of years after the ordinary fashion. I found the vast plain intersected by roads as intricate as the veins of the human body. The comparison is not unapt, by the way, and may be even carried out much further; for the *grandes routes* can be compared to the arteries, the *chemins vicinaux*, or cross-roads, to the veins, and the innumerable paths that intersect the open fields in all directions, to the more minute blood-vessels, circulation being the object common to all. I mount my horse and gallop into the fields at random, merely taking care not to quit the paths. By the latter, one can go in almost any direction; and as they are very winding, there is a certain pleasure in following their sinuosities, doubtful whither they tend. Much of the plain is in vegetables, for the use of Paris; but there are occasional vineyards and fields of grain. The weather has become settled and autumnal, and is equally without the chilling moisture of winter, or the fickleness of the spring. The kind-hearted peasants see me pass among them without distrust, and my salutations are answered with cheerfulness and civility. One of my rides is over the plain that lies between St. Ouen and Montmartre, ascending the latter by its rear to the windmills that, night and day, are whirling their ragged arms over the capital of France. A view from this height is like a glimpse into the pages of history; for every foot of land it commands, and more than half the artificial accessories, are pregnant with the past. Looking down into the fissures between the houses, men appear like the mites they are; and one gets to have a philosophical indifference to human vanities by obtaining these bird's-eye views of them in the mass. It was a happy thought that first suggested the summits of mountains for religious contemplation. The cathedral of Notre Dame should have been reared on this noble and isolated height, that the airs of heaven might whisper through its fane, breathing chants in honor of God."

The scene of "The Red Rover," as the reader is already aware, lies at Newport. After leaving the navy, while living at Angevine, Mr. Cooper became interested in a whaling ship, as one of its owners. The name of this ship was the

"Union;" her port was Sag Harbor, but on several occasions she made short trips for repairs, or other purposes, to different points of the coast, and in two or three instances, more probably from pleasure than any other motive, Mr. Cooper played skipper as she passed to and fro under his direction. One of these trips carried him to Newport. He was much pleased with the spot, and some years later laid the opening scene of "The Rover" in that port. Of course he had explored the famous ruin, which not even the genius of romance, however, could induce him to see in any other light than that of a windmill. The reader is probably already familiar with the deed which degrades the old mill from the dignity of temple or fastness to the humble duties of agricultural labor in behalf of the nearest farmer; and he has also, no doubt, made merry over that very clever and rather wicked Yankee *jeu d'ésprit* which so sadly bewildered the very venerable Society of Antiquaries at Copenhagen.

A pleasant little gift was made to the author of "The Red Rover" not long after its publication, by some gentlemen of Newport. It would seem that the keel of the "Endeavor," the famous exploring ship of Cooke, after going round the world, found its way into Newport harbor; a box, bearing a silver plate and engraving on its lid, was made from this wood, black as ebony with age and adventure, and sent to France to the writer, who was much gratified by the friendly remembrance.

In one of Sir Walter Scott's works, which appeared subsequently to "The Red Rover," allusion is made to a famous corsair of olden times, whose craft bore the same name. So far, however, as any previous knowledge of it may go, this name was original with Mr. Cooper. Of the old Scotch corsair he had never heard. The alliterations alone naturally suggested the title.

THE WRECK OF THE ROYAL CAROLINE.

"It might be done!" muttered our adventurer; "it might be done! A few busy hours would do it, with this wind. Mr. Earing!"—

The mate was instantly at his elbow. Wilder pointed to the dim object to leeward, and, handing him the glass, desired that he would take another view. Each looked, in his turn, long and closely.

"He shows no more sail!" said the commander, impatiently, when his own prolonged gaze was ended.

"Not a cloth, sir. But what matters it, to such a craft, how much canvas is spread, or how the wind blows?"

"Earing, I think there is too much southing in this breeze; and there is more brewing in yonder streak of dusky clouds on our beam. Let the ship fall off a couple of points, or more, and take the strain off the spars by a pull upon the weather braces."

The simple-minded mate heard the order with an astonishment he did not care to conceal. There needed no explanation, to teach his experienced faculties, that the effect would be to go over the same track they had just passed, and that it was, in substance, abandoning the objects of the voyage. He presumed to defer his compliance, in order to remonstrate.

"I hope there is no offence for an elderly seaman, like myself, Captain Wilder, in venturing an opinion on the weather," he said. "When the pocket of the owner is interested, my judgment approves of going about, for I have no taste for land that the wind blows on, instead of off. But, by easing the ship with a reef or two, she would be jogging seaward; and all we gain would be clear gain; because it is so much off the Hatteras. Besides, who can say that to-morrow, or the next day, we sha'n't have a puff out of America, here at north-west?"

The Red Rover: The limb stiffened and fell, though
the eyes still continued their affectionate and glaring
gaze on that countenance he had so long loved, and
which, in the midst of all his long endured wrongs,
had never refused to meet his look of love in kindness.

"A couple of points fall off, and a pull upon your weather-braces," said Wilder, with startling quickness.

It would have exceeded the peaceful and submissive temperament of the honest Earing to have delayed any longer.   The orders were given to the inferiors; and, as a matter of course, they were obeyed—though ill-suppressed and portentous sounds of discontent, at the undetermined, and seemingly unreasonable, changes in their officer's mind might have been heard issuing from the mouths of Nighthead and other veterans of the crew.

But to all these symptoms of disaffection Wilder remained, as before, utterly indifferent.   If he heard them at all, he either disdained to yield them any notice, or, guided by a temporizing policy, he chose to appear unconscious of their import.   In the mean time, the vessel, like a bird whose wing had wearied with struggling against the tempest, and which inclines from the gale to dart along an easier course, glided swiftly away, quartering the crests of the waves, or sinking gracefully into their troughs, as she yielded to the force of a wind that was now made to be favorable. The sea rolled on, in a direction that was no longer adverse to her course; and, as she receded from the breeze, the quantity of sail she had spread was no longer found trying to her powers of endurance.   Still she had, in the opinion of all her crew, quite enough canvas exposed to a night of such a portentous aspect.   But not so in the judgment of the stranger who was charged with the guidance of her destinies.   In a voice that still admonished his inferiors of the danger of disobedience, he commanded several broad sheets of studding-sails to be set, in quick succession.   Urged by these new impulses, the ship went careering over the waves, leaving a train of foam in her track that rivalled, in its volume and brightness, the tumbling summit of the largest swell.

When sail after sail had been set, until even Wilder was obliged to confess to himself that the "Royal Caroline," stanch as she was, would bear no more, our adventurer began to pace the deck again, and to cast his eyes about him, in order to watch the fruits of his new experiment.   The change in the course of the Bristol trader had made a corresponding change in the apparent direction of the stranger, who yet floated in the horizon like a diminutive and misty shadow.   Still the unerring compass told the watchful mariner that she continued to maintain the same relative position as when first seen.   No effort, on the part of Wilder, could apparently alter her bearing an inch.   Another hour soon passed away, during which, as the log told him, the "Caroline" had rolled through more than three leagues of water, and still there lay the stranger in the west, as though it were merely a lessened shadow of herself, cast by the "Caroline" upon the distant and dusky clouds.   An alteration in his course exposed a broader surface of his canvas to the eyes of the spectators, but in nothing else was there any visible change.   If his sails had been materially increased, the distance and the obscurity prevented even the understanding Earing from detecting it. Perhaps the excited mind of the worthy mate was too much disposed to believe in the miraculous powers possessed by his unaccountable neighbor, to admit of the full exercise of his experienced faculties on the occasion; but even Wilder, who vexed his sight, in often-repeated examinations, was obliged to confess to himself that the stranger seemed to glide across the waste of waters more like a body floating in the air, than a ship resorting to the ordinary expedients of mariners.

Mrs. Wyllys and her charge had, by this time, retired to their cabin; the former secretly felicitating herself on the prospect of soon quitting a vessel that had commenced its voyage under such sinister circumstances as to have deranged the equilibrium of even her well-governed and highly-disciplined mind. Gertrude was left in ignorance of the change. To her uninstructed eye, all appeared the same on the wilderness of the ocean; Wilder having it in his power to alter the direction of his vessel as often as he pleased, without his fairer and more youthful passenger being any the wiser for the same.

Not so, however, with the intelligent commander of the "Caroline" himself. To him there was neither obscurity nor doubt, in the midst of his midnight path. His eye had long been familiar with every star that rose from out the waving bed of the sea, to set in another dark and ragged outline of the element; nor was there a blast that swept across the ocean, that his burning cheek could not tell from what quarter of the heavens it poured out its power. He knew, and understood, each inclination made by the bows of his ship; his mind kept even pace with her windings and turnings, in all her trackless wanderings; and he had little need to consult any of the accessories of his art, to tell him what course to steer, or in what manner to guide the movements of the nice machine he governed. Still was he unable to explain the extraordinary evolutions of the stranger. His smallest change seemed rather anticipated than followed; and his hopes of eluding a vigilance that proved so watchful, were baffled by a facility of manœuvring, and a superiority of sailing, that really began to assume, even to his intelligent eye, the appearance of some unaccountable agency.

While our adventurer was engaged in the gloomy musings that such impressions were not ill adapted to excite, the heavens and the sea began to exhibit another aspect. The bright streak which had so long hung along the eastern horizon, as though the curtain of the firmament had been slightly opened to admit a passage for the winds, was now suddenly closed; and heavy masses of black clouds began to gather in that quarter, until vast volumes of the vapor were piled upon the water, blending the two elements in one. On the other hand, the dark canopy lifted in the west, and a long belt of lurid light was shed over the view. In this flood of bright and portentous mist the stranger still floated, though there were moments when his faint and fanciful outlines seemed to be melting into thin air.

Our watchful adventurer was not blind to these well-known and sinister omens. No sooner did the peculiar atmosphere by which the mysterious image that he so often examined was suddenly surrounded, catch his eye, than his voice was heard in the clear, powerful, and exciting notes of warning.

"Stand by," he called aloud, "to in all studding sails! Down with them!" he added, scarcely giving his former words time to reach the ears of his subordinates. "Down with every rag of them, fore and aft the ship! Man the topgallant clew-lines, Mr. Earing. Clew up, and clew down! In with every thing, cheerily, men! In!"

This was a language to which the crew of the "Caroline" were no strangers, and one which was doubly welcome; since the meanest seaman of them all had long thought that his unknown commander had been heedlessly trifling with the safety of the vessel, by the hardy manner in which he disregarded the wild symptoms of the weather. But they undervalued the keen-eyed vigilance of Wilder. He had certainly driven the Bristol trader through the water at a rate she had never been known to have gone before; but, thus far, the facts themselves attested in his favor, since no injury was the consequence of what they deemed his temerity. At the quick, sudden order just given, however, the whole ship was instantly in an uproar. A dozen seamen called to each other, from different parts of the vessel, each striving to lift his voice above the roaring ocean; and there was every appearance of a general and inextricable confusion; but the same authority which had aroused them, thus unexpectedly, into activity, produced order from their ill-directed though vigorous efforts.

Wilder had spoken, to awaken the drowsy, and to excite the torpid. The instant he found each man on the alert, he resumed his orders, with a calmness that gave a direction to the powers of all, but still with an energy that he well knew was called for by the occasion. The enormous sheets of duck, which had looked like so many light clouds in the murky and threatening heavens, were soon seen fluttering wildly, as they descended from their high places; and, in a few minutes, the ship was reduced to the action of her more secure and heavier canvas. To effect this object, every man in the ship had exerted his powers to the utmost, under the guidance of the steady but rapid mandates of their commander. Then followed a short and apprehensive breathing pause. Every eye was turned toward the quarter where the ominous signs had been discovered; and each individual endeavored to read their import, with an intelligence correspondent to the degree of skill he might have acquired, during his particular period of service, on that treacherous element which was now his home.

The dim tracery of the stranger's form had been swallowed by the flood of misty light, which, by this time, rolled along the sea like drifting vapor, semi-pellucid, preternatural, and seemingly tangible. The ocean itself appeared admonished that a quick and violent change was nigh. The waves had ceased to break in their former foaming and brilliant crests; but black masses of the water were seen lifting their surly summits against the eastern horizon, no longer relieved by their scintillating brightness, or shedding their own peculiar and lucid atmosphere around them. The breeze which had been so fresh, and which had even blown, at times, with a force that nearly amounted to a little gale, was lulling and becoming uncertain, as though awed by the more violent power that was gathering along the borders of the sea, in the direction of the neighboring continent.   Each moment, the eastern puffs of air lost their strength, and became more and more feeble, until, in an incredibly short period, the heavy sails were heard flapping against the mast—a frightful and ominous calm succeeding.   At this instant, a glancing, flashing gleam lighted the fearful obscurity of the ocean; and a roar, like that of a sudden burst of thunder, bellowed along the waters.   The seamen turned their startled looks on each other, and stood stupid, as though a warning had been given, from the heavens themselves, of what was to follow.   But their calm and more sagacious commander put a different construction on the signal.   His lip curled, in high professional pride, and his mouth moved rapidly, while he muttered to himself, with a species of scorn—

"Does he think we sleep?   Aye, he has got it himself, and would open our eyes to what is coming!   What does he imagine we have been about, since the middle watch was set?"

Then Wilder made a swift turn or two on the quarter-deck, never ceasing to bend his quick glances from one quarter of the heavens to another; from the black and lulling water on which his vessel was rolling, to the sails; and from his silent and profoundly expectant crew, to the dim lines of spars that were waving above his head, like so many pencils tracing their curvilinear and wanton images over the murky volumes of the superincumbent clouds.

"Lay the after-yards square!" he said, in a voice which was heard by every man on deck, though his words were apparently spoken but little above his breath.   Even the creaking of the blocks, as the spars came slowly and heavily round to the indicated position, contributed to the imposing character of the moment, and sounded, in the ears of all the instructed listeners, like notes of fearful preparation.

"Haul up the courses!" resumed Wilder, after a thoughtful, brief interval, with the same eloquent calmness of manner.   Then, taking another glance at the threatening horizon, he added, with emphasis, "Furl them—furl them both: away aloft, and hand your courses," he continued, in a shout; "roll them up, cheerily; in with them, boys, cheerily; in!"

The conscious seamen took their impulses from the tones of their commander.   In a moment, twenty dark forms were seen leaping up the rigging, with the alacrity of so many quadrupeds; and, in another minute, the vast and powerful sheets of canvas were effectually rendered harmless, by securing them in tight rolls to their respective spars. The men descended as swiftly as they had mounted to the yards; and then succeeded another short and breathing pause.   At this moment, a candle would have sent its flame perpendicularly toward the heavens.   The ship, missing the steadying power of the wind, rolled heavily in the troughs of the seas, which, however, began to be more diminutive at each instant; as though the startled element was recalling, into the security of its own vast bosom, that portion of its particles which had, just before, been permitted to gambol so madly over its surface.   The water washed sullenly along the side of the ship, or, as she laboring rose from one of her frequent falls into the hollows of the waves, it shot back into the ocean from her decks, in numberless little glittering cascades. Every hue of the heavens, every sound of the element, and each dusky and anxious countenance that was visible, helped to proclaim the intense interest of the moment. It was in this brief interval of expectation and inactivity that the mates again approached their commander.

"It is an awful night, Captain Wilder!" said Earing, presuming on his rank to be the first of the two to speak.

"I have known far less notice given of a shift of wind," was the steady answer.

"We have had time to gather in our kites, 'tis true, sir; but there are signs and warnings, that come with this change, at which the oldest seaman has reason to take heed!"

"Yes," continued Nighthead, in a voice that sounded hoarse and powerful, even amid the fearful accessories of that scene; "yes, it is no trifling commission that can call people, that I shall not name, out upon the water in such a night as this. It was in just such weather that I saw the 'Vesuvius' ketch go to a place so deep, that her own mortar would not have been able to have sent a bomb into the open air, had hands and fire been there fit to let it off!"

"Aye; and it was in such a time that the Greenlandman was cast upon the Orkneys, in as flat a calm as ever lay on the sea."

"Gentlemen," said Wilder, with a peculiar and perhaps an ironical emphasis on the word, "what is it you would have? There is not a breath of air stirring, and the ship is naked to her topsails!"

It would have been difficult for either of the two malcontents to have given a very satisfactory answer to this question. Both were secretly goaded by mysterious and superstitious apprehensions, that were powerfully aided by the more real and intelligible aspect of the night; but neither had so far forgotten his manhood and his professional pride, as to lay bare the full extent of his own weakness, at a moment when he was liable to be called upon for the exhibition of qualities of a far more positive and determined character. Still, the feeling that was uppermost betrayed itself in the reply of Earing, though in an indirect and covert manner.

"Yes, the vessel is snug enough now," he said, "though eyesight has shown us all it is no easy matter to drive a freighted ship through the water as fast as one of your flying craft can go, aboard of which no man can say who stands at the helm, by what compass she steers, or what is her draught!"

"Aye," resumed Nighthead; "I call the 'Caroline' fast for an honest trader, and few square-rigged boats are there, who do not wear the pennants of the king, that can eat her out of the wind, or bring her into their wake, with studding-sails abroad. But this is a time, and an hour, to make a seaman think. Look at yon hazy light, here, in with the land, that is coming so fast down upon us, and then tell me whether it comes from the coast of America, or whether it comes from out of the stranger who has been so long running under our lee, but who has got, or is fast getting, the wind of us at last, and yet none here can say how or why. I have just this much, and no more, to say: give me for consort a craft whose captain I know, or give me none!"

"Such is your taste, Mr. Nighthead," said Wilder, coldly; "mine may, by some accident, be very different."

"Yes, yes," observed the more cautious and prudent Earing, "in time of war, and with letters of marque aboard, a man may honestly hope the sail he sees should have a stranger for her master; or otherwise he would never fall in with an enemy. But, though an Englishman born myself, I should rather give the ship in that mist a clear sea, seeing that I neither know her nation nor her cruise. Ah, Captain Wilder, yonder is an awful sight for the morning watch! Often, and often, have I seen the sun rise in the east, and no harm done; but little good can come of a day when the light first breaks in the west. Cheerfully would I give the owners the last month's pay, hard as I have earned it with my toil, did I but know under what flag yonder stranger sails."

"Frenchman, Don, or Devil, yonder he comes!" cried Wilder. Then, turning toward the silent and attentive crew, he shouted, in a voice that was appalling by its vehemence and warning, "Let run the after-halyards! round with the fore-yard! round with it, men, with a will!"

These were cries that the startled crew perfectly understood. Every nerve and muscle were exerted to execute the orders, in time to be in readiness for the approaching tempest. No man spoke; but each expended the utmost of his power and skill in direct and manly efforts. Nor was there, in verity, a moment to lose, or a particle of human strength expended here without a sufficient object.

The lucid and fearful-looking mist, which, for the last quarter of an hour, had been gathering in the north-west, was now driving down upon them with the speed of a race-horse. The air had already lost the damp and peculiar feeling of an easterly breeze; and little eddies were beginning to flutter among the masts—precursors of the coming squall. Then, a rushing, roaring sound was heard moaning along the ocean, whose surface was first dimpled, next ruffled, and finally covered with one sheet of clear, white, and spotless foam. At the next moment, the power of the wind fell full upon the inert and laboring Bristol trader.

As the gust approached, Wilder had seized the slight opportunity afforded by the changeful puffs of air, to get the ship as much as possible before the wind; but the sluggish movement of the vessel met neither the wishes of his own impatience nor the exigencies of the moment. Her bows had slowly and heavily fallen off from the north, leaving her precisely in a situation to receive the first shock on her broadside. Happy it was for all who had life at risk in that defenceless vessel, that she was not fated to receive the whole weight of the tempest at a blow. The sails fluttered and trembled on their massive yards, bellying and collapsing alternately for a minute, and then the rushing wind swept over them in a hurricane.

The "Caroline" received the blast like a stout and buoyant ship, yielding readily to its impulse, until her side lay nearly incumbent on the element in which she floated; and then, as if the fearful fabric were conscious of its jeopardy, it seemed to lift its reclining masts again, struggling to work its way heavily through the water.

"Keep the helm aweather! Jam it aweather, for your life!" shouted Wilder, amid the roar of the gust.

The veteran seaman at the wheel obeyed the order with steadiness, but in vain he kept his eyes riveted on the margin of his head-sail in order to watch the manner the ship would obey its power. Twice more, in as many moments, the tall masts fell toward the horizon, waving as often gracefully upward, and then they yielded to the mighty pressure of the wind, until the whole machine lay prostrate on the water.

"Reflect!" said Wilder, seizing the bewildered Earing by the arm, as the latter rushed madly up the steep of the deck; "it is our duty to be calm: bring hither an axe."

Quick as the thought which gave the order, the admonished mate complied, jumping into the mizzen-channels of the ship, to execute, with his own hands, the mandate that he well knew must follow.

"Shall I cut?" he demanded, with uplifted arms, and in a voice that atoned for his momentary confusion, by its steadiness and force.

"Hold! Does the ship mind her helm at all?"

"Not an inch, sir."

"Then cut," Wilder clearly and calmly added.

A single blow sufficed for the discharge of the momentary act. Extended to the utmost powers of endurance, by the vast weight it upheld, the lanyard struck by Earing no sooner parted than each of its fellows snapped in succession, leaving the mast dependent on itself alone for the support of all its ponderous and complicated hamper. The cracking of the wood came next; and then the rigging fell, like a tree that had been sapped at its foundation, the little distance that still existed between it and the sea.

"Does she fall off?" instantly called Wilder to the observant seaman at the wheel.

"She yielded a little, sir; but this new squall is bringing her up again."

"Shall I cut?" shouted Earing from the main rigging, whither he had leaped, like a tiger who had bounded on his prey.

"Cut!" was the answer.

A loud and imposing crash soon succeeded this order, though not before several heavy blows had been struck into the massive mast itself. As before, the seas received the tumbling maze of spars, rigging, and sails; the vessel surging, at the same instant, from its recumbent position, and rolling far and heavily to windward.

"She rights! she rights!" exclaimed twenty voices which had been hitherto mute, in a suspense that involved life and death.

"Keep her dead away!" added the still calm but deeply authoritative voice of the young commander. "Stand by to furl the fore-topsail—let it hang a moment to drag the ship clear of the wreck—cut, cut—cheerily, men—hatchets and knives—cut *with* all, and cut *off* all!"

As the men now worked with the freshened vigor of revived hope, the ropes that still confined the fallen spars to the vessel were quickly severed; and the "Caroline," by this time dead before the gale, appeared barely to touch the foam that covered the sea, like a bird that was swift upon the wing skimming the waters. The wind came over the waste in gusts that rumbled like distant thunder, and with a power that seemed to threaten to lift the ship and its contents from its proper element, to deliver it to one still more variable and treacherous. As a prudent and sagacious seaman had let fly the halyards of the solitary sail that remained, at the moment when the squall approached, the loosened but lowered topsail was now distended in a manner that threatened to drag after it the only mast which still stood. Wilder instantly saw the necessity of getting rid of this sail, and he also saw the utter impossibility of securing it. Calling Earing to his side, he pointed out the danger, and gave the necessary order.

"Yon spar cannot stand such shocks much longer," he concluded; "and, should it go over the bows, some fatal blow might be given to the ship at the rate she is moving. A man or two must be sent aloft to cut the sail from the yards."

"The stick is bending like a willow whip," returned the mate; "and the lower mast itself is sprung. There would be great danger in trusting a life in that top, while such wild squalls as these are breathing around us."

"You may be right," answered Wilder, with a sudden conviction of the truth of what the other had said. "Stay you then here; and, if any thing befall me, try to get the vessel into port as far north as the Capes of Virginia at least; on no account attempt Hatteras in the present condition of"——

"What would you do, Captain Wilder?" interrupted the mate, laying his hand powerfully on the shoulder of his commander, who, he observed, had already thrown his sea-cap on the deck, and was preparing to divest himself of some of his outer garments.

"I go aloft, to ease the mast of that topsail, without which we lose the spar, and possibly the ship."

"Aye, aye, I see that plain enough; but shall it be said, another did the duty of Edward Earing? It is your business to carry the vessel into the Capes of Virginia, and mine to cut the topsail adrift. If harm comes to me, why, put it in the log, with a word or two about the manner in which I played my part. That is always the best and most proper epitaph for a sailor."

Wilder made no resistance, but resumed his watchful and reflecting attitude, with

J. Hamilton feet.

J. A. Thompson sculpt.

The Red Rover: The Red Rover and The Bristol Trader

the simplicity of one who had been too long trained to the discharge of certain obliga-
tions himself, to manifest surprise that another should acknowledge their imperative
character.   In the mean time, Earing proceeded steadily to perform what he had just
promised.   Passing into the waist of the ship, he provided himself with a suitable
hatchet; and then, without speaking a syllable to any of the mute but attentive seamen,
he sprang into the fore-rigging, every strand and rope-yarn of which was tightened by
the strain nearly to snapping.   The understanding eyes of his observers comprehended
his intention; and, with precisely the same pride of station as had urged him to the
dangerous undertaking, four or five of the older mariners jumped upon the ratlines,
to mount with him into an air that apparently teemed with a hundred hurricanes.

"Lie down out of that fore-rigging," shouted Wilder, through a deck trumpet;
"lie down, all but the mate, lie down!"   His words were borne past the inattentive
ears of the excited and mortified followers of Earing, but they failed of their effect.
Each man was too much bent on his own earnest purpose to listen to the sounds of
recall.   In less than a minute, the whole were scattered along the yards, prepared to
obey the signal of their officer.   The mate cast a look about him; and, perceiving
that the time was comparatively favorable, he struck a blow upon the large rope that
confined one of the angles of the distended and bursting sail to the lower yard.   The
effect was much the same as would be produced by knocking away the keystone of an
ill-cemented arch.   The canvas broke from all its fastenings with a loud explosion, and,
for an instant, was seen sailing in the air ahead of the ship, as though sustained on the
wings of an eagle.   The vessel rose on a sluggish wave—the lingering remains of the
former breeze—and then settled heavily over the rolling surge, borne down alike by
its own weight, and the renewed violence of the gusts.   At this critical instant, while
the seamen aloft were still gazing in the direction in which the little cloud of canvas
had disappeared, a lanyard of the lower rigging parted with a crack that even reached
the ears of Wilder.

"Lie down!" he shouted fearfully through his trumpet; "down by the backstays;
down for your lives; every man of you, down!"

A solitary individual, of them all, profited by the warning, and was seen gliding
toward the deck with the velocity of the wind.   But rope parted after rope, and the
fatal snapping of the wood instantly followed.   For a moment, the towering maze
tottered, and seemed to wave toward every quarter of the heavens; and then, yielding
to the movements of the hull, the whole fell, with a heavy crash, into the sea.   Each
cord, lanyard, or stay snapped, when it received the strain of its new position, as though
it had been made of thread, leaving the naked and despoiled hull of the "Caroline" to
drive onward before the tempest as if nothing had occurred to impede its progress.

A mute and eloquent pause succeeded this disaster.   It appeared as if the elements
themselves were appeased by their work, and something like a momentary lull in the
awful rushing of the winds might have been fancied.   Wilder sprang to the side of the

vessel, and distinctly beheld the victims, who still clung to their frail support. He even saw Earing waving his hand, in adieu, with a seaman's heart, and like a man who not only felt how desperate was his situation, but one who knew how to meet his fate with resignation. Then the wreck of spars, with all who clung to it, was swallowed up in the body of the frightful, preternatural-looking mist which extended on every side of them, from the ocean to the clouds.

"Stand by, to clear away a boat!" shouted Wilder, without pausing to think of the impossibility of one's swimming, or of effecting the least good, in so violent a tornado.

But the amazed and confounded seamen who remained needed not instruction in this matter. No man moved, nor was the smallest symptom of obedience given. The mariners looked wildly around them, each endeavoring to trace, in the dusky countenance of the other, his opinion of the extent of the evil; but not a mouth was opened among them all.

"It is too late—it is too late!" murmured Wilder to himself; "human skill and human efforts could not save them!"

"Sail, ho!" Nighthead muttered at his elbow, in a voice that teemed with a species of superstitious awe.

"Let him come on," returned his young commander, bitterly; "the mischief is ready finished to his hands!"

"Should yon be a mortal ship, it is our duty to the owners and the passengers to speak her, if a man can make his voice heard in this tempest," the second mate continued, pointing through the haze at the dim object that was certainly at hand.

"Speak her!—passengers!" muttered Wilder, involuntarily repeating his words. "No; any thing is better than speaking her. Do you see the vessel that is driving down upon us so fast?" he sternly demanded of the watchful seaman who still clung to the wheel of the "Caroline."

"Aye, aye, sir," was the brief, professional reply.

"Give her a berth—sheer away hard to port—perhaps he may pass us in the gloom, now we are no higher than our decks. Give the ship a broad sheer, I say, sir."

The same laconic answer as before was given, and, for a few moments, the Bristol trader was seen diverging a little from the line in which the other approached; but a second glance assured Wilder that the attempt was useless. The strange ship (and every man on board felt certain it was the same that had so long been seen hanging in the north-western horizon) came on, through the mist, with a swiftness that nearly equalled the velocity of the tempestuous winds themselves. Not a thread of canvas was seen on board her. Each line of spars, even to the tapering and delicate top-gallant-masts, was in its place, preserving the beauty and symmetry of the whole fabric; but nowhere was the smallest fragment of a sail opened to the gale. Under her bows rolled a volume of foam, that was even discernible amid the universal agitation of the ocean; and, as she came within sound, the sullen roar of the water might have been likened to the noise of a cascade. At first, the spectators on the decks of the " Caroline" believed they were not seen, and some of the men called madly for lights, in order that the disasters of the night might not terminate in the dreaded encounter.

" No !" exclaimed Wilder ; " too many see us there already !"

" No, no," muttered Nighthead ; " no fear but we are seen ; and by such eyes, too, as never yet looked out of mortal head !"

The seamen paused. In another instant, the long-seen and mysterious ship was within a hundred feet of them. The very power of that wind, which was wont usually to raise the billows, now pressed the element, with the weight of mountains, into its bed. The sea was everywhere a sheet of froth, but no water swelled above the level of the surface. The instant a wave lifted itself from the security of the vast depths, the fluid was borne away before the tornado in driving, glittering spray. Along this frothy but comparatively motionless surface, then, the stranger came booming, with the steadiness and grandeur with which a dark cloud is seen to sail before the hurricane. No sign of life was anywhere discovered about her. If men looked out from their secret places upon the straitened and discomfited wreck of the Bristol trader, it was covertly, and as darkly as the tempest before which they drove. Wilder held his breath, for the moment the stranger drew nighest, in the very excess of suspense ; but, as he saw no signal of recognition, no human form, nor any intention to arrest, if possible, the furious career of the other, a smile of exultation gleamed across his countenance, and his lips moved rapidly, as though he found pleasure in being abandoned to his distress. The stranger drove by, like a dark vision, and, ere another minute, her form was beginning to grow less distinct, in a thickening body of the spray to leeward.

"She is going out of sight in the mist !" exclaimed Wilder, when he drew his breath, after the fearful suspense of the few last moments.

"Aye ; in mist or clouds," responded Nighthead, who now kept obstinately at his elbow, watching with the most jealous distrust, the smallest movements of his unknown commander.

" In the heavens, or in the sea ; I care not, provided she be gone."

"Most seamen would rejoice to see a strange sail from the hull of a vessel shaved to the deck like this."

"Men often court their destruction, from ignorance of their own interests. Let him drive on, say I, and pray I ! He goes four feet to our one ; and now I ask no better favor than that this hurricane may blow until the sun shall rise."

Nighthead started, and cast an oblique glance, which resembled denunciation, at his companion. To his blunted faculties, and superstitious mind, there was profanity in thus invoking the tempest at a moment when the winds seemed already to be pouring out their utmost wrath.

"This is a heavy squall, I will allow," he said; "and such a one as many mariners pass whole lives without seeing; but he knows little of the sea who thinks there is not more wind where this comes from."

"Let it blow!" cried the other, striking his hands together a little wildly; "I pray only for wind!"

All the doubts of Nighthead, as to the character of the young stranger who had so unaccountably got possession of the office of Nicholas Nichols, if, indeed, any remained, were now removed. He walked forward among the silent and thoughtful crew with the air of a man whose opinion was settled. Wilder, however, paid no attention to the movements of his subordinate, but continued pacing the deck for hours; now casting his eyes at the heavens, or now sending frequent and anxious glances around the limited horizon, while the "Royal Caroline" still continued drifting before 'the wind, a shorn and naked wreck.

IX.

THE WEPT OF WISH-TON-WISH.

THE summer of 1828 was passed in Switzerland. Those were very happy months. The sublime grandeur of the ancient mountains, and the loveliness of the pastoral valleys at their feet, far surpassed in the reality all previous conceptions of the same nature. The daily morning ride, or evening stroll, was rich in picturesque charm, while language could scarcely convey a full sense of the feeling aroused when climbing the more commanding heights, and beholding the wonders of Alpine glory revealed there. The first glimpse of the hoary Alps which the American traveller received, was unexpected at the moment:

"The day was lovely, and I had persuaded —— to share my seat on the carriage-box. As we rounded the little height on which the ruin is seated (a ruined tower in Franche Comté, said to be a castle of Roland), she exclaimed: 'What a beautifully white cloud!' Taking the direction from her finger, I saw an accurately-defined mass, that resembled the highest wreath of a cloud whose volume lay concealed beyond the mountains of the Jura, which by this time were so near as to be quite distinct. There was something that was not cloudy, too, in its appearance. Its outline was like that of a chiselled rock, and its whiteness greatly surpassed the brilliancy of vapor. I called to the postillion, and pointed out this extraordinary object: 'Mont Blanc, monsieur!' We were, according to the maps, at least seventy miles from it, in an air line! I shall never forget the thrill of that moment. There is a feeling allied to the universal love of the mysterious that causes us all to look with pleasure at any distant object which insensibly leads the mind to the contemplation of things that are invisible. The imagination steals down the sides of distant peaks into the valleys, which it is apt to people with creatures from its stores of recollections, or, perhaps, from its own creative powers.   This glimpse of the glacier, for it was only a glimpse, the shining mass settling beyond the Jura, as we descended on a gallop toward Dôle, transported us over a long line of road into the very heart of the country toward which we were hastening.   Mont Blanc, it is true, is not in Switzerland, but it is a part of the same wonderful formation that renders Switzerland so remarkable, and the eye swept across two cantons, and half of Savoy, to take in this speck of aerial brightness.   I never before so ardently longed for wings, though their possession used to be one of the most constant of my youthful aspirations."

Berne was the destination of the travellers.   From motives of economy, and for the enjoyment of that quiet home-life which he always preferred, it was his habit, as soon as possible after reaching new ground, to secure some private dwelling for his little family band.   In Europe such a step is easily taken, furnished lodgings and houses abounding everywhere.   A modest country house, called La Lorraine, was soon secured.   "We are in one of the pretty, little, retired villas that dot the landscape, and at the distance of only half a mile from the town.   The sinuous Aar glances between us, but it has burrowed so low in the earth that no part of it is visible until we stand on its very banks.   Graceful footpaths wind among the fields, which are little encumbered with fences, or even hedges, and we have roads as narrow and good as those one sees in pleasure-grounds.   Our house is of stone, about as large as one of the ordinary boxes of Manhattan Island, and on the whole sufficiently comfortable.   We found both house and furniture faultlessly neat."   The position of La Lorraine was very quiet and retired, well shaded by lindens and other trees, and with its little trim garden and half-ruined fountain, its adjoining farm-house and barn-yard, thoroughly Swiss in all their details, was just the ground for children to roam over at will, in full enjoyment of a summer holiday.   Near by there was a common, too, where hoops and jumping-ropes and kites could be used, and where parents and children often strolled together.   From this common there was a very beautiful view of the Alps, which indeed were always in sight from the cottage windows—a source of unfailing delight, but especially so during the evening hours.

"I shall attempt to give you some notion of the two grandest aspects that the Alps, when seen from this place, assume.   One of these appearances is often alluded to; but I do not remember to have ever heard the other mentioned.   The first is produced by the setting sun, whose rays, of a cloudless evening, are the parents of hues and changes of a singularly lovely character.   The lustre of the glacier slowly retires, and is gradually succeeded by a tint of rose color ; which, falling on so luminous a body, produces a sort of roseate light—the whole of the vast range being mellowed, and subdued into indescribable softness. This appearance gradually increases in intensity ; varying on different evenings, however, according to the state of the atmosphere. At the very moment, perhaps, when the eye is resting most eagerly on this extraordinary view, the light vanishes. No scenic change is more sudden than that which follows. All the forms remain unaltered ; but so varied in hue, as to look like the ghosts of mountains. You see the same vast range of eternal snow ; but you see it ghastly, and spectral. You fancy that the spirits of the Alps are ranging themselves before you. Watching the peaks for a few minutes longer, the light slowly departs. The spectres, like the magnificent images of the phantasmagoria, grow more and more faint, less and less material, until lost in the firmament. What renders all this more thrillingly exquisite, is the circumstance that these changes do not occur until after evening has fallen on the lower world—giving, to the whole, the air of nature sporting, in the upper regions, with some of her spare and detached materials. This sight is far from uncommon. It is usually seen during the summer, in greater or less perfection, twice or thrice a week. The other view is much less frequent. The Aar flows toward Berne in a north-west direction, through a valley of some width, and several leagues in length. To this fact the Bernese are indebted for their view of the Oberland Alps, which range themselves exactly across the mouth of the gorge, at the distance of forty miles in an air line. These giants are supported by a row of advanced sentinels, any one of which would be a spectacle in another country. One in particular, the Niesen, is distinguished by its conical form. It is nearly in a line with the Jungfrau, the virgin queen of the Oberland, and is some eight or ten miles in advance of the mighty range; though to the eye, at Berne, all these accessories appear tumbled, without order, at the very feet of their principals. The height of the Niesen is some eight thousand feet above the sea—rather higher than the tallest peak of the White Mountains. The Jungfrau rises, directly in the rear of this mountain, more than a mile nearer to heaven. The day was clouded ; and as a great deal of mist was clinging to all the lesser mountains, the lower atmosphere was much charged with vapor. The cap of the Niesen was quite hid, and a wide pall of watery cloud entirely overhung the summits of the nearer range ; leaving, however, their broad sides misty, but quite visible. In short, the Niesen and its immediate neighbors looked like any other range of noble mountains whose heads were hid in the clouds. The vapor must have caused a good deal of refraction, for above these clouds rose the whole of the Oberland Alps to an altitude which certainly seemed even greater than usual. Every peak, and all the majestic formation, was perfectly visible, though the whole range appeared to be severed from the earth, and to float in air. The line of connection was veiled; and, while all below was watery or enfeebled by mist, the glaciers threw back the fierce light of the sun with powerful splendor. The separation from the lower world was made the more complete from the contrast between the sombre hues beneath, and the calm, but bright magnificence above. One had some difficulty in believing that both belonged to the same orb. The effect of the whole was to create a picture, of which I can give no other idea than by saying it resembled a glimpse through the windows of heaven at such a gorgeous but chastened grandeur as the imagination might conceive to suit the place. There were moments when the spectral aspect, just mentioned, dimmed the lustre of the snows, without impairing their forms, and no language can do justice to the sublimity of the effect. It was impossible to look at them without religious awe; and, irreverent though it may seem, I could hardly persuade myself I was not gazing at some of the sublime mysteries that lie beyond the grave."

The nearer country, hill and dale, in the immediate neighborhood of La Lorraine was also charming. The drives were of course beautiful: often along narrow roads, smooth and even as garden-walks—amid open fields, rich and neat with the highest degree of culture, the passing wheel almost touching the crops, so narrow were the tracks. And then the Alps, ever in view, or at least always the hope of beholding them at the next turn, when some nearer hill or wood shut out the grand panorama for a moment! And the cottages, so exquisitely rural and rustic, and local—with their broad, projecting roofs, and low balconies, and quaint inscriptions, rude in lettering, devout in meaning! How thrifty the whole aspect of things: a dilapidated cottage, or a carelessly tilled field, seeming blots on the face of the land unknown in the good canton of Berne. Over these beautiful scenes the eye of the American traveller, eager, observant, and appreciative, wandered with delight, gathering some fresh incident of interest from every evening drive. When harvest-time came, the traveller was very much interested by the gleaners; these poor people were spread through the grain-fields in large parties. They came chiefly from the mountains, where the land lies almost wholly in pasture; and, for many, the little barley, or rye, or wheat, for their winter store, must be gathered wholly in that way, picked up by the ear, from the richer fields of the lowland farmers. Old and young, men, women, and children, they came flocking down from the Oberland in household parties, scattering themselves through the harvest-fields many a weary mile from their mountain homes. Their varied costumes were often faded and tattered, and yet pleasing, since the interest of inheritance and prolonged local growth—like that of the plants—lingered about each. Pausing, one evening, before a field where these poor people were gathered, Mr. Cooper counted one hundred and twenty-nine of them, young and old, men and women, in a field of less than six acres. We give an extract of this date :

"The day after meeting this herd of gleaners, who, by the way, were of all ages, and both sexes, we went to Hindelbank, to see the celebrated monument in the village church. The history of this monument has been often told, but it is so touchingly beautiful that it will bear to be repeated. Hindelbank is no more than a sequestered and insignificant hamlet, at the distance of two leagues from Berne. The church also is positively one of the very smallest and humblest of all the parish churches I remember to have seen in Europe. Small as it is, however, it contains the tomb of the Erlachs, whose principal residence is at a short distance from the village. A German artist, of the name of Nahl, was employed to execute something for this distinguished family, and, while engaged in the work, he took up his residence in the house of the parish priest, whose name was Langhans. The good pastor had been recently married, and tradition hath it that his young wife was eminently beautiful. She died at the birth of her first child, and while the sculptor was yet an inmate of the family. Touched by the sorrow of his host, and inspired by the virtues and beauty of the deceased, Nahl struck out the idea of this monument at a heat, and executed it on the spot, as a homage to friendship and conjugal worth ; looking to the Erlachs alone for the vulgar dross through which genius too commonly receives its impulses. We saw the château of the Erlachs, at a little distance on our right, before reaching the village. It is a house of no great size, but is historical on account of its connection with this ancient family. The humble little church was readily opened, and we entered filled with expectation. A large, labored, and magnificent, but, I think, tasteless monument, nearly covered one side of the building. It was richly wrought in marbles of different colors, but was confused and meretricious, wanting certainly the simplicity that belongs to every thing of this nature that is truly admirable. I had come to the spot without particularly attending to the history of the pastor's family, expecting to see a piece of sculpture of rare merit, without exactly knowing what. At that moment I knew nothing of the Erlachs' having a tomb at Hindelbank, and, seeing nothing but an exceedingly rustic and plain village church, which was nearly half occupied by this labored work of art, quite naturally supposed this was the object of our excursion. I was already endeavoring to dissect the confused details, in order to find out the grain of wheat among the heaps of tares, when I was called to the rest of the party. The sexton had ascended a little platform, at the head of the church, which seemed to be covered with boards thrown loosely on the joists. Raising one or two of these, the monument appeared below. An ordinary flat tombstone, with armorial bearings and inscriptions, lay at the depth of about six inches below the floor. The idea was that of the grave giving up its dead for judgment. The stone was rent longitudinally in twain, until near the head, where a fragment was so broken as to expose the faces and busts of those who were summoned to the resurrection. The child lies tranquilly on the bosom of its mother, as if its innocence were passive, while the countenance of the latter is beaming with holy joy. One hand is a little raised, as if reverently greeting her Redeemer. The sculpture is equal to the thought, and the artist, probably from the circumstances of moulding the features after death, while he has preserved the beauty of a fine symmetry, has imparted to them a look entirely suited to the mystery of the grave. These things too often savor of conceit; and after the momentary feeling of wonder into which, perhaps, you have been surprised is a little abated, the mind turns with greater pleasure to the more severe models of classic taste. Such is not the case with this extraordinary monument. It grows upon you by study, and its rare simplicity is quite as remarkable as the boldness and poetry of the conception. Even the material, perishable and plain as it is, helps to sustain the interest, for it betrays the poverty which could not restrain, though it might trammel, genius. There it lay, in noble contrast to the more ostentatious sorrow of the Erlachs! I would not have changed it into marble, if I could, although it is no more than the common friable sandstone of the adjoining hills, of a grayish-blue color, and of which half the houses in Berne are constructed. I have heard it said that the thought of this monument is not original. For this I will not vouch: but I think it has all the appearance of being produced under the pure inspiration of the imagination, quickened by strong generous feeling. One seldom sees or hears a particularly clever thing without setting about hunting for the original; ideas which are the most natural and beautiful usually striking us with the force of old acquaintances, on account of their fitness and truth.

"There is a monument in Westminster Abbey, in which Death, in the form of a skeleton, appears opening the gates of a tomb, ready to strike his victim. This is a conceit of Roubilliac, and nothing but a conceit. The cumbrous allegory of this work can no more compare with the sublime and evangelical thought of Nahl, than the labored couplets of Racine can sustain a parallel with the vigorous images of Shakespeare. No work of art—not even the Apollo—ever produced so strong an effect on me as this monument, which—because the most

The Wept of Wish-Ton-Wish: "Lord!" said Meek,
stretching his meagre arms, with the palms of the
hands open, high above the head of his flock, "at thy
bidding we go forth."

exquisite blending of natural sentiment with a supernatural and revealed future —I take to be the most sublime production of its kind in the world."

At the foot of the Alps, a new book was planned. Mind and memory, however, turned affectionately westward; and scenes of home-life, incidents connected with the annals of his native soil, formed once more the materials selected for the work. As usual, it was no sooner planned than the first pages were written. The period and ground chosen were the early colonial time in Connecticut. The American Puritan and the Indian were to be thrown together, while the chief point of interest is a child, a lovely little girl, torn from her mother's arms, and borne away into the wilderness by the savage band: according to a custom prevailing throughout the tribes of northern America, the captive girl is formally adopted, and engrafted into a family of the red race. Years pass over; the bereaved mother—a very beautiful character, colored with great truth, purity, and tenderness—lives drooping and mourning on the spot where the blow had fallen upon her head. The father—a fine and highly favorable picture of the colonist of that day and that ground—carries about with him, under a calm exterior, and beneath his stiff Puritan garb, a sad heart. Brother, and sister, and companions, grow to maturity, and all throw many a yearning look backward, in memory of the lost sister, the Wept of Wish-ton-Wish. A fresh outbreak of the savages occurs: the lost girl returns to her father's roof one of the marauding band, the wife of a Narragansett warrior, the mother of an Indian boy.

Such was the book planned and commenced in the little uncarpeted study at La Lorraine.   Long excursions, however, made in succession to some of the many points of interest in the country about him, interfered more than usual with the progress of his work.   Occasionally he went off through the more level cantons in a carriage or char-à-banc, with a part of his family; at other times he made excursions into the heart of the Alps, on foot, with a guide for his only companion.   Always a good pedestrian, he enjoyed extremely these excursions on foot.   While at Paris, a year or two earlier, he had undertaken to walk around the walls of that city, with an officer in the navy, an old comrade and messmate, Captain Wolcott Chauncey, for a companion, performing the feat in four hours. The distance was said to be, at that time, some eighteen miles.   At length autumnal gusts began to whistle through the linden-trees about La Lorraine, showers of snow fell upon the little garden; it was declared expedient to move southward ere the Alpine passes were closed.   A couple of *voituriers* were engaged to transport the party, after the usual fashion, to Florence; Caspar, the principal of the two, acting as *postillon-en-chef*, had been a cuirassier of the first Napoleon's wars; he had many a long tale of the camp to tell, and with much *bonhomie*, a hearty, jovial nature, and perfectly respectful manner, was soon in high favor with his employer, who in later years frequently alluded to him.   The Lake of Geneva was reached.   " A more ravishing view than that we now beheld can scarcely be imagined.   Nearly the whole of the lake was visible.   The north shore was studded with towns, towers, castles, and villages, for the distance of thirty miles; the rampart-like rocks of Savoy rose, for three or four thousand feet, like walls, above the water, and solitary villages were built against their bases, in spots where there scarcely appeared room to rest a human foot.   The solemn, magnificent gorge, rather than valley, of the Rhone, and the river glittering like silver among its meadows, were in the distant front, while the immediate foreground was composed of a shore which also had its walls of rocks, and its towns laved by the water, its castles, its hamlets, half-concealed by fruit-trees, and its broad, mountain bosom thrown into terraces to the elevation of two thousand feet, on which reposed almost every object of rural art that can adorn a picture.   The beauty of the panorama was singularly heightened by some thirty or forty large barks, with *latine* sails, a rig peculiarly Italian, and which, to my eye, was redolent of the Mediterranean, a sea I had not beheld for twenty years.   They were lying lazily on the glassy lake, as if placed there by Claude himself, to serve as models."

The Simplon was crossed.   The first glimpse of Italy gave great delight : " Suddenly we burst upon a little verdant valley that gave us a foretaste of Italy.

The valley widened, and, on one side, the mountain became less abrupt, in a way to admit of cultivation, and the abodes of men. The habitable tract was very limited, being no more than a sharp acclivity of some two or three thousand acres; but it was literally teeming with the objects of a rural civilization. The whole côte was a leafy cloud of lovely foliage, above which peeped the roofs of cottages, wherever a cottage could stand. Tall, gaunt-looking church-towers rose out of this grateful forest. Again the mountains approached each other, and we went rolling down a gentle declivity for miles, through gorges less wild than those above, but always imposing and savage. Here the torrent was spanned by several beautiful bridges, that were to receive foot-passengers, or, at most, a packhorse. They were of hewn stone, with pointed arches, and of extreme lightness and boldness. One or two were in ruins—a fact that bespoke their antiquity, and contributed to their interest. At length the mountains terminated, and an open space appeared. A transverse valley spread itself athwart the jaws of the gorge, and a massive bridge was thrown across the torrent at right angles to our course. Old Caspar cracked his whip, and soon whirled us into an entirely new region. The country was still Alpine—the valley into which we now entered being completely imbedded in sublime mountains; but the severity of the scenery unaccountably disappeared, and was replaced by softer hues, and a gentler nature; even the naked rocks appearing less stern and repulsive than those we had left on the banks of the Rhone. The vegetation was more exuberant, and it had been less nipped by frosts; the fruits were much more generous, and all the appliances of civilization were more abundant, and more genial. As we turned out of the gorge of the Doveria, into the valley of the Toccia, the carriage passed a huge column of marble, that lay, half-completed, by the side of the rock whence it had been quarried. This was a fit emblem of Italy; nor was its effect thrown away."

Florence was the destination of the travellers. As usual, a temporary home was soon arranged. The lodgings secured for the winter were in one of those old piles, half house, half fortalice, such as the warlike nobles of Florence were wont to build centuries ago, and which still form a severe feature in the aspect of that joyous and sunny city. Buildings which within are full of elegance and noble works of art, without throw a stern and frowning shade over the narrow streets. The house in which the American traveller, with his family, had been received, belonged to a lady of the family of Ricasoli, a widow with two sons—the elder a page attached to the court of the Grand Duke, the second, a tonsured Abbé still in his minority. The older brother, Baron Ricasoli, is now achieving for himself a highly honorable name, as the leader of the patriotic party in his

native country.   Mr. Cooper's residence in Florence was always remembered by
him with great pleasure ; he enjoyed extremely the society into which he was so
kindly received.   The higher Italian element of that society surpassed in intelligence, in activity of mind, and in elevated tone what he had anticipated, from
the general condition of the country at that period.   Among other gentlemen
whom he met frequently, the late Marchese Capponi was remembered by him
with especial and respectful regard, from his high personal character.   Baron
Poerio and the Cavalier Alessandro Poerio, exiles themselves, and the father and
brother of the present distinguished Neapolitan exile of the same name, were
frequent visitors at his house ; the latter gentleman being a poet and a linguist,
considered second only to Mezzofanti in acquirements of that nature.   The Prince
Napoleon, the elder brother of the present emperor, and the Princess Charlotte
Bonaparte, he also saw frequently ; for the first Mr. Cooper had anticipated a
brilliant career, from his character and talents, while for the princess he cherished
a most sincere regard, in common with many friends she had already won in
America.   These are all now deceased.   It was the delight of the American
traveller to enliven the hearthstone of the Casa Ricasoli with the cheery glow
of wood fires, such as might have done honor to his paternal home, in the Otsego
Hills ; through life a bright wood-fire, in cool weather, was a necessity for him—
he was very critical in the art of laying the wood, and in nursing the bright
blaze, in which his cheerful nature rejoiced.   While the Italian servants held up
their hands with horror at such waste of fuel, the friends who gathered about the
hearthstone when the chill tramontana was blowing from the Apennines, all professed great admiration of this fashion, deemed by them especially American.
Among those cheered by the firelight, and to whom its charm was no novelty,
was one in whom Mr. Cooper soon learned to feel a deep interest—Mr. Horatio
Greenough, the sculptor.

Daily life now flowed in a double current.   A traveller's pleasures filled up
many hours.   Mr. Cooper's enjoyment of works of art, painting, sculpture,
and architecture, was very great ; the society of artists had always given him
especial pleasure ; the antiquities and beautiful natural scenery of the country
were of course full of interest, while many a graver thought was given to the
character and condition of the people, their life and education, and the government influencing both.   To the native character of the Italians, in its better
aspects, he was partial, believing them capable of far more than during the last
centuries they have accomplished.   But while throwing himself, with his usual
zest and animation, into the outward movement of the hour, a portion of every
morning was given to his pen ; and wide, indeed, was the difference between the

living groups among which he moved abroad, the gay, impulsive, laughing, singing, brown-skinned Italians, and the demure, ideal, Puritan band which surrounded him when in his study in the Casa Ricasoli. In all Italy, from the Alps to Mount Etna, the like of these could not be found—never had existed—the soil of Italy could yield no such growth—their virtues and their vices belonged alike to a very different zone of the moral world. The two currents, however, remained wholly distinct in the writer's mind; the family of the Wish-ton-Wish were as clearly drawn as if the book had been written in the valley of the Connecticut, rather than on the banks of the Arno. Ere long the work was sufficiently advanced for printing. Here, however, the author met with great and unforeseen difficulties. The first obstacle to be overcome was the censorship of the press. In Tuscany, however, the restraints of this nature were light compared to those in other parts of Italy, and the necessary permission to print was readily granted. To carry out the plan was a task much more difficult. There was no regular English printing establishment in Florence, and several efforts which were made to procure English compositors, and set them to work in an Italian office, successively failed. Despairing of effecting his object, Mr. Cooper at length reluctantly determined to leave his family at Florence, and endeavor to make arrangements for printing at Marseilles. During the carnival he set out for Marseilles, following the beautiful road along the coast. A few extracts of that date are given :

"Genoa lies at the base of a large cove, which has been converted into a fine harbor by means of two moles. One quarter of the town actually stands on low cliffs that are washed by the sea, which must sometimes throw its spray into the streets. Its position consequently unites the several beauties of a gorgeous capital with all its works of art, the movement and bustle of a port, the view of a sea with passing ships and its varying aspects of calms and tempests, with a background of stupendous hills; for at this point the Alps send out those grand accessories to their magnificence, the Apennines. The place is fortified, and the nature of the ground requiring that the adjacent hill should be included, the *enceinte* is large enough to contain all Paris. I took a horse and made the circuit of the walls. The day was mild, but had passing clouds, and some of the views toward the interior were of an extraordinary character. A deep valley separated us from the works; and there were several fine glimpses, in a sort of wild perspective, among the recesses of the mountains. I scarcely remember a scene of more peculiar wildness, blended with beauty, than some of these glimpses offered, though the passing cloud and the season perhaps contributed to the effect. The inland views resembled some of the backgrounds of the pictures of Leonardo da Vinci. Indeed, it is only in Italy, and among its romantic heights, with their castle-like villages and towns, that one gets an accurate notion of the models that the older masters copied. Seaward the prospect was truly glorious. The day was mild, and twenty sail were loitering along, quaint in rig as usual, and wallowing to the heavy ground swell. Here I had almost a bird's-eye view of the town, port, and offing, with the noble range of coast southward, and a pile of purple mountains whose feet were lined with villages. * * I took the *malle-poste*, and left Genoa for Nice. The road ran on the very margin of the sea, the carriage literally rolling along the beach. Many were the pretty little fishing and trading hamlets we gallopped through in this manner, and now and then we had a town. The coast was fairly lined with them. Inland the mountains soon began to tower upward to an Alpine elevation. Imagination cannot portray bits of scenery more picturesque than some that offered on the beach. Wild ravines, down which broad and rapid torrents poured their contributions, opened toward the hills; and bridges of singular construction and of great antiquity spanned these, in bold and imposing flights. Many of those wide arches were half ruined. As for the beach, it was principally of sand, and wherever a hamlet occurred, it was certain to be lined with boats and feluccas, some lying on their bilges, and others shored up on their keels, with perchance a sail or net spread to dry. How some of these crafts, vessels of forty or fifty tons, were got there in the absence of tides, and how they were to be got off again, exceeded my skill at conjecture; the *conduc-*

teur affirmed that they sailed upon the sands, and would sail off again when they wished to put to sea! Here and there a prettily-modelled felucca was on the ways. Altogether, it was an extraordinary passage, differing entirely from any I had ever made before. For several hours we travelled in darkness; when day dawned it opened on an entirely different scene. There was no longer a beach; the coast had become rocky and broken; the land was heaving itself up into gigantic forms, and on our right appeared Monte Finale, the last summit of the Alps! The huge background of mountains protects all this coast from the north winds, and the sun of a low latitude beating against it, joined to the bland airs of this miraculous sea, conspire to render all this region precocious. Even the palm was growing in one or two places, though early in March we felt all the symptoms of a young spring. This harmony between the weather and the views contributed largely to my pleasures. Soon after quitting Mentone, the road began to wind its way across the broad and naked breast of a huge mountain. This was, in truth, the point where we crossed the Maritime Alps, the rest of the mounting and descending being merely coquetting on their skirts. The town of Monaco appeared in the distance, seated on a low rocky promontory, with the sea laving one of its sides, and the other opening toward a pretty and secluded port. The whole of this coast is as picturesque and glorious as the imagination can paint; and then the associations, which are oriental, and sometimes even scriptural, come in to throw a hue over all. I observed to-day a polacre rolling at her anchor, while boats were carrying off to her oil and olives from the spot where the latter had grown. As I sat leaning back in the carriage, the line of sight, by clearing the bottom of the carriage window, struck another vessel under her canvas, at the distance of half a league from the shore. We may have been, at the moment, a thousand feet above the sea. The panoramas seen from these advanced eminences were as magnificent as land and water could form—the more so from the hue of the Mediterranean, a tint eminently beautiful. Indeed, one who has seen no other sea but that which is visible from the American coast, can scarcely form a notion of the beauty of the ocean; for there the tint is a dull green, while in many other parts of the world it is a marine blue. After climbing a league we reached the summit of the pass, which was a sort of shoulder of the range, and had a short distance of tolerably level route. From this elevation we caught a glimpse of a deep bay, with a town at its head, called Villa Franca; and one of the most extraordinary of all the wasp-like looking villages I had yet seen presented itself. It literally capped the apex of a cone, whose sides were so steep as to render ascending and descending a work of toil, and even risk. I should think that a child falling from the verge of the village must roll down two hundred feet. On this extraordinary pinnacle were perched some fifty or sixty houses built of stone, resembling, as usual, one single and quaint edifice, from the manner in which they were compressed together. The *conducteur* deemed this village the most extraordinary object on his route; and when I asked him what could have induced men to select such a position for a town, he answered: '*The bears!*' Protection was unquestionably the motive, and the village is probably very ancient. My companion thought there must be a well of great depth to furnish water, and he added that the inhabitants were chiefly shepherds. It is necessary to see a landscape embellished by towns, convents, castles, and churches, occupying sites like this, to form any accurate notion of the manner in which they render it quaint and striking."

At Marseilles the printing plan was varied. Unwilling to be absent from his temporary home longer than was possible, he succeeded in finding an English compositor, who consented to return with him to Florence, and work under Mr. Cooper's directions in an Italian office. This man, whose name was Richard Heavisides, was unfortunately deaf and dumb. The author returned to Florence with him, however; and a room in some corner of that spacious Italian dwelling, the Casa Ricasoli, was found for the printer, who received his meals from his employer's table, while his working hours were passed in the Italian office. He proved, however, but an indifferent printer; the work went on very slowly, and the plan would probably have been abandoned from this cause alone, when the ungovernable temper of the man—a failing said to be common with mutes—rendered it necessary to send him back to Marseilles again. At length, with the kind assistance of the grand duke's librarian, other arrangements were made, and a small edition of the Wish-ton-Wish was printed, the early sheets of which were sent to Paris, London, and Philadelphia, to meet engagements with the author's publishers in those cities. In England, the book received the name of "The Borderers," which it still bears in that country. The word Wish-ton-Wish, the author had taken from an Indian vocabulary, professing to give it the meaning of Whip-poor-Will, in a dialect of one of the eastern tribes; the correctness of the translation he had afterward reason to doubt, when too late, however, to change the name. An American work, of no little interest, whose leading idea was very similar to that of the Wish-ton-Wish, appeared rather earlier: Hope Leslie, by Miss Sedgwick. It was a singular coincidence that two American writers should have been led to plan, at the same moment, works so similar in outline. Hope Leslie had the honors of the earlier publication, still it is simply true that the idea of Mr. Cooper's book was quite original with himself; at the time of the publication of the Wish-ton-Wish he had never read Hope Leslie. Both authors probably drew their outline from the same sources, the annals of Deerfield, and Cherry Valley, and Wyoming.

The success of the Wish-ton-Wish was moderate only. This was especially the case in America; in England and in France it was more liked. Is it an error to believe that the book has been undervalued? May we not assert that if no other work more brilliant in character had been given us by the same pen, the Wish-ton-Wish would have ranked more highly? There is a vein of deep pathetic interest running through the narrative; and many beautiful pictures might be drawn from its pages. The principal characters are well sketched, and there is a purity and freshness in the general tone like the odor of the newly-turned sod— the fragrance of bud and briar in the newly opened wood. Mr. Cooper was very far from being an admirer of Puritan peculiarities, or the fruits their principles have yielded in later times; but in the Wish-ton-Wish impartial justice has been done to all that was sound and healthful in their system: to their courage, their thrifty industry, their self-denial and simple habits of life, their shrewdness, and their indomitable resolution; while the less pleasing traits have been softened down, and a subdued poetical light, in perfect harmony with the pathetic nature of the subject, thrown over the whole. As a picture of pure family love—that between husband and wife, parent and child, brother and sister—the narrative is beautiful. The spirit of that love glows throughout; it throws a light, sweet and serene, yet clear and strong, over every page; while in no instance is there the least taint of exaggeration or conceit. Some time after the publication of the book, when revising its pages for a new edition, the writer expressed a regret that his plan

had not varied in one particular; the leading idea, the abduction of the daughter
of the Puritan family and her adoption by the savages, would have remained the
same, but instead of bringing Narra-mattah to her old home again with the
Narragansett marauders, he would have carried the heart-stricken father into the
wilderness on the trail of his lost child; he would have followed the parent step
by step through the forest, as he was led onward—now deceived by some false
rumor, then again guided by the right clue, wandering far and wide, along unex-
plored streams, over nameless lakes, through pathless valleys, until, at length, in
some remote wigwam of the red man, he finds her as she is now drawn, a beautiful
picture of sweet natural instincts, and wild grace, appearing one moment in that
subdued forest light which belongs to the red man's daughter, and then again
brightening under some clearer ray of her earlier Christian nurture. We can
imagine something, at least, of the higher interest, and the beauty of original
detail, which would have been given to the work under this form.

NARRA-MATTAH.

THE short twilight was already passed, when old Mark Heathcote ended the evening prayer. The mixed character of the remarkable events of that day had given birth to a feeling which could find no other relief than that which flowed from the usual zealous, confiding, and exalted outpouring of the spirit. On the present occasion, he had even resorted to an extraordinary, and, what one less devout might be tempted to think, a supererogatory offering of thanksgiving and praise. After dismissing the dependants of the establishment, supported by the arm of his son, he had withdrawn into an inner apartment, and there, surrounded only by those who had the nearest claims on his affections, the old man again raised his voice to laud the Being who, in the midst of so much general grief, had deigned to look upon his particular race with the eyes of remembrance and of favor. He spoke of his recovered grandchild by name, and he dealt with the whole subject of her captivity among the heathen, and her restoration to the foot of the altar, with the fervor of one who saw the wise decrees of Providence in the event, and with a tenderness of sentiment that age was far from having extinguished. It was at the close of this private and peculiar worship that we return into the presence of the family.

When Ruth Heathcote arose from her knees, it was with a hand clasped in that of the child whom her recent devotion was well suited to make her think had been rescued from a condition far more gloomy than that of the grave. She had used a gentle violence to force the wondering being at her side to join, so far as externals could go, in the prayer; and, now it was ended, she sought the countenance of her daughter, in order to read the impression the scene had produced, with all the solicitude of a Christian, heightened by the tenderest maternal love.

Narra-mattah, as we shall continue to call her, in air, expression, and attitude, resembled one who had a fancied existence in the delusion of some exciting dream. Her ear remembered sounds which had so often been repeated in her infancy, and her memory recalled indistinct recollections of most of the objects and usages that were so suddenly replaced before her eyes ; but the former now conveyed their meaning to a mind that had gained its strength under a very different system of theology, and the latter came too late to supplant usages that were rooted in her affections by the aid of all those wild and seductive habits that are known to become nearly unconquerable in those who have long been subject to their influence. She stood, therefore, in the centre of the grave, self-restrained group of her nearest kin, like an alien to their blood, resembling some timid and but half-tamed tenant of the air, that human art had endeavored to domesticate, by placing it in the society of the more tranquil and confiding inhabitants of the aviary.

Notwithstanding the strength of her affections, and her devotion to all the natural duties of her station, Ruth Heathcote was not now to learn the manner in which she was to subdue any violence in their exhibition. The first indulgence of joy and gratitude was over, and in its place appeared the never-tiring, vigilant, engrossing, but regulated watchfulness which the events would naturally create. The doubts, misgivings, and even fearful apprehensions, that beset her, were smothered in an appearance of satisfaction; and something like gleamings of happiness were again seen playing about a brow that had so long been clouded with an unobtrusive but corroding care.

"And thou recallest thine infancy, my Ruth?" asked the mother, when the respectful period of silence, which ever succeeded prayer in that family, was passed; "thy thoughts have not been altogether strangers to us, but nature hath had its place in thy heart. Tell us, child, of thy wanderings in the forest, and of the sufferings that one so tender must have undergone among a barbarous people. There is pleasure in listening to all thou hast seen and felt, now that we know there is an end to unhappiness."

She spoke to an ear that was deaf to language like this. Narra-mattah evidently understood her words, while their meaning was wrapped in an obscurity that she neither wished to nor was capable of comprehending. Keeping a gaze, in which pleasure and wonder were powerfully blended, on that soft look of affection which beamed from her mother's eye, she felt hurriedly among the folds of her dress, and drawing a belt that was gayly ornamented after the most ingenious fashion of her adopted people, she approached her half-pleased, half-distressed parent, and, with hands that trembled equally with timidity and pleasure, she arranged it around her person in a manner to show its richness to the best advantage. Pleased with her performance, the artless being eagerly sought approbation in eyes that bespoke little else than regret. Alarmed at an expression she could not translate, the gaze of Narra-mattah wandered, as if it sought support against some sensation to which she was a stranger. Whittal Ring had stolen into the room, and missing the customary features of her own cherished home, the looks of the startled creature rested on the countenance of the witless wanderer. She pointed eagerly to the work of her hands, appealing by an eloquent and artless gesture to the taste of one who should know whether she had done well.

"Bravely!" returned Whittal, approaching nearer to the subject of his admiration; "'tis a brave belt, and none but the wife of a Sachem could make so rare a gift!"

The girl folded her arms meekly on her bosom, and again appeared satisfied with herself and with the world.

"Here is the hand of him visible who dealeth in all wickedness," said the Puritan. "To corrupt the heart with vanities, and to mislead the affections by luring them to the things of life, is the guile in which he delighteth. A fallen nature lendeth but too ready aid. We must deal with the child in fervor and watchfulness, or better that her bones were lying by the side of those little ones of thy flock, who are already inheritors of the promise."

Respect kept Ruth silent; but, while she sorrowed over the ignorance of her child, natural affection was strong at her heart. With the tact of a woman, and the tenderness of a mother, she both saw and felt that severity was not the means to effect the improvement they desired. Taking a seat herself, she drew her child to her person, and, first imploring silence by a glance at those around her, she proceeded, in a manner that was dictated by the mysterious influences of nature, to fathom the depth of her daughter's mind.

"Come nearer, Narra-mattah," she said, using the name to which the other would alone answer. "Thou art still in thy youth, my child; but it hath pleased Him whose will is law, to have made thee the witness of many changes in this varying life. Tell me if thou recallest the days of infancy, and if thy thoughts ever returned to thy father's house, during those weary years thou wast kept from our view?"

Ruth used gentle force to draw her daughter nearer while speaking, and the latter sunk into that posture from which she had just arisen, kneeling, as she had often done in infancy at her mother's side. The attitude was too full of tender recollections not to be grateful, and the half-alarmed being of the forest was suffered to retain it during most of the dialogue that followed. But while she was thus obedient in person, by the vacancy, or rather wonder of an eye that was so eloquent to express all the emotions and knowledge of which she was the mistress, Narra-mattah plainly manifested that little more than the endearment of her mother's words and manner was intelligible. Ruth saw the meaning of her hesitation, and smothering the pang it caused, she endeavored to adapt her language to the habits of one so artless.

"Even the gray heads of thy people were once young," she resumed; "and they remember the lodges of their fathers. Does my daughter ever think of the time when she played among the children of the pale-faces?"

The attentive creature at the knee of Ruth listened greedily. Her knowledge of the language of her childhood had been sufficiently implanted before her captivity, and it had been too often exercised by intercourse with the whites, and more particularly with Whittal Ring, to leave her in any doubt of the meaning of what she now heard. Stealing a timid look over a shoulder, she sought the countenance of Martha, and, studying her lineaments for near a minute with intense regard, she laughed aloud in the contagious merriment of an Indian girl.

"Thou hast not forgotten us! That glance at her who was the companion of thy infancy assures me, and we shall soon again possess our Ruth in affection, as we now possess her in the body. I will not speak to thee of that fearful night when the violence of the savage robbed us of thy presence, nor of the bitter sorrow which beset us at thy loss; but there is one who must still be known to thee, my child: He who sitteth above the clouds, who holdeth the earth in the hollow of his hand, and who looketh in mercy on all that journey on the path to which his own finger pointeth. Hath he yet a place in thy thoughts? Thou rememberest His holy name, and still thinkest of his power?"

The listener bent her head aside, as if to catch the full meaning of what she heard, the shadows of deep reverence passing over a face that had so lately been smiling. After a pause she audibly murmured the word—

"Manitou!"

"Manitou, or Jehovah; God, or King of kings, and Lord of lords! it mattereth little which term is used to express his power. Thou knowest him, then, and hast never ceased to call upon his name?"

"Narra-mattah is a woman. She is afraid to speak to the Manitou aloud. He knows the voices of the chiefs, and opens his ears when they ask help."

The Puritan groaned, but Ruth succeeded in quelling her own anguish, lest she should disturb the reviving confidence of her daughter.

"This may be the Manitou of an Indian," she said; "but it is not the Christian's God. Thou art of a race which worships differently, and it is proper that thou shouldst call on the name of the Deity of thy fathers. Even the Narragansett teacheth this truth! Thy skin is white, and thy ears should hearken to the traditions of the men of thy blood."

The head of the daughter drooped at this allusion to her color, as if she would fain conceal the mortifying truth from every eye; but she had not time for answer, ere Whittal Ring drew near, and pointing to the burning color of her cheeks, that were deepened as much with shame as with the heats of an American sun, he said—

"The wife of the Sachem hath begun to change. She will soon be like Nipset, all red. See!" he added, laying a finger on a part of his own arm, where the sun and the winds had not yet destroyed the original color; "the Evil Spirit poured water into his blood too, but it will come out again. As soon as he is so dark that the Evil Spirit will not know him, he will go on the war-path; and then the lying pale-faces may dig up the bones of their fathers, and move toward the sunrise, or his lodge will be lined with hair of the color of a deer!"

"And thou, my daughter! canst thou hear this threat against the people of thy nation—of thy blood—of thy God—without a shudder?"

The eye of Narra-mattah seemed in doubt; still it regarded Whittal with its accustomed look of kindness. The innocent, full of his imaginary glory, raised his hand in exultation, and by gestures that could not easily be misunderstood, he indicated the manner in which he intended to rob his victims of the usual trophy. While the youth was enacting the disgusting but expressive pantomime, Ruth watched the countenance of her child in nearly breathless agony. She would have been relieved by a single glance of disapprobation, by a solitary movement of a rebellious muscle, or by the smallest sign that the tender nature of one so lovely, and otherwise so gentle, revolted at so unequivocal evidence of the barbarous practices of her adopted people. But no empress of Rome could have witnessed the dying agonies of the hapless gladiator, no consort of a more modern prince could read the bloody list of the victims of her husband's triumphs, nor any betrothed fair listen to the murderous deeds of him her imagination had painted as a hero, with less indifference to human suffering, than that with which the wife of the sachem of the Narragansetts looked on the mimic representation of those exploits which had purchased for her husband a renown so highly prized. It was but too apparent that the representation, rude and savage as it was, conveyed to her mind nothing but pictures in which the chosen companion of a warrior should rejoice. The varying features and answering eye too plainly proclaimed the sympathy of one taught to exult in the success of the combatant; and when Whittal, excited by his own exertions, broke out into an exhibition of a violence more ruthless even than common, he was openly rewarded by another laugh. The soft, exquisitely feminine tones of this involuntary burst of pleasure, sounded in the ears of Ruth like a knell over the moral beauty of her child. Still, subduing her feelings, she passed a hand thoughtfully over her own pallid brow, and appeared to muse long on the desolation of a mind that had once promised to be so pure.

But the efforts of maternal love are not easily repulsed. An idea flashed upon her brain, and she proceeded to try the efficacy of the experiment it suggested. Nature had endowed her with a melodious voice, and an ear that taught her to regulate sounds in a manner that seldom failed to touch the heart. Drawing her daughter nearer to her knee, she commenced one of the songs then much used by the mothers of the colony, her voice scarcely rising above the whispering of the evening air, in its first notes, but gradually gaining, as she proceeded, the richness and compass that a strain so simple required.

At the first low breathing notes of this nursery song, Narra-mattah became as motionless as if her rounded and unfettered form had been wrought in marble. Pleasure lighted her eye, as strain succeeded strain; and ere the second verse was ended, her look, her attitude, and every muscle of her ingenuous features, were eloquent in the expression of delight. Ruth did not hazard the experiment without trembling for its result. Emotion imparted feeling to the music, and when, for the third time in the course of her song, she addressed her child, she saw the soft blue eyes that gazed wistfully on her face swimming in tears. Encouraged by this unequivocal evidence of success, nature grew still more powerful in its efforts, and the closing verse was sung to an ear that nestled near her heart, as it had often done during the early years of Narra-mattah, while listening to its melancholy melody.

Content was a quiet but an anxious witness of this touching evidence of a reviving intelligence between his wife and child. He best understood the look that beamed in the eyes of the former, while her arms were, with extreme caution, folded around her who still leaned upon her bosom, as if fearful one so timid might be frightened from her security by any sudden or unaccustomed interruption. A minute passed in the deepest silence. Even Whittal Ring was lulled into quiet, and long and sorrowing years had passed since Ruth enjoyed moments of happiness so pure and unalloyed. The stillness was broken by a heavy step in the outer room; a door was thrown open by a hand more violent than common, and then young Mark appeared, his face flushed with exertion, his brow seemingly retaining the frown of battle, and with a tread that betrayed a spirit goaded by some fierce and unwelcome passion. The burden of Conanchet was on his arm. He laid it upon a table; then pointing, in a manner that appeared to challenge attention, he turned, and left the room as abruptly as he had entered.

A cry of joy burst from the lips of Narra-mattah, the instant the beaded belts caught her eye. The arms of Ruth relaxed their hold in surprise, and before amazement had time to give place to more connected ideas, the wild being at her knee had flown to the table, returned, resumed her former posture, opened the folds of the cloth, and was holding before the bewildered gaze of her mother the patient features of an Indian babe.

It would exceed the powers of the unambitious pen we wield, to convey to the reader a just idea of the mixed emotions that struggled for mastery in the countenance of Ruth. The innate and never-dying sentiment of maternal joy was opposed by all those feelings of pride that prejudice could not fail to implant even in the bosom of one so meek. There was no need to tell the history of the parentage of the little suppliant, who already looked up into her face, with that peculiar calm which renders his race so remarkable. Though its glance was weakened by infancy, the dark glittering eye of Conanchet was there; there were also to be seen the receding forehead and the compressed lip of the father; but all these marks of his origin were softened by touches of that beauty which had rendered the infancy of her own child so remarkable.

"See!" said Narra-mattah, raising the infant still nearer to the riveted gaze of Ruth; "'tis a sachem of the red men! The little eagle hath left his nest too soon."

Ruth could not resist the appeal of her beloved. Bending her head low, so as entirely to conceal her own flushed face, she imprinted a kiss on the forehead of the Indian boy. But the jealous eye of the young mother was not to be deceived. Narra-mattah detected the difference between the cold salute and those fervent embraces she had herself received, and disappointment produced a chill about her own heart. Replacing the folds of the cloth with quiet dignity, she arose from her knees, and withdrew in sadness to a distant corner of the room. There she took a seat, and with a glance that might almost be termed reproachful, she commenced a low Indian song to her infant.

"The wisdom of Providence is in this, as in all its dispensations," whispered Content over the shoulder of his nearly insensible partner. "Had we received her as she was lost, the favor might have exceeded our deservings. Our daughter is grieved that thou turnest a cold eye on her babe."

The appeal was sufficient for one whose affections had been wounded rather than chilled. It recalled Ruth to recollection, and it served at once to dissipate the shades of regret that had been unconsciously permitted to gather around her brow. The displeasure—or it would be more true to term it sorrow—of the young mother was easily appeased. A smile on her infant brought the blood back to her heart in a swift and tumultuous current; and Ruth herself soon forgot that she had any reason for regret, in the innocent delight with which her own daughter now hastened to display the physical excellence of the boy. From this scene of natural feeling, Content was too quickly summoned by the intelligence that some one without awaited his presence, on business of the last importance to the welfare of the settlement.

X

THE WATER-WITCH.

WITH the early spring of Italy came longings for the freedom of the fields. A villa was secured, on a side-hill, just beyond the walls of Florence. The dwelling was trim and spruce rather than picturesque, and received its name of St. Illario from a little rustic church, which would have touched its walls but for a very narrow lane which lay between them. There were two square projecting wings to the villa, each crowned with a belvedere and roofed terrace, one of these last being connected with the author's study. We give a sketch of the spot in his own words: "Among other recommendations the Villa St. Illario has two covered belvederes, where one can sit in the breeze, and overlook the groves of olive-trees with all the crowded objects of an Italian landscape. The valley of the Arno, though sufficiently wide, and cultivated chiefly with the spade, is broken by many abrupt and irregular heights, the advanced spurs of the ranges of the Apennines which bound it. On nearly all of these eminences stands a stone building, topped by a belvedere, with or without terraces, here and there a tree, and olive-groves beneath. The whole country is intersected by very narrow roads leading up to the heights, and these lanes usually run between close and high walls. They are commonly paved, to prevent the wash of the rains, and nothing can be less attractive, though we find the shade of the walls beginning to be necessary as the season advances. To obtain a view one is obliged to ascend to some one of the look-outs on the hills, of which there are many; though the rides and walks on the level land, above and behind us, occasionally furnish glorious glimpses. We are much in the habit of strolling to one of the heights,

Hamilton fecit

M Gorfon Sculpt

The Water Witch: The Chase through Hurl Gate

rightly enough called Bellosguardo, for a better bird's-eye view of a town is not often had than this affords of Florence. In addition, we get the panorama of the valley and mountains, and the delicate lights and shades of the misty Apennines. These mountains are generally to be distinguished from the lower ranges of the Alps, or those whose elevation comes nearest to their own, by a softer and more sunny hue, which is often rendered dreamy and indolent by the sleepy haziness of the atmosphere. Indeed, every thing in these regions appears to invite to contemplation and repose, at this particular season. There is an admixture of the savage and the refined in the ragged ravines of the hills, the villas, the polished town, the cultivated plain, the distant chestnut-covered peaks, the costumes, the songs of the peasants, the oriental olive, the monasteries and churches, that keeps the mind constantly attuned to poetry. . . . . The songs of Tuscany are often remarkable. There is one air in particular that is heard in every key, used to all sorts of words, and is in the mouths of all of the lower classes of both sexes. The soldier sings of war to it, the sailor of storms and the seas, the gallant of his adventures, and the young girl of her love. The air is full of melody. It is, withal, a little wild, and has a *la ral, lal, la* to it that just suits the idea of heartiness which is perhaps necessary, for the simplicity of such a thing may be hurt by too much sophistication. I first heard this air in the town, at a particular hour, every evening. On inquiry, I found it was a baker boy singing it in the street as he dispensed his cakes. I often hear it, as I sit in my belvedere, rising from among the vines or olives, on different heights: sometimes it is sung in falsetto, sometimes in a deep bass, sometimes in a rich contralto. Walking to Bellosguardo the other evening, I heard it in a vineyard, and getting on a stone that overlooked the wall, I found it came from a beautiful *contadina* who was singing of love as she trimmed her vines ; disturbed by my motions, she turned, blushed, laughed, hid her face, and ran among the leaves. This is not our only music. One of the very narrow lanes separates my end of the house from the church of St. Illario and the dwelling of the priest. From the belvedere communicating with my own room we have frequent passages of civility across the lane with the good old *curato*, who discusses the weather and the state of the crops with great unction. The old man has some excellent figs, and our cook, having discovered it, lays his trees under contribution. And here I will record what I conceive to be the very perfection of epicurism, or rather of taste, in the matter of eating. A single fresh fig, as a corrective after the soup, I hold to be one of those sublime touches of art that are oftener discovered by accident than by the investigations of science. I do not mean that I have even the equivocal merit of this accidental discovery, for I was told the secret, and French ingenuity had come pretty near it already, in the way of melons. But no melon is like a fig; nor will a French fig, certainly not a Paris fig, answer the purpose at all. It must be such a fig as one gets in Italy. At Paris you are always offered a glass of Madeira after the soup, the only one taken at table; but it is a pitiful sub stitute for the fig. After communicating this improvement on human happiness, let me add that it is almost destructive of the pleasure derived from the first, to take a second. *One* small green-coated fresh fig is the precise point of gastro-nomic felicity in this respect. But the good *curato*, besides his figs, has a pair of uneasy bells in his church-tower, which are exactly forty-three feet from my ears, and which invariably ring in pairs six or eight times daily. There are matins, noon-tide, angelus, vespers, regularly, to say nothing of christenings, funerals, weddings. The effect of bells is delightful when heard in the distance, and they are ringing all over the valley, morning, noon, and night; but these are too near. Still I get now and then rare touches of the picturesque from this proximity to the church. Lounging in the belvedere lately, at night, we saw torches gleaming in a distant lane. Presently the sounds of the funeral chant reached us; these gradually deepened, until we had the imposing and solemn chant for the dead echoing beneath our own walls, as if in the nave of a church. It is necessary to witness such a scene, to appreciate its beauty, on a still and dark night beneath an Italian sky."

The sight of the Mediterranean, enjoyed during the winter journey to Mar-seilles, had suggested the idea of another tale of the sea; a return of the fever, however, from which the writer had suffered at home, and which was now brought on again, though in a milder form, by exposure to the summer sun of Italy, prevented the progress of the work. About midsummer an entire change of air was planned. There was a longing for the sea-breezes, a wish to find a dwelling somewhere within sight and sound of the blue waves of the Mediterranean. A movement southward, and by the water, was decided upon. Leghorn was the first step:

"After passing the night at Pisa, we galloped across the plain to Leghorn. The salt air was grateful, and I snuffed the odor of this delightful sea with a feeling that was 'redolent of joy and youth.' We hurried off to the port. Here we feasted our eyes on the different picturesque rigs and peculiar barks of those poetical waters. Long years had gone by since I had seen the felucca, the polacre, the xebec, and the sparanara, with all the other quaint-looking craft of the Mediterranean. As we strolled along the mole and quays, we met several men from the Levant; and an Algerine Rais was calmly smoking his chibouque on the deck of his polacre. A good many Sardinians lay scattered about the harbor. Of Tuscans there were few, and these all small. Three Russians were laid up on account of the war with Turkey! Rowing under the bows of a Yankee, I found one of his people seated on the windlass, playing on the flute—as cool a piece of impudence as can well be imagined for a Massachusettsman to practise in Italy! The delicious odors of the sea-port were inhaled with a delight that no language can describe. I had been living in an atmosphere of poetry for many months, and this was truly an atmosphere of life. The fragrance of the bales of merchandise, of the piles of oranges—of even the mud, saturated as it was with salt—to say nothing of the high seasoning of occasional breathings of tar and pitch, to me were pregnant with 'odors of delight.' "

At Leghorn a Genoese felucca was engaged for the voyage to Naples. "La Bella Genovese" was a craft of about thirty tons, and of beautiful mould; she was latine-rigged, carrying two sails of that description, and a jib; her crew numbered ten men! "I myself," continues the author, "have been one of eleven hands, officers included, to navigate a ship of some three hundred tons across the Atlantic ocean; and, what is more, we often reefed topsails with the watch. Having engaged the felucca, we passed another day in gazing at the hazy Apennines, whose lights and shadows, particularly the noble piles that buttress the coast to the northward, render them pictures to study. The entire northern shore of this luxurious sea, in summer, is one scene of magnificent nature, relieved by a bewitching softness, such as perhaps no other portion of the globe can equal. I can best liken it to an extremely fine woman, whose stateliness and beauty are softened by the eloquent and speaking expression of feminine sentiment."

The voyage in the "Bella Genovese," along the coast of Tuscany, Romagna, and Naples, lasted some six days—a week of great enjoyment to one who, though now numbered among men of letters, was ever a sailor at heart, and who felt so deeply the charm of Italian nature. The very atmosphere of Italy was a perpetual delight to him.

After two or three weeks passed in a hotel at Naples, the family party were again housed in a temporary home of their own, on the cliffs of Sorrento.

" This is a town of a few thousand inhabitants, directly opposite Naples, at a distance of some eighteen miles across the bay. The fertile plain on which Sorrento stands is surrounded by mountains, in a half-circle, facing the sea. The whole formation is volcanic, large fissures of the tufa appearing, in the shape of deep ravines, in various places. Advantage has been taken of the accidental position of these ravines, to form a deep natural ditch around the place, which stands on the margin of the plain overlooking the sea. This plain is six or seven miles in length, a continued village, very fertile, and extremely populous. Its elevation above the bay varies from one to two hundred feet, the verge being a perpendicular cliff of tufa, nearly the whole distance. The house we have taken is said to have been the one in which Tasso was born; it stands on the brow of the cliffs, within the walls of the town, and in plain sight of every object of interest on the bay, from Ischia to the promontory of Vico, Castelamare and a short reach of the shore in that vicinity excepted. The foundation of the house rests on narrow shelves of the cliffs, which just at this spot are about one hundred and fifty feet in perpendicular height, or possibly even more. It has a treacherous look to see the substratum of a building standing on a projection of this sort. There are two or three stories below us down among the cliffs. All the dwellings along these rocks, many of which are convents, have subterraneous communications with the sea, the outlets being visible as we row along beneath the heights. The government, however, has caused them to be closed, without distinction, to prevent smuggling. We occupy the principal floor only, though I have taken the entire house. There is a chapel beneath the great *sala*, and I believe there are kitchens and offices somewhere in those lower regions; but I have never visited any portion of the substratum but the chapel. We enter by a heavy *porte-cochère* into a court, which has a well with a handsome marble covering, or curb, and a flight of broad marble steps fit for a palace. These two objects, coupled with the interest of Tasso's name, have been thought worthy of an engraving. Seaward, two or three large ante-chambers lead to the sala, which faces the water, and is a room fifty feet long, with width and height in proportion. The floors, or rather *pavements*, are of a mud-colored composition, resembling pudding-stone; the furniture is no great matter, being reduced to the very minimum in quality, but it is not unsuited to the heat of the climate and the *villeggiatura;* there are old-fashioned gilded couches and chairs, with a modern lounge or two. There are several marble medallions and busts of merit—one, on what authority I cannot say, is declared to be an antique of Alexander the Great. The windows of this sala, facing northward, open on the sea. A narrow street, that leads among convents, winds downward toward the great landing and the bay. Toward the water there is a terrace—the great charm of the house; it is only fifty feet long, and perhaps half as wide; but it hangs over the blue Mediterranean, and, by its position and height, commands a view of three-fourths of the glorious objects of the region. It has a solid stone balustrade to protect it, massive and carved, with banisters as big as my body. This renders it perfectly safe, as you will understand when I tell you that, hearing an outcry from P—— the other day, I found him with his head fast between two of the latter, in a way that frightened me, as well as the youngster himself. It was like being imbedded in a rock. Immediately below the terrace runs a narrow beach, where our children delight to play, picking up shells of the Mediterranean—and more than shells: among the treasures gleaned here by them are fragments of ancient mosaics, small semitransparent and glass-like squares of different colors, chiefly blue, green, and red—relics, no doubt, of some ancient villa of the Romans, many of which once lined these shores. The foundations of some ancient edifice—said to have been a temple of Neptune—are still seen, at times, by us, as we look down upon the sea from the terrace; they lie wholly beneath the waves, and when the water is still and clear, may be distinctly traced. The sea limits our view from the terrace to the west. Ischia, dark, broken, and volcanic, but softened by vegetation and the tints of this luxurious atmosphere, rises at the farther entrance of the bay; then Procida, low, verdant, and peopled. The misty, abrupt bluff of Mysenum is the first land on the continent, with its memories of the Elysian fields, the port of the Roman galleys, and the 'Hundred Chambers.' The site of delicious Baiæ is pointed out by the huge pile of castle on the hillside, and by the ruined condition of all those surrounding objects of interest. Behind yon little island, called Nisida, the bark of St. Paul must have sailed, when he landed at Puteoli on his way to Rome. The Palace of Queen Joan, the grotto of Posilippo, the teeming city, and the bay, dotted with sails, follow. Then the eye passes over a broad expanse of rich level country, between Vesuvius and the heights of the town. This is the celebrated Felice Campagna, with Capua in its bosom ; and the misty background is a wall of broken rocks, which in form are not unlike our own palisades, but which, a grand range of the Apennines, have probably six or seven times their elevation.   These mountains, at times, are scarcely visible, just marking the outline of the view, in a sort of shadowy frame, and then again they come forth distinct, noble, and dark, the piles they really are.   The base of Vesuvius, a continued hamlet of white edifices, including palaces and cottages, with its cone for the background, follows ; and a pile of dingy earth, or ashes, marks the position of Pompeii.   There is a little room partitioned off from the terrace, which I use for writing, and where I can sit at the window, and see most of these objects.   The distance impairs the effect but little ; so great is the purity of the atmosphere, at times, that we may faintly hear the din of Naples, across the water."

*   *   *   *   *   *   *

" Our daily excursions under the cliffs are peculiarly Italian.   We cannot move until the day is drawing to a close ; but about four, the shadows of the rocks are thrown so far on the waters as to form a complete protection against the rays of a fierce sun ; and we glide along, sometimes with a boatman, but oftener by ourselves.

" We as much affect the inland walks, however, as this lazy navigation.   Our excursions are of two sorts—the 'donkey,' and the 'non-donkey.'   In the 'non-donkey,' we roam over the hills near the town, which are covered with fruit-trees, and intersected with narrow paths ; the kind and gentle peasants smiling as we pass, never offering rudeness of any kind.   The Capo di Monte, overlooking the landing of the town, is a favorite resting-spot in these walks.   The view of the beach, strewed with crafts of different sizes, including boats to the number of a hundred ; the domestic groups between them and the houses ; the children sporting in the sands ; the costumes and gay colors of the female dresses ; the nets spread to dry, and all the other little accessories of such a spot, that you can so readily imagine, make a perfect picture.   The men usually wear a shirt, and loose trowsers that reach to little below the knee, and they have a Phrygian cap, oftener red than any other color.

" The great number of beggars, that torment one like gnats, was at first a drawback to our pleasure.   It was no unusual thing to have dozens of them in chase.   We are now relieved of their assiduities, however ; and as the means of relief are characteristic, they may be worth knowing.   Walking one day on the terrace that overhangs the bay, I happened to cast my eye over the balustrade into the street, where there is a public seat—a long stone bench, immediately beneath our sala windows.   It was occupied, at the moment, by an old fellow with a lame leg, as fine an old mendicant as one shall see in a thousand. This man was enjoying himself, and keeping an eye on the gate, in expectation of our daily sortie. Seeing me, the beggar rose, and pulled off his cap. As I had no change I called a servant to bring me a *grano*. This little ceremony established a sort of intercourse between us. The next day the thing was repeated. As I usually wrote in the cabinet of a morning, and walked on the terrace at stated hours, my new acquaintance became very punctual; and there is such a pleasure in thinking you are making a fellow-creature comfortable for a day, at so cheap a rate, that I began to expect him. This lasted ten days, perhaps, when I found *two*, one fine morning, instead of the *one* I had known. Another *grano* was given, and the next day I had *three* visitors. These *three* swelled, like the men in buckram, and were soon a dozen. From that moment no one asked charity of us in our walks. We frequently met beggars; but they invariably drew modestly aside, permitting us to pass without question. We might have been a month getting up to the dozen; after which the ranks increased with singular rapidity. Seeing many strange faces, I inquired of Roberto whence they came; he told me that many were from villages five or six miles distant, it having been bruited that at noon, each day, all applicants were accommodated with a *grano* apiece by the *American admiral!* By this fact alone we may learn the extreme poverty and the value of money in this country. We went on recruiting, until I now daily review some forty or fifty *gaberlunzies*. As my time here is limited, I have determined to persevere; and the only precaution taken is to drive off those who do not seem worthy to be enrolled on a list so eminently mendicant. A new-comer from St. Agata, a village across the mountains, had the indiscretion, lately, as he got his *grano*, to wish me only a hundred years of life. 'A hundred years!' repeated the king of the gang; 'you blackguard, do you wish a signor, who gives you a *grano* every day, only a hundred years? Knock him down! away with him!' '*Mille anni, signor!* a thousand years; may you live a thousand years!' shouted the blunderer, amid some such tumult as one would see around a kettle of maccaroni in the streets of Naples, were its contents declared free. 'A thousand years, and *long* ones!'"

Among the many charming excursions made over the mountains, and along the shores of the sea, there was one which had an especial influence on the book last planned. The lovely plain of Sorrento forms part of the noble promontory which, projecting westward into the Mediterranean, divides the bay of Naples from the still broader gulf of Salerno. Toward Naples, this promontory bears several beautiful plains, or valleys, on its bosom, divided by different ridges; but to the southward rises a range of high mountains, dark and wild on

their southern face. "We had often explored these heights, and had often admired the loveliness of the view, overlooking both bays, and all their radiant scenery. On the present occasion we dismissed the donkeys at the highest point of the road, and prepared to make a descent on foot. The spot toward which we were descending, and in particular the path which leads to it, has great local celebrity, and that deservedly, among the lovers of the picturesque, under the name of the Scaricatojo, which signifies a place to discharge at, or a landing; and really it is one of the last places where one would expect to find a marine landing. The precipice is very high—many times higher than that of Sorrento, and almost as abrupt. We went down the face of the rock by a zigzag, half stairs, half path, or what —————— would call an *amphibious* road, wondering what there could be at the bottom but the sea! We found, however, a landing just large enough to receive a boat or two, and the site of a small house, in which lived several custom-house officers; for so extreme is the jealousy of the government in matters of revenue, that every point at which a boat can throw its crew ashore is closely watched. At the Scaricatojo we took a small boat, with a pair of oars, and launched upon the water, bound for Amalfi, some six or eight miles further up the gulf, toward Salerno. The cradle of old Neptune was lazily rocking, as it is ever known to do, gale or calm. Occasionally, as we rounded the cliffs, the send of the sea would carry us close in, giving us the appearance of one of the bubbles, though in fact there was no risk. I had often rowed under mountains in Switzerland; but not often so immediately beneath rocks of the same elevation; for some of these peaks between the Scaricatojo and Amalfi are said to be six thousand feet high. In Switzerland one sees cottages, even churches, convents, and chateaux, on the spurs of mountains, but I do not remember to have ever met with habitations of the same pretension so crowded on rocks so nearly perpendicular as was the case to-day, a few miles before we reached Amalfi. Some of the country-houses seemed absolutely clinging to the rocks; but no doubt there was ample room for safety, and even for gardens. Just before reaching the town, a convent appeared built into the cliffs, in a most picturesque manner, the wall of rock rising above the buildings, half-way to the clouds."

This excursion to the Scaricatojo, coming after other glimpses of the same nature, all uniting to prove the extreme watchfulness of these European governments on points connected with the customs, led to the idea of introducing a smuggling craft into the new book. The scene, however, was laid in American waters, on the shores of Staten Island, while the time chosen was the period shortly after the English had taken possession of New Amsterdam—the Dutch element of the colony figuring largely in the book. A great portion of the Water-Witch was very rapidly written, in the little study on the beautiful terrace of the Casa Tasso, in sight of Vesuvius. Mr. Cooper lingered on the cliffs of Sorrento until the latest moment possible; but when, at length, not only the dark tufa mountains, but the green orange groves of the plain also, were powdered with snow, it became necessary to abandon a dwelling so vast and open, in which but one fire could be kindled. Braziers, after the regular Italian fashion, albeit of elegant workmanship and great size, and filled with choice charcoal of olive-wood, were not to be endured by such a votary of the Yule-log. A most reluctant adieu to the beautiful plain of Sorrento was forced from the traveller by the chill tramontana, and a movement northward was made. The morning of the departure from Sorrento, the mendicant corps, to the number of ninety-six, paraded in the court of the Casa Tasso.

The winter of 1830 was passed at Rome. Travellers have written so many volumes about Rome—where every fallen column and time-worn stone has found a hundred pens to describe it—that the few passages allowed us shall be given rather to other ground. Laying no claim whatever to the honors of high scholarship in the field of antiquity, the American traveller was yet most deeply interested by the present aspect of the great city. So much has been given to the world, in connection with its ruins, by learned men, that even without profound erudition the intelligent traveller may easily comprehend and appreciate much which would otherwise be dark to him. It was the especial delight of the American author to ride for hours over the Campagna, lingering here about some ruin, now pausing a moment to enjoy an impressive view, or dismounting, perchance, to examine more closely a statue or fragment of ancient days. He seldom rode alone; ever social in feeling and tastes, he generally found some agreeable companion for the morning ride among the European friends who, at Rome, as at Florence, took pleasure in the cheerful American fireside. Among those who rode with him, there was none, perhaps, whose society gave the author more pleasure than that of the distinguished Polish poet Mickiewicz, a man whose appearance, manner, and conversation, were full of originality and genius, while the sad fate of his country enlisted Mr. Cooper's warmest sympathies in his behalf. The two writers were constantly roaming together over the Campagna, or amid the ruins of Rome.

The new work being nearly finished, the author was desirous of printing a small edition at Rome. The usual applications were made, and several Italian friends, gentlemen of influence, very kindly interested themselves in behalf of the American writer. Some encouragement was given at first; the nature and character of the book were explained, and the preliminary permission was granted. The Italian friends were quite sanguine as to the success of the little enterprise—and as such it was considered by them. The first chapters of the book were copied, and placed with all due form in the hands of the authorities —the official censor of the press. Days passed. No answer was received. Anxious to know the result, a renewed application was made to the gentlemen in authority. At length came a very polite, very dignified, but slightly severe communication; a particular passage on the second page of the book was referred to as wholly unfit for publication :

" It would seem that, as Nature has given its periods to the stages of animal life, it has also set limits to all moral and political ascendency. While the city of the Medici is receding from its crumbling walls, like the human form shrinking into the ' lean and slippered pantaloon,' the Queen of the Adriatic is sleeping on her muddy isles, and Rome itself is only to be traced by fallen temples and buried columns, the youthful vigor of America is fast covering the wilds of the West with the happiest fruits of human industry."

This passage was utterly condemned. It was declared to be false in principle —untrue, in fact. There were hints also that nothing at all similar could possibly be received. The whole book must be rigidly revised, this ominous opening having excited the gravest fears as to the nature of subsequent pages. Foreseeing constant annoyance from an attempt to carry out the plan, Mr. Cooper abandoned immediately all idea of printing at Rome. The MS. was finished, and laid aside for a few weeks, until in the spring the author left Rome, and commenced his migration northward. Passing along the shores of the Adriatic to Venice, he proceeded through the Tyrol to Munich. After a brief pause in the capital of Bavaria, where he much admired the works of art collected by the king, he moved onward to Dresden. Here some months were passed very pleasantly, in a cheerful apartment looking out upon the Alt-Market, and the quaint and busy show of homely German life, so different from that of Italy, seen there at the weekly fairs. The town was admired, its fine public grounds, noble river and bridge, and, above all, its gallery, worthy of Italy. Still there were regrets for the country south of the great mountains; the author frequently observing that every traveller should visit Germany before crossing the Alps. One object of his residence in Dresden was easily accomplished. The book, chiefly written in the Casa Tasso, was printed without the least difficulty—the obstacles which wrecked "The Water-Witch" on the Tiber, forming no impediment to her being safely launched on the broader waters of the Elbe. The book was published in America in 1830, by Messrs. Carey & Lea. This was rather a drama of the coast than a tale of the sea; the movements of the vessels being confined entirely to the waters connected with the harbor of New York. If less brilliant than "The Red Rover," the spirit and interest which pervade "The Water-Witch" are still very striking; there is an atmosphere of romance infused into the narrative, singularly different from the sober coloring of Puritan life in "The Wish-ton-Wish." It is strikingly picturesque also, more so than most works from the same pen. But on the other hand, there is less of high moral tone in the book than was usual with Mr. Cooper; it carries a carnival aspect about it; the shell was gay and brilliant, the kernel was less nourishing than usual.

FIRE!

THE Skimmer paused, for at that moment a fierce light glared upon the ocean, the ship, and all in it. The two seamen gazed at each other in silence, and both recoiled, as men recede before an unexpected and fearful attack. But a bright and wavering light, which rose out of the forward hatch of the vessel, explained all. At the same moment, the deep stillness which, since the bustle of making sail had ceased, pervaded the ship, was broken by the appalling cry of "Fire!"

The alarm which brings the blood in the swiftest current to a seaman's heart, was now heard in the depths of the vessel. The smothered sounds below, the advancing uproar, and the rush on deck, with the awful summons in the open air, succeeded each other with the rapidity of lightning. A dozen voices repeated the word, "The grenade!" proclaiming in a breath both the danger and the cause. But an instant before, the swelling canvas, the dusky spars, and the faint lines of the cordage, were only to be traced by the glimmering light of the stars; and now the whole hamper of the ship was the more conspicuous, from the obscure background against which it was drawn in distinct lines. The sight was fearfully beautiful;—beautiful, for it showed the symmetry and fine outlines of the vessel's rig, resembling the effect of a group of statuary seen by torch-light,—and fearful, since the dark void beyond seemed to declare their isolated and helpless state.

There was one breathless, eloquent moment, in which all were seen gazing at the grand spectacle in mute awe,—and then a voice rose, clear, distinct, and commanding, above the sullen sound of the torrent of fire, which was roaring among the avenues of the ship.

The Water Witch: "What means this," said Ludlow hastily –
"She, Claudio, that you wronged, look you restore,
– love her, Angelo,
I have confessed her, and I know her virtue."

"Call all hands to extinguish fire! Gentlemen, to your stations. Be cool, men; and be silent!"

There was a calmness and an authority in the tones of the young commander, that curbed the impetuous feelings of the startled crew. Accustomed to obedience, and trained to order, each man broke out of his trance, and eagerly commenced the discharge of his allotted duty. At that instant, an erect and unmoved form stood on the combings of the main-hatch. A hand was raised in the air, and the call, which came from the deep chest, was like that of one used to speak in the tempest.

"Where are my brigantines?" it said—"Come away there, my sea-dogs; wet the light sails, and follow!"

A group of grave and submissive mariners gathered about the "Skimmer of the Seas," at the sound of his voice. Glancing an eye over them, as if to scan their quality and number, he smiled, with a look in which high daring and practised self-command was blended with a constitutional *gaîté de cœur*.

"One deck, or two!"—he added; "what avails a plank, more or less, in an explosion?—Follow!"

The free-trader and his people disappeared in the interior of the ship. An interval of great and resolute exertion succeeded. Blankets, sails, and every thing which offered, and which promised to be of use, were wetted and cast upon the flames. The engine was brought to bear, and the ship was deluged with water. But the confined space, with the heat and smoke, rendered it impossible to penetrate to those parts of the vessel where the conflagration raged. The ardor of the men abated as hope lessened, and after half an hour of fruitless exertion, Ludlow saw, with pain, that his assistants began to yield to the inextinguishable principle of nature. The appearance of the Skimmer on deck, followed by all his people, destroyed hope, and every effort ceased as suddenly as it had commenced.

"Think of your wounded," whispered the free-trader, with a steadiness no danger could disturb. "We stand on a raging volcano!"

"I have ordered the gunner to drown the magazine."

"He was too late. The hold of the ship is a fiery furnace. I heard him fall among the store-rooms, and it surpassed the power of man to give the wretch succor. The grenade has fallen near some combustibles, and, painful as it is to part with a ship so loved, Ludlow, thou wilt meet the loss like a man! Think of thy wounded; my boats are still hanging at the stern."

Ludlow reluctantly, but firmly, gave the order to bear the wounded to the boats. This was an arduous and delicate duty. The smallest boy in the ship knew the whole extent of the danger, and that a moment, by the explosion of the powder, might precipitate them all into eternity. The deck forward was getting too hot to be endured, and there were places even in which the beams had given symptoms of yielding.

But the poop, elevated still above the fire, offered a momentary refuge. Thither all retired, while the weak and wounded were lowered, with the caution circumstances would permit, into the whale-boats of the smugglers.

Ludlow stood at one ladder and the free-trader at the other, in order to be certain that none proved recreant in so trying a moment. Near them were Alida, Seadrift, and the Alderman, with the attendants of the former.

It seemed an age, before this humane and tender duty was performed. At length the cry of "all in!" was uttered, in a manner to betray the extent of the self-command that had been necessary to effect it.

"Now, Alida, we may think of thee!" said Ludlow, turning to the spot occupied by the silent heiress.

"And you!" she said, hesitating to move.

"Duty demands that I should be the last——"

A sharp explosion beneath, and fragments of fire flying upward through a hatch, interrupted his words. Plunges into the sea, and a rush of the people to the boats, followed. All order and authority were completely lost, in the instinct of life. In vain did Ludlow call on his men to be cool, and to wait for those who were still above. His words were lost, in the uproar of clamorous voices. For a moment it seemed, however, as if the Skimmer of the Seas would overcome the confusion. Throwing himself on a ladder, he glided into the bows of one of the boats, and, holding by the ropes with a vigorous arm, he resisted the efforts of all the oars and boat-hooks, while he denounced destruction on him who dared to quit the ship. Had not the two crews been mingled, the high authority and determined mien of the free-trader would have prevailed; but while some were disposed to obey, others raised the cry of "throw the dealer in witchcraft into the sea!"—Boat-hooks were already pointed at his breast, and the horrors of the fearful moment were about to be increased by the violence of a mutinous contention, when a second explosion nerved the arms of the rowers to madness. With a common and desperate effort, they overcame all resistance. Swinging off upon the ladder, the furious seaman saw the boat glide from his grasp, and depart. The execration that was uttered, beneath the stern of the Coquette, was deep and powerful; but, in another moment, the Skimmer stood on the poop, calm and undejected, in the centre of the deserted group.

"The explosion of a few of the officers' pistols has frightened the miscreants," he said, cheerfully. "But hope is not yet lost!—they linger in the distance, and may return!"

The sight of the helpless party on the poop, and the consciousness of being less exposed themselves, had indeed arrested the progress of the fugitives. Still, selfishness predominated; and while most regretted their danger, none but the young and unheeded midshipmen, who were neither of an age nor rank to wield sufficient authority, proposed to return. There was little argument necessary to show that the perils increased at each moment; and finding that no other expedient remained, the gallant youths encouraged the men to pull toward the land, intending themselves to return instantly to the assistance of their commander and his friends. The oars dashed into the water again, and the retiring boats were soon lost to view in the body of darkness.

While the fire had been raging within, another element, without, had aided to lessen hope for those who were abandoned. The wind from the land had continued to rise, and, during the time lost in useless exertion, the ship had been permitted to run nearly before it. When hope was gone, the helm had been deserted, and as all the lower sails had been hauled up to avoid the flames, the vessel had drifted, many minutes, nearly dead to leeward. The mistaken youths, who had not attended to these circumstances, were already miles from that beach they hoped to reach so soon; and ere the boats had separated from the ship five minutes, they were hopelessly asunder. Ludlow had early thought of the expedient of stranding the vessel, as the means of saving her people; but his better knowledge of their position soon showed him the utter futility of the attempt.

Of the progress of the flames beneath, the mariners could only judge by circumstances. The Skimmer glanced his eye about him, on regaining the poop, and appeared to scan the amount and quality of the physical force that was still at their disposal. He saw that the Alderman, the faithful François, and two of his own seamen, with four of the petty officers of the ship, remained. The six latter, even in that moment of desperation, had calmly refused to desert their officers.

"The flames are in the state-rooms!" he whispered to Ludlow.

"No further aft, I think, than the berths of the midshipmen—else we should hear more pistols."

"True—they are fearful signals to let us know the progress of the fire!—our resource is a raft."

Ludlow looked as if he despaired of the means; but, concealing the discouraging fear, he answered cheerfully in the affirmative. The orders were instantly given, and all on board gave themselves to the task, heart and hand. The danger was one that admitted of no ordinary or half-conceived expedients; but, in such an emergency, it required all the readiness of their art, and even the greatness of that conception which is the property of genius. All distinctions of rank and authority had ceased, except as deference was paid to natural qualities and the intelligence of experience. Under such circumstances, the "Skimmer of the Seas" took the lead; and though Ludlow caught his ideas with professional quickness, it was the mind of the free-trader that controlled, throughout, the succeeding exertions of that fearful night.

The cheek of Alida was blanched to a deadly paleness; but there rested about the bright and wild eyes of Seadrift an expression of supernatural resolution.

When the crew abandoned the hope of extinguishing the flames, they had closed all the hatches, to retard the crisis as much as possible. Here and there, however, little torch-like lights were beginning to show themselves through the planks, and the whole deck, forward of the main-mast, was already in a critical and sinking state. One or two of the beams had failed, but, as yet, the form of the construction was preserved. Still, the seamen distrusted the treacherous footing, and, had the heat permitted the experiment, they would have shrunk from a risk which at any unexpected moment might commit them to the fiery furnace beneath.

The smoke ceased, and a clear, powerful light illuminated the ship to her trucks. In consequence of the care and exertions of her people, the sails and masts were yet untouched; and as the graceful canvas swelled with the breeze, it still urged the blazing hull through the water.

The forms of the Skimmer and his assistants were visible in the midst of the gallant gear, perched on the giddy yards. Seen by that light, with his peculiar attire, his firm and certain step, and his resolute air, the free-trader resembled some fancied sea-god, who, secure in his immortal immunities, had come to act his part in that awful but exciting trial of hardihood and skill. Seconded by the common men, he was employed in cutting the canvas from the yards. Sail after sail fell upon the deck, and in an incredibly short space of time, the whole of the fore-mast was naked to its spars and rigging.

In the mean time, Ludlow, assisted by the Alderman and François, had not been idle below. Passing forward between the empty ridge-ropes, lanyard after lanyard parted under the blows of their little boarding-axes. The mast now depended on the strength of the wood and the support of a single back-stay.

"Lay down!" shouted Ludlow. "All is gone aft, but this stay!"

The Skimmer leaped upon the firm rope, followed by all aloft, and, gliding downward, he was instantly in the hammock-cloths. A crash followed their descent, and an explosion, which caused the whole of the burning fabric to tremble to its centre, seemed to announce the end of all. Even the free-trader recoiled before the horrible din; but when he stood near Seadrift and the heiress again, there was cheerfulness in his tones, and a look of high and even of gay resolution in his firm countenance.

"The deck has failed forward," he said, "and our artillery is beginning to utter fearful signal-guns! Be of cheer! the magazine of a ship lies deep, and many sheathed bulkheads still protect us."

Another discharge from a heated gun, however, proclaimed the rapid progress of the flames. The fire broke out of the interior anew, and the fore-mast kindled.

"There must be an end of this!" said Alida, clasping her hands in a terror that could not be controlled. "Save yourselves, if possible, you who have strength and courage, and leave us to the mercy of Him whose eye is over all!"

"Go!" added Seadrift, whose sex could no longer be concealed. "Human courage can do no more; leave us to die."

The looks that were returned to these sad requests were melancholy but unmoved.

The Skimmer caught a rope, and still holding it in his hand, he descended to the quarter-deck, on which he at first trusted his weight with jealous caution. Then looking up, he smiled encouragingly, and said : " Where a gun still stands, there is no danger for the weight of a man !"

" It is our only resource," cried Ludlow, imitating his example. " On, my men, while the beams will still hold us."

In a moment all were on the quarter-deck, though the excessive heat rendered it impossible to remain stationary an instant. A gun on each side was run in, its tackles loosened, and its muzzle pointed toward the tottering, unsupported, but still upright fore-mast.

" Aim at the cleets !" said Ludlow to the Skimmer, who pointed one gun, while he did the same office at the other.

" Hold !" cried the latter. " Throw in shot—it is but the chance between a bursting gun and a lighted magazine !"

Additional balls were introduced into each piece, and then, with steady hands, the gallant mariners applied burning brands to the priming. The discharges were simultaneous, and, for an instant, volumes of smoke rolled along the deck, and seemed to triumph over the conflagration. The rending of wood was audible. It was followed by a sweeping noise in the air, and the fall of the fore-mast, with all its burden of spars, into the sea. The motion of the ship was instantly arrested, and, as the heavy timbers were still attached to the bowsprits by the forward stays, her head came to the wind, when the remaining topsails flapped, shivered, and took aback.

The vessel was now, for the first time during the fire, stationary. The common mariners profited by the circumstance, and, darting past the mounting flame along the bulwarks, they gained the topgallant-forecastle, which, though heated, was yet untouched. The Skimmer glanced an eye about him, and seizing Seadrift by the waist, as if the mimic seaman had been a child, he pushed forward between the ridge-ropes. Ludlow followed with Alida, and the others imitated their example in the best manner they could. All reached the head of the ship in safety; though Ludlow had been driven by the flames into the fore-channels, and thence nearly into the sea.

The petty officers were already on the floating spars, separating them from each other, cutting away the unnecessary weight of rigging, bringing the several parts of the wood in parallel lines, and lashing them anew. Ever and anon, these rapid movements were quickened by one of those fearful signals from the officers' berths, which, by announcing the progress of the flames beneath, betrayed their increasing proximity to the still slumbering volcano. The boats had been gone an hour, and yet it seemed, to all in the ship, but a minute. The conflagration had, for the last ten minutes, advanced with renewed fury ; and the whole of the confined flame, which had been so long pent in the depths of the vessel, now glared high in the open air.

"This heat can no longer be borne," said Ludlow ; "we must to our raft, for breath."

"To the raft, then!" returned the cheerful voice of the free-trader. " Haul in upon your fasts, men, and stand by to receive the precious freight."

The seamen obeyed, Alida and her companions were lowered safely to the place prepared for their reception. The fore-mast had gone over the side with all its spars aloft; for preparation had been made, before the fire commenced, to carry sail to the utmost, in order to escape the enemy. The skilful and active seamen, directed and aided by Ludlow and the Skimmer, had made a simple but happy disposition of those buoyant materials on which their all now depended. In settling in the water, the yards, still crossed, had happily fallen uppermost. The booms and all the light spars had been floated near the top, and laid across, reaching from the lower to the topsail-yard. A few light spars, stowed outboard, had been cut away and added to the number, and the whole were secured with the readiness and ingenuity of seamen. On the first alarm of fire, some of the crew had seized a few light articles that would float, and rushed to the head, as the place most remote from the magazine, in the blind hope of saving life by swimming. Most of these articles had been deserted, when the people were rallied to exertion by their officers. A couple of empty shot-boxes and a mess-chest were among them, and on the latter were seated the females, while the former served to keep their feet from the water. As the arrangement of the spars forced the principal mast entirely beneath the element, and the ship was so small as to need little artificial work in her masting, the port around the top, which contained the staging, was scarcely submerged. Although a ton in weight was added to the inherent gravity of the wood, still, as the latter was of the lightest description, and freed as much as possible of every thing that was unnecessary to the safety of those it supported, the spars floated sufficiently buoyant for the temporary security of the fugitives.

" Cut the fast!" said Ludlow, involuntarily starting at several explosions in the interior, which followed each other in quick succession, and which were succeeded by one which sent fragments of burning wood into the air. " Cut, and bear the raft off the ship!—God knows, we have need to be further asunder!"

" Cut not!" cried the half-frantic Seadrift; "my brave!—my devoted!—"

" Is safe," calmly said the Skimmer, appearing in the rattling of the main-rigging, which was still untouched by the fire. " Cut off all! I stay to brace the mizen-topsail more firmly back."

The duty was done, and for a moment the fine figure of the free-trader was seen standing on the edge of the burning ship, looking with regret at the glowing mass.

" 'Tis the end of a lovely craft !" he said, loud enough to be heard by those beneath. Then he appeared in the air, and sank into the sea. " The last signal was from the ward-room," added the dauntless and dexterous mariner, as he rose from the water, and, shaking the brine from his head, he took his place on the stage. " Would to God the wind would blow, for we have need of greater distance !"

The precaution the free-trader had taken, in adjusting the sails, was not without its use. Motion the raft had none, but as the topsails of the Coquette were still aback, the flaming mass, no longer arrested by the clogs in the water, began slowly to separate from the floating spars, though the tottering and half-burnt masts threatened at each moment to fall.

Never did moments seem so long as those which succeeded. Even the Skimmer and Ludlow watched, in speechless interest, the tardy movements of the ship. By little and little she receded; and, after ten minutes of intense expectation, the seamen, whose anxiety had increased as their exertions ended, began to breathe more freely. They were still fearfully near the dangerous fabric, but destruction from the explosion was no longer inevitable. The flames began to glide upward, and then the heavens appeared on fire, as one heated sail after another kindled and flared wildly in the breeze.

Still the stern of the vessel was entire. The body of the master was seated against the mizen-mast, and even the stern visage of the old seaman was distinctly visible, under the broad light of the conflagration. Ludlow gazed at it in melancholy, and for a time he ceased to think of his ship, while memory dwelt, in sadness, on those scenes of boyish happiness, and of professional pleasures, in which his ancient shipmate had so largely participated. The roar of a gun, whose stream of fire flashed nearly to their faces, and the sullen whistling of its shot, which crossed the raft, failed to awaken him from his trance.

"Stand firm to the mess-chest!" half-whispered the Skimmer, motioning to his companions to place themselves in attitudes to support the weaker of their party, while, with sedulous care, he braced his own athletic person in a manner to throw all of its weight and strength against the seat. "Stand firm, and be ready!"

Ludlow complied, though his eye scarce changed its direction. He saw the bright flame that was rising above the arm-chest, and he fancied that it came from the funeral pile of the young Dumont, whose fate, at that moment, he was almost disposed to envy. Then his look returned to the grim countenance of Trysail. At moments, it seemed as if the dead master spoke; and so strong did the illusion become, that our young sailor more than once bent forward to listen. While under this delusion, the body rose, with the arms stretched upward. The air was filled with a sheet of streaming fire, while the ocean and the heavens glowed with one glare of intense and fiery red. Notwithstanding the precaution of the "Skimmer of the Seas," the chest was driven from its place, and those by whom it was held were nearly precipitated into the water. A deep, heavy detonation proceeded, as it were, from the bosom of the sea, which, while it wounded the ear less than the sharp explosion that had just before issued from the gun, was audible at the distant capes of the Delaware. The body of Trysail sailed upward for fifty fathoms, in the centre of a flood of flame, and, describing a short curve, it came toward the raft, and cut the water within reach of the captain's arm. A sullen plunge of a gun followed, and proclaimed the tremendous power of the explosion; while a ponderous yard fell athwart a part of the raft, sweeping away the four petty officers of Ludlow, as if they had been dust driving before a gale. To increase the wild and fearful grandeur of the dissolution of the royal cruiser, one of the cannon emitted its fiery contents while sailing in the void.

The burning spars, the falling fragments, the blazing and scattered canvas and cordage, the glowing shot, and all the torn particles of the ship, were seen descending. Then followed the gurgling of water, as the ocean swallowed all that remained of the cruiser which had so long been the pride of the American seas. The fiery glow disappeared, and a gloom like that which succeeds the glare of vivid lightning, fell on the scene.

XI.

THE BRAVO.

It was during the choice days of an Italian spring, when the country was in all the luxuriant freshness of its beautiful vegetation, that the American author left Rome, after the winter passed there. "The first stopping-place was Città Castellana; a town which, like Sorrento, has a natural ditch, formed by the crevices of the volcanic rock. * * * A bridge carried us over the Tiber, and we began to ascend the Apennines. We breakfasted on their side, at a hamlet, and leaving the horses to bait, I walked ahead. It was a solitary, wild mountain road, though perfectly good; and I soon fell in company with a party of pilgrims on their return from Rome. These men carried the staves and scrips, and wore a species of light cloak, with the capes covered with scallop-shells. They were conversable, and any thing but solemn or wayworn. They had been attending some of the recent ceremonies at Rome. Passing through vineyards, olive-trees, and fruit-trees, we reached the little city of Terni, prettily placed on the river Nera, in the centre of a very fertile region. The falls are more than a league from the town, as we found to our cost, for we made the mistake of undertaking to walk to them. These celebrated falls are artificial, having been made by the Romans some centuries before Christ, by turning the course of a pretty little stream. They are reputed the finest waterfalls in Europe—a quarter of the world that, with many cascades, has few fine cataracts.   There is a "method in the madness" of these falls, however, which I think slightly impairs their beauty, though very beautiful they are.   Between Terni and Spoleto we had another reach of mountains and mountain scenery.   There are Roman remains at the latter town, which is prettily placed on a rocky and irregular hill, thought to be an extinct crater. A long aqueduct, called Roman in the books, has gothic arches.   There is also a high bridge across a valley, leading to a hermitage; a proof of what religious feeling can effect, even when ill-directed.   There is a poetry, notwithstanding, about these hermitages, which makes them pleasing objects to a traveller.   I may have seen, first and last, a hundred of them in Europe.   Very few are now tenanted.   Those of Italy are generally the finest in position.   The valley beyond Spoleto was very beautiful.   On one side there is a *côte*, as the French term it, and houses and churches were clinging to its sides, almost buried in fruit-trees. While trotting along pleasantly, beneath this teeming hill-side, we came to a small brick edifice, standing near the highway, while meadows were spreading themselves on our left, more like a country north than south of the Alps.   This is the temple of the Clitumnus, standing near the sources of that classical stream; it is now a Christian chapel.   You would be surprised to find these temples so small.   This is the twentieth I have seen, not much larger than a good-sized maize crib of a Yankee farmer.   The workmanship of this is neat, but plain; though its marbles may have shared the fate of so many despoiled amphitheatres, theatres, forums, and temples, found all over Italy.   It is with these ruins as with our departed friends; we never truly prize them until they are irretrievably lost.   Beyond Foligno the road was beautiful, carrying us over a spur of the Apennines called the Col Fiorito. It had at first a sort of camera-lucide wildness about it—a boldness that was quite striking, though in miniature after the Alps; and as the day drew toward a close, we rolled, by a gradual and almost imperceptible descent, into a lovely region, affluent in towns, villas, hamlets, and all other appliances of civilized life.   This was the March of Ancona.   The fine country continued next day; the Adriatic becoming visible, a silvery belt on the horizon, distant some eight or ten leagues. All the towns in this region appear to be built on isolated hills, that once admitted of being strongly fortified.   About three in the afternoon we came to the foot of another ridge, running at right angles to the coast of the Adriatic, from which it might be distant about a league.   The ascent was long, but not difficult. Having overcome it, we reached a village of a single long street, terminated by a pretty good square, and a large church, with other ecclesiastical edifices, tolerably spacious even for the States of the Church.   These were the village and shrine of Loretto.   *   *   *   The history of this shrine, as it is given in books sold on the spot, is as follows: The house, of course, is asserted to have been built in Naza-reth, where the Saviour was reared. In 1291, angels raised it from its foundations, and transported it to Dalmatia. There it remained four or five years, when angels again transferred it to Italy. It was first placed in a wood near Reconati, on the land of a lady named Lauretta, whence the present name of Loretto. The road to it being much infested by robbers, the angels again removed it a short distance, leaving it on the property of two brothers. These brothers quarrelled and fought about the profits of the pilgrims, who began to frequent the shrine in throngs, and both were killed; whereupon the house was finally removed to its present site. What is one to think of such a history? Do they who promulgate it believe it themselves; or is it a mere fiction invented to deceive? *Can* it be true? Certainly it might, as well as that this earth could be created, and continue to roll in its orbit. *Is* it true? That is far more than I should affirm, or even believe, supported by such incomplete proofs, accompanied with circumstances of so little dignity, and facts so little worthy of the display of Divine power. Do the people themselves, who frequent the shrine, believe it? Of that I should think there could be little doubt, as respects the majority. I cannot express to you the feelings with which I saw my fellow-creatures kneeling at this shrine, and manifesting every sign of a devout reliance on the truth of this extraordinary legend. The *Santa Casa*, or the shrine, stands near the centre of the church erected around it as an honorable canopy. The house has been cased externally with Carrara marble, wrought beautifully, after designs of Bramanti. The image of the Virgin, which is separated from those within the house by a grating, is said to be made of the cedar of Lebanon, and it wears a triple crown. It is gorgeously attired, bears a figure of the Child in one arm, and has the bronzed, mysterious countenance that is common to find about all the more re-nowned images of Mary. I cannot discover how far the Church of Rome, at this day, attaches importance to belief in the history of the *Santa Casa*. So far as I can discover, intelligent Catholics, especially those out of Italy, wish to overlook this shrine. Certainly I should say that the more enlightened Catholics, even here, regard the whole account with distrust; for he who really believes that God had made such a manifestation of His will, could scarcely hesitate about worshipping at the shrine, if he worshipped at all, since the building would not have been transferred by a miracle without a motive. It is fair, then, to suppose that few among the intelligent now put any faith in the tradition; for it is certain, few of that class continue to make pilgrimages to the spot. The time will probably come when shrine and legend will be abandoned together."

At Ancona the American traveller first stood on the shores of the Adriatic.

His sailor's instincts hurried him as usual to the port. Such, indeed, was ever his habit while travelling, especially after having been shut up for a time in some inland situation—his friends often smiling at the almost boyish eagerness with which he enjoyed the odor of rope, pitch, and tar, and the lively interest with which he would examine two or three rusty-looking craft, in some insignificant harbor. "The port of Ancona is formed by the bluff, against the side of which the town is principally built, aided by a mole of considerable extent. A part of this mole is very ancient, for there is an arch on it raised in honor of Trajan. Another arch farther advanced, shows that the Popes have greatly added to the work. The harbor is pretty safe, but it appears to want water. Here we first stood on the shores of the Adriatic. The color of this sea is less beautiful than that of the Mediterranean; its waters having a stronger resemblance to those of our own coast than to those of the neighboring sea. * * * On leaving Ancona next morning, we commenced a journey of some twenty or thirty leagues along the coast, within a mile or two of the Adriatic, and with constant views of the sea. The first stage was to Sinigaglia, a pretty little town, with a sort of port; for all the places along this shore have some pretensions to be considered seaports, although the coast is a low, sandy beach, almost without points, or bays, or headlands; a small creek has usually sufficed to commence a harbor, and by means of excavations, and perhaps a small mole at the outlet, to prevent the accumulation of sands by the south winds, the thing has usually been effected. We saw the remains of a considerable castle near La Cattolica. It was rather a striking structure of the sort for Italy; this country not being at all remarkable for buildings of that nature. One reads of moated castles among the Apennines in Mrs. Radcliffe's novels; but I have not yet seen an edifice in all Italy that would at all justify her descriptions. Such things may be, but none have lain in my path. With the exception of Castel Guelfo, near Modena, and the regular forts and citadels, I do not remember to have seen a moated building in the country. Some of the castles on the heights are gloriously picturesque, it is true, that of Ischia being a striking example. But, on the whole, I should say few parts of Europe have so little embellishment in this way as Italy. Most of the fortresses of the middle ages, in this part of the world, were made out of the ruins of Roman works. Walking ahead of the carriage this morning, we amused ourselves for several hours on the beach; the children gathering shells on the shores of the Adriatic. The scenery improved as we advanced, the mountains drawing nearer to the coast, and the foreground becoming undulating and verdant. We had the sea always on our right, and seized every good occasion for strolling on the banks."

After a brief pause at Bologna, and another at Ferrara, the American traveller

moved eastward toward Venice: "I cannot say that the villas on the Brente at all equalled my expectation. The monotony of a country as level as Holland, and the landscape gardening that is confined to flowers, and *allees*, and exotics, compare ill with the broader beauties of the Hudson, or the high finish of the lawns on the Thames. The road and river showed signs of a crowded population, and we were amused in that way, but scarcely in raptures with the sylvan charms of the scenery. A part of our road, however, ran athwart a common. At this point, looking across the bay on our right, a town appeared rising above the water, singularly resembling New York, as seen from the low lands near Powles' Hook. The presence of domes, and the absence of shipping, told of the difference, however. I need scarcely add, the town was Venice—the water, the intervening lagoons. We were soon afloat. Venice has recently been declared a free port; a line of wooden posts, with painted tops, encircles the whole town, perhaps a mile from the islands. After a pull of an hour, the boat entered a broad canal, lined with palaces and noble houses. Passing through this, we came to another, which seemed to be the main artery, smaller lateral canals communicating with it, at short distances. Across the lesser canals we could see, among dark ravines of houses, numberless narrow bridges trodden by foot-passengers. Over the larger channel, which was the Grand Canal, there was but one; this was of stone, covered with low buildings; its length was great; its single arch was high and pointed, though not Gothic. As we glided beneath it, vessels that might contend with the Adriatic appeared beyond, the water gradually widening. The bridge was the Rialto, the water the Canal Grande, and the opening beyond the port. We disembarked at the *Leone Bianco*. We were in the centre of a civilization entirely novel. On entering the inn we found ourselves in a large paved hall, only a step or two above the water, and in the corner lay a gondola. From the windows we saw boats gliding about in all directions, but no noise was heard beyond the plash of an oar—no sound of wheel or hoof rattling over pavement. The fall of a rope in the water might be heard a considerable distance. Every thing was strange—though a sailor, and accustomed to water, I had never seen a city afloat. It was now evening; but a fine moon was shedding its light on the scene, rendering it fairy-like. C—— and myself quitted the inn, for he told me there was something he wished me to see before I slept. Instead of taking a boat, we passed into the rear of the inn, and found ourselves in a street. I had believed until then that Venice had no streets. On the contrary, the whole town is intersected in this way; the bridges over the smaller canals serving as communication between these streets, which, however, are usually only eight or ten feet wide. That we followed was lined with shops, and it seemed a great thoroughfare. Its width varied from ten to twenty feet. Following this passage, in itself a novelty, we inclined a little to the right, passed beneath an arch, and issued into the great Square of St. Mark. No other scene in a town ever struck me with so much surprise and pleasure. Three sides of this large area were surrounded by palaces, with arcades; on the fourth stood a low ancient church, of an architecture so quaint—having oriental domes, and external ornaments so peculiar —that I felt as if transported to a scene in the Arabian Nights. The moon, with its mild delusive light, aided the deception, the forms rising beneath it still more fanciful and quaint. You will know, at once, this was the Church of St. Mark. Another area communicates with the first, extending from it, at right angles, to the bay. Two sides only of this square, which is called the Piazzetta, were built on; the side next the Piazza, or Great Square, and that toward the sea, being open. On one of the other sides of this area the line of palaces was continued, and on the other rose the celebrated Ducal residence. This was, if possible, still more oriental and quaint than the church, transferring the mind at once to the events of the East, and to the days of Venetian greatness and power. On every side were objects of interest. The two large columns near the sea were trophies of one conquest; the ranges of little columns on the church were trophies of a hundred more; the great stairway, at which we looked through an arch, were the 'Giant's Stairs,' and the openings in the walls above them the Lions' Mouths! This huge tower is the Campanile, which has stood there a thousand years rooted in mud; and those spars let into the pavement, in front of the church, are the very same on which the conquered standards of Cyprus, and Candia, and the Morea, were wont to flap. The noble group of horses in bronze, above the great door, is *the* group restored at last to its resting-place of centuries. Passing the front of the palace of the Doge, facing the sea, by an area that lines its noble exterior—which is the celebrated Broglio, where none but the noble once walked, and where intrigues were formerly so rife—we came to the bridge which spans the canal that girts the rear of church and palace. The covered gallery, thrown across this canal, at the height of a story or two above the ground, connecting the palace with the prisons opposite, was the Bridge of Sighs! By the side of the water-gate beneath were the submarine dungeons, and I had only to look toward the roof to imagine the position of the *Piombi*. Then there was the port, lighted by a soft moon, and dotted with vessels of quaint rigs, with the sea-breeze fanning the cheek—the distant Lido beyond—and dark, hearse-like gondolas, gliding in every direction. Certainly no other place ever struck my imagination so forcibly ; and never before did I experience so much pleasure, from novel objects, in so short a time. * * * I have set up my own gondola, and we have been regularly at work looking at sights for the last week. We have visited half the churches picture-hunting ; and a queer thing it is to draw up to a noble portico in your gondola, to land, and find yourself in one of the noblest edifices of Europe. The sea-breezes fan the shrine, and sometimes the spray and surf are leaping about them, as if they were rocks on a strand. St. Mark's is as quaint internally as its exterior. It is an odd jumble of magnificence, and of tastes that are almost barbarous. The imitation mosaics, in particular, are something like what one might expect to see at the court of the Incas. The pavement of this church is undulating, like low waves—a sort of sleeping ground-swell. C—— thinks it intentional, by way of marine poetry, to denote the habits of the people ; but I fancy it is more probably poetical justice, a reward for not driving home the piles. The effect is odd, for you almost fancy you are afloat, as you walk over the undulating surface. * * * Titian, Tintoretto, and Paul Veronese, are seen only in Venice ; good pictures of the first are certainly found elsewhere, but here you find him in a blaze of glory. You know the French carried away every work of art they could. They even attempted to remove fresco paintings—a desecration that merited the overthrow of their power. One great picture in Venice, however, escaped them ; it stood in a dark chapel, so completely covered with dust and smoke that no one attended to it. Within a few years, however, some artist had the curiosity to examine into the subject of this unknown altar-piece. The picture was taken down, and being thoroughly cleaned, it proved to be one of the most gorgeous Titians extant. Some think it his *chef-d'œuvre*. The subject is the Assumption, which he has treated in a manner very different from that of Murillo, all of whose virgins are in white, while this of Titian's is red.   The picture is now kept in the Academy, and imitations of it are seen on half the ornamental manufactures of Venice.   All the painters who create, or revive their art, commence with the head, which they paint well long before they can draw the form at all.   The works of the old masters exhibit heavenly countenances on spiders' legs, as any one knows who has ever seen a picture of Geotto.   A picture here by John of Bellino, the master of Titian, has much of this about it; but it is a gem.   I liked it better than any thing I saw, one fresco painting excepted.   Some of the carvings in the churches, in *high relief*, surpass any thing of the sort I have ever seen; and, in general, there is an affluence of ornaments and of works of merit that renders these edifices second to few besides those of Rome.   A monument by Canova, designed for Titian, has received a new destination, by being erected in honor of the sculptor himself; it is an extraordinary work, quite unique.   Besides the main group, there are detached figures, standing several feet aloof; and the effect of this work, which is beautifully chiselled out of spotless marble, beneath the gloomy arches of the church, is singularly dramatic and startling.   One is afraid to commend the conceit, and yet it is impossible not to admire the result.   Still I think the admirable thought of Nahl renders his humble Swiss tomb the sublimest thing of the kind in Europe."

The mind of the American author was very deeply impressed with these views of Venice—that very Nereid among earth's gorgeous capitals, whose whole existence for long ages has been a brilliant marvel; most picturesque among municipalities; most poetical among the daughters of commerce; most thrifty, most politic among the daughters of art; most oriental among the children of Christian Europe; most stately, most beautiful, most elegant, among the proud daughters of the sea; most gay and gorgeous, most heartless, most tyrannical Queen among earth's crowning cities.   Here was just the material to attract the imagination of one who was both seaman and poet at heart.   For weeks the traveller went gliding along the noiseless canals, in the easy gondola—reminding him in form and lightness, as he tells us, of the Indian canoe of bark; now stepping from the graceful and shadowy skiff into the portal of some sacred pile, and now leaping from the boat into the aquatic hall of some old palace, all marble to the eye, between water and sky. Until now he had had but a vague general idea of the history of Venice—of the spirit of her government. The first glow of enchantment, excited by the outward aspect of the beautiful city, had scarcely passed away, when he became very curious with regard to the details of the political history of that singular government. He procured several of the principal works on this subject, and read them with lively interest. An insight into the interior working of that political system filled him with indignation. Its heartless trifling with the most sacred rights of individuals, where these came in the remotest degree into conflict with the one great object—the aggrandisement of the power of San Marco—excited his horror. The singular blending of admiration for the outward aspect of the marvellous city, and indignation against the tyranny of the political system which for ages lived a life of crime in the secret chambers of its councils, soon led him to form the idea of writing a work in which views of both, as distinct and just as his pen could draw them, should be given to the reader. The tale called "The Bravo" was the result of this attempt—a romance especially political in its character, and among the very first, it is believed, of books of that class, since then become quite numerous. The task the author had allotted himself was thoroughly carried out; a fearful picture of the heartless cruelty of the Venetian oligarchy, in its secret workings, is laid before the reader—and yet it is a picture which, in no particular, surpasses, in the darkness of its coloring, what history has revealed on the same subject. It was the opinion of Mr. Cooper that an aristocracy must, from its very nature, be a dangerous form of government; as a general rule, he believed a prolonged aristocracy more likely to prove coldly selfish, tyrannical, and treacherous, than either a monarchy or a democracy. And this danger he believed to flow from its irresponsible character, united to the great strength to which such a form of government may attain by the concentration of talent, wealth, legislative and executive power, within a circle sufficiently narrow for the most decisive action, while, like all corporate bodies, it is lacking in the restraints of individual responsibility. Even in an absolute monarchy, he held that there would be greater hope, during an evil hour, from change of counsel, and from the responsibility inevitably connected with a single head. While, fearful as he knew the latent power for evil to be in a democracy, he believed it to be ever tempered by that latent power for good, flowing, in an educated Christian community, from its higher principles of natural justice and truth—which, in a system allowing full freedom of action, may at any moment, by constitutional means, be rendered more or less available. Such were his views on these subjects—views adopted early in life, and to which he always adhered. Venice appeared to him altogether the most striking picture of an oligarchy which Christendom has ever seen, and he endeavored to give the reader a sketch of the system as strong and as just as his pen could draw it.

"The Bravo" was written in Paris, after the author's return from Germany, and was published in America in the summer of 1831, by Messrs. Carey & Lea. In Europe the book was much liked, particularly in France and Germany; the distinctions it draws between a nominal republic, and the higher principle of a free Christian government, were considered just; while the power, the pathetic incidents of the narrative, the pure moral tone, and the beautiful poetical spirit pervading the whole work, were greatly admired. In America, on the contrary, the book was pronounced a decided failure, and was very generally decried. The author was repeatedly accused by his countrymen of having closely copied the novel of Lewis, bearing the title of "The Bravo of Venice," and also of imitating a drama taken from that romance, and called "Abellino." These criticisms and accusations may be scarcely remembered to-day, but it will be well, perhaps, simply to assert the fact that before writing this tale of Venice, Mr. Cooper had never read a line of either work—the romance of Lewis, or the drama referred to. "The Bravo" was as entirely original with him, in its general conception and in its details, as "The Prairie," or "The Pioneers."

"The Bravo" is connected with one of the most audacious and most extraordinary attempts at a literary forgery to be found on record. Mr. Fenimore Cooper had lain but a few weeks in his grave, in the parish church-yard of the little village which was his home, when there appeared in Paris, in a French periodical, a very flattering notice of his works, purporting to be written by an intimate personal friend, and openly bearing the signature of a literary man of some local reputation. Allusion was made to the years passed by the American author in France, and the writer, declaring himself to have been on terms of the closest intimacy with him, deplored in his death the decease of a friend—one who for years had been a constant companion—one who was in the habit of going almost daily with him to this *café* and that theatre. But it was not only a friend whom the French *littérateur* had lost; he had also been deprived of a constant correspondent—one whose letters filled his portfolio; a few of these letters he now lays before the public; a volume of them should shortly be published. While travelling in Italy, these letters had been particularly interesting. At Venice, however, where Mr. Cooper wrote his celebrated romance of "The Bravo," the *littérateur* was so fortunate as to have been his constant companion—having visited with him the spot marked for the death of Antonio, the jailer's dwelling in which Gelsomina had lived, and the Piombi, where the wretched father of Jacopo had died. Remarks made by Mr. Cooper on these occasions were given—extracts from several letters of his were printed. Would it have been thought possible that such an article, from the very first to the very last line, in so far as Mr. Fenimore Cooper was concerned, was a most daring fabrication? It was falsehood throughout. Mr. Cooper had no French friend bearing the name of this writer. It is probable that he never wrote one line to that person. It is very doubtful if that individual ever crossed his threshold. The cafés alluded to Mr. Cooper never frequented; rarely, indeed, did he go to a theatre. The only gentlemen who accompanied him to the prisons of Venice chanced to be Americans; he had, on those occasions, no European companion whatever. A brief denial of this most flagrant falsehood was published at the time, by the family of Mr. Cooper; allusion to it in these pages was scarcely needed, excepting as showing the audacity to which similar attempts may be carried.

The reader may remember the jailer's daughter, with the sweet Italian name of Gelsomina—one of the most delicately drawn of all the author's female characters—a creature to whom the imagination unconsciously gives one of those lovely Italian countenances painted by Raphael. The name was a real one, and possibly something in the general character may have been drawn from life. While the American family were living on the cliffs of Sorrento, a young peasant girl of the neighborhood became one of the household—half nurse, half play-fellow to the children of the party. She bore the sweet name of Gelsomina. Simple and child-like, yet singularly faithful to duty, Gelsomina was soon in high favor with great and small, and, in charge of the young flock, made one of every family party in the little excursions about the bay. On these occasions she was always in gay costume: a light blue silken jacket, garnished with gold lace; a flowery chintz skirt; her dark hair well garnished with long golden pins and bodkins; while a gold chain of manifold strands encircled her throat, and drops long and heavy hung from her ears. It chanced one afternoon that, after playing with her young charge among the orange groves of the garden, Gelsomina went for a draught of water, to the well in the court—that picturesque marble well. There, while bending over the curbstone, and drawing up the bucket, like Zara of Moorish fame, she dropped one of the long, heavy ear-rings into the water. Great was the lamentation of the simple creature! Warm was the sympathy of the household! The ear-rings, like most of the jewelry of the Italian peasants, were as much an heir-loom—a family treasure—as the diamonds of a Duchess.

But the well was very deep; the jewel was irretrievably lost.   Gelsomina's tears, like those of Moorish Zara, fell on the marble curbstone in vain:

> "The well is deep—far down they lie, beneath the cold blue water!
> My ear-rings! my ear-rings! oh! luckless, luckless well!"

The warm-hearted and faithful Gelsomina would gladly have followed her American friends to the northward; but there was a portly aunt, stately and dignified as a Roman matron, who would not trust her so far away from the orange groves of Sorrento.   When the hour of parting came, she received from her mistress a fine pair of new ear-rings, as a reward for her simple fidelity; and tears of gratitude and of sorrow fell upon the trinkets, as she kissed the hand of the giver.   Something of the simplicity, innocence, and fidelity of this young creature would seem to have been given, with her name, to the jailer's daughter, in "The Bravo."

The Bravo: Stretching his arms toward the stars,
he pronounced the absolution in a voice that was
"touched with pious fervor."

THE DEATH OF ANTONIO.

"O pescator! dell' onda,
Fi da lin;
O pescator! dell' onda.
Fi da lin;
Vien pescar in qua,
Colla bella tua barca,
Colla bella se ne va,
Fi da lin, lin, la—"

THE moon was at its height. Its rays fell in a flood on the swelling domes and massive roofs of Venice; while the margin of the town was brilliantly defined by the glittering bay. The natural and gorgeous setting was more than worthy of that picture of human magnificence; for, at that moment, rich as was the Queen of the Adriatic in her works of art, the grandeur of her public monuments, the number and splendor of her palaces, and most else that the ingenuity and ambition of man could attempt, she was but secondary in the glories of the hour.

Above was the firmament, gemmed with worlds, and sublime in immensity. Beneath lay the broad expanse of the Adriatic, endless to the eye, tranquil as the vault it reflected, and luminous with its borrowed light. Here and there a low island, reclaimed from the sea by the patient toil of a thousand years, dotted the lagunes, burdened with the group of some conventual dwellings, or picturesque with the modest roofs of a hamlet of the fishermen. Neither oar, nor song, nor laugh, nor flap of sail, nor jest of mariner, disturbed the stillness. All in the near view was clothed in midnight loveliness, and all in the distance bespoke the solemnity of nature at peace. The city and the lagunes, the gulf and the dreamy Alps, the interminable plain of Lombardy, and the blue void of heaven, lay alike, in a common and grand repose.

There suddenly appeared a gondola. It issued from among the watery channels of the town, and glided upon the vast bosom of the bay, noiseless as the fancied progress of a spirit.   A practised and nervous arm guided its movement, which was unceasing and rapid.   So swift, indeed, was the passage of the boat, as to denote pressing haste on the part of the solitary individual it contained.   It held the direction of the Adriatic, steering between one of the more southern outlets of the bay and the well-known island of St. Giorgio.   For half-an-hour the exertions of the gondolier were unrelaxed ; though his eye was often cast behind him, as if he distrusted pursuit ; and as often did he gaze ahead, betraying an anxious desire to reach some object that was yet invisible. When a wide reach of water lay between him and the town, however, he permitted his oar to rest, and he lent all his faculties to a keen and anxious search.

A small dark spot was discovered on the water still nearer to the sea.   The oar of the gondolier dashed the element behind him, and his boat again glided away, so far altering its course as to show that all indecision was now ended.   The darker spot was shortly beheld quivering in the rays of the moon, and it soon assumed the form and dimensions of a boat at anchor.   Again the gondolier ceased his efforts, and he leaned forward, gazing intently at this undefined object, as if he would aid his powers of sight by the sympathy of his other faculties.   Just then the notes of music came softly across the lagunes.   The voice was feeble even to trembling, but it had the sweetness of tone and the accuracy of execution which belong so peculiarly to Venice.   It was the solitary man, in the distant boat, indulging in the song of a fisherman.   The strains were sweet, and the intonations plaintive to melancholy.   The air was common to all who plied the oar in the canals, and familiar to the ear of the listener.   He waited until the close of a verse had died away, and then he answered with a strain of his own.   The alternate parts were thus maintained until the music ceased, by the two singing a final verse in chorus.

When the song was ended, the oar of the gondolier stirred the water again, and he was quickly by the other's side.

"Thou art busy with thy hook betimes, Antonio," said he who had just arrived, as he stepped into the boat of the old fisherman already so well known to the reader. "There are men that an interview with the Council of Three would have sent to their prayers and a sleepless bed."

"There is not a chapel in Venice, Jacopo, in which a sinner may so well lay bare his soul as in this.   I have been here on the empty lagunes, alone with God, having the gates of Paradise open before my eyes."

"One like thee hath no need of images to quicken his devotion."

"I see the image of my Saviour, Jacopo, in those bright stars, that moon, the blue heavens, the misty bank of mountain, the waters on which we float—ay, even in my own sinking form—as in all which has come from his wisdom and power.   I have prayed much since the moon has risen."

"And is habit so strong in thee, that thou thinkest of God and thy sins, whilst thou anglest?"

"The poor must toil, and the sinful must pray. My thoughts have dwelt so much of late on the boy, that I have forgotten to provide myself with food. If I fish later or earlier than common, 'tis because a man cannot live on grief."

"I have bethought me of thy situation, honest Antonio; here is that which will support life, and raise thy courage. See," added the Bravo, stretching forth an arm into his own gondola, from which he drew a basket, "here is bread from Dalmatia, wine of Lower Italy, and figs from the Levant; eat, then, and be of cheer."

The fisherman threw a wistful glance at the viands, for hunger was making powerful appeals to the weakness of nature, but his hand did not relinquish its hold of the line, with which he still continued to angle.

"And these are thy gifts, Jacopo?" he asked, in a voice that, spite of his resignation, betrayed the longings of appetite.

"Antonio, they are the offerings of one who respects thy courage, and honors thy nature."

"Bought with his earnings?"

"Can it be otherwise? I am no beggar, for the love of the saints, and few in Venice give unasked. Eat, then, without fear; seldom wilt thou be more welcome."

"Take them away, Jacopo, if thou lovest me. Do not tempt me beyond what I can bear."

"How! art thou commanded to a penance?" hastily exclaimed the other.

"Not so—not so. It is long since I have found leisure or heart for the confessional."

"Then why refuse the gift of a friend? Remember thy years and necessities."

"I cannot feed on the price of blood."

The hand of the Bravo was withdrawn, as if repelled by an electric touch. The action caused the rays of the moon to fall athwart his kindling eye, and firm as Antonio was in honesty and principle, he felt the blood creep into his heart, as he encountered the fierce and sudden glance of his companion. A long pause succeeded, during which the fisherman diligently plied his line, though utterly regardless of the object for which it had been cast.

"I have said it, Jacopo," he added at length; "and tongue of mine shall not belie the thought of my heart. Take away thy food, then, and forget all that is past; for what I have said hath not been said in scorn, but out of regard to my own soul. Thou knowest how I have sorrowed for the boy, but next to his loss I could mourn over thee—ay, more bitterly than over any other of the fallen!"

The hard breathing of the Bravo was audible, but still he spoke not.

"Jacopo," continued the anxious fisherman, "do not mistake me. The pity of the suffering and poor is not like the scorn of the rich and worldly. If I touch a sore, I do not bruise it with my heel. Thy present pain is better than the greatest of all thy former joys."

"Enough, old man," said the other, in a smothered voice; "thy words are forgotten. Eat without fear, for the offering is bought with earnings as pure as the gleanings of a mendicant friar."

"I will trust to the kindness of St. Anthony, and the fortune of my hook," simply returned Antonio. "'Tis common for us of the lagunes to go to a supperless bed; take away the basket, good Jacopo, and let us speak of other things."

The Bravo ceased to press his food upon the fisherman. Laying aside his basket he sat brooding over what had occurred.

"Hast thou come thus far for naught else, good Jacopo?" demanded the old man, willing to weaken the shock of his refusal.

The question appeared to restore Jacopo to a recollection of his errand. He stood erect, and looked about him, for more than a minute, with a keen eye and an entire intentness of purpose. The look in the direction of the city was longer and more earnest than those thrown toward the sea and the main, nor was it withdrawn until an involuntary start betrayed equally surprise and alarm.

"Is there not a boat here, in a line with the tower of the campanile?" he asked quickly, pointing toward the city.

"It so seems. It is early for my comrades to be abroad, but the draughts have not been heavy of late, and the revelry of yesterday drew many of our people from their toil. The patricians must eat, and the poor must labor, or both would die."

The Bravo slowly seated himself, and he looked with concern into the countenance of his companion.

"Art thou long here, Antonio?"

"But an hour. When they turned us away from the palace, thou knowest that I told thee of my necessities. There is not, in common, a more certain spot on the lagunes than this, and yet have I long played the line in vain. The trial of hunger is hard, but, like all other trials, it must be borne. I have prayed to my patron thrice, and sooner or later he will listen to my wants. Thou art used to the manners of these masked nobles, Jacopo; dost thou think them likely to hearken to reason? I hope I did the cause no wrong for want of breeding, but I spoke them fair and plainly as fathers and men with hearts."

"As senators they have none. Thou little understandest, Antonio, the distinctions of these patricians. In the gaiety of their palaces, and among the companions of their pleasures, none will speak you fairer of humanity and justice—aye, even of God! but when met to discuss what they call the interests of St. Mark, there is not a rock on the coldest peak of yonder Alps with less humanity, or a wolf among their valleys more heartless!"

"Thy words are strong, Jacopo—I would not do injustice even to those who have done me this wrong. The senators are men, and God has given all feelings and nature alike."

"The gift is then abused. Thou hast felt the want of thy daily assistant, fisherman, and thou hast sorrowed for thy child; for thee it is easy to enter into another's griefs; but the senators know nothing of suffering. Their children are not dragged to the galleys; their hopes are never destroyed by laws coming from hard taskmasters; nor are their tears shed for sons ruined by being made companions of the dregs of the republic. They will talk of public virtue and services to the state, but in their own cases they mean the virtue of renown, and services that bring with them honors and rewards. The wants of the state is their conscience, though they take heed those wants shall do themselves no harm."

"Jacopo, Providence itself hath made a difference in men. One is large, another small; one weak, another strong; one wise, another foolish. At what Providence hath done, we should not murmur!"

"Providence did not make the senate; 'tis an invention of man. Mark me, Antonio, thy language hath given offence, and thou art not safe in Venice. They will pardon all but complaints against their justice. That is too true to be forgiven."

"Can they wish to harm one who seeks his own child?"

"If thou wert great and respected, they would undermine thy fortune and character, ere thou should'st put their system in danger—as thou art weak and poor, they will do thee some direct injury, unless thou art moderate. Before all, I warn thee that their system must stand!"

"Will God suffer this?"

"We may not enter into his secrets," returned the Bravo, devoutly crossing himself. "Did his reign end with this world, there might be injustice in suffering the wicked to triumph, but, as it is, we—— Yon boat approaches fast! I little like its air and movements."

"They are not fishermen, truly, for there are many oars and a canopy!"

"It is a gondola of the state!" exclaimed Jacopo, rising and stepping into his own boat, which he cast loose from that of his companion, when he stood in evident doubt as to his future proceedings. "Antonio, we should do well to row away."

"Thy fears are natural," said the unmoved fisherman, "and 'tis a thousand pities that there is cause for them. There is yet time for one skilful as thou to outstrip the fleetest gondola on the canals."

"Quick, lift thy anchor, old man, and depart—my eye is sure—I know the boat."

"Poor Jacopo! what a curse is a tender conscience! Thou hast been kind to me in my need, and if prayers, from a sincere heart, can do thee service, thou shalt not want them."

"Antonio!" cried the other, causing his boat to whirl away, and then pausing an instant like a man undecided—"I can stay no longer—trust them not—they are false as fiends—there is no time to lose—I must away."

The fisherman murmured an ejaculation of pity, as he waved a hand in adieu.

"Holy St. Anthony watch over my own child, lest he come to some such miserable life!" he added, in an audible prayer. "There hath been good seed cast on a rock, in that youth, for a warmer or kinder heart is not in man. That one like Jacopo should live by striking the assassin's blow!"

The near approach of the strange gondola now attracted the whole attention of the old man. It came swiftly toward him, impelled by six strong oars, and his eye turned feverishly in the direction of the fugitive. Jacopo, with a readiness that necessity and long practice rendered nearly instinctive, had taken a direction which blended his wake in a line with one of those bright streaks that the moon drew on the water, and which, by dazzling the eye, effectually concealed the objects within its width. When the fisherman saw that the Bravo had disappeared, he smiled, and seemed at ease.

"Aye, let them come here," he said; "it will give Jacopo more time. I doubt not the poor fellow hath struck a blow, since quitting the palace, that the council will not forgive! The sight of gold hath been too strong, and he hath offended those who have so long borne with him. God forgive me, that I have had communion with such a man! but when the heart is heavy, the pity of even a dog will warm our feelings. Few care for me, now, or the friendship of such as he could never have been welcome."

Antonio ceased, for the gondola of the state came with a rushing noise to the side of his own boat, where it was suddenly stopped by a backward sweep of the oars. The water was still in ebullition, when a form passing into the gondola of the fisherman, the larger boat shot away again, to the distance of a few hundred feet, and remained at rest.

Antonio witnessed this movement in silent curiosity; but when he saw the gondoliers of the state lying on their oars, he glanced his eye again furtively in the direction of Jacopo, saw that all was safe, and faced his companion with confidence. The brightness of the moon enabled him to distinguish the dress and aspect of a bare-footed Carmelite. The latter seemed more confounded than his companion, by the rapidity of the movement, and the novelty of his situation. Notwithstanding his confusion, however, an evident look of wonder crossed his mortified features when he first beheld the humble condition, the thin and whitened locks, and the general air and bearing of the old man with whom he now found himself.

"Who art thou?" escaped him, in the impulse of surprise.

"Antonio of the Lagunes! A fisherman that owes much to St. Anthony, for favors little deserved."

"And why hath one like thee fallen beneath the senate's displeasure?"

"I am honest, and ready to do justice to others. If that offend the great, they are men more to be pitied than envied."

"The convicted are always more disposed to believe themselves unfortunate than guilty. The error is fatal, and it should be eradicated from the mind, lest it lead to death."

"Go tell this to the patricians. They have need of plain counsel, and a warning from the church."

"My son, there is pride, and anger, and a perverse heart in thy replies. The sins of the senators—and as they are men, they are not without spot—can in no manner whiten thine own. Though an unjust sentence should condemn one to punishment, it leaves the offences against God in their native deformity. Men may pity him who hath wrongfully undergone the anger of the world, but the church will only pronounce pardon on him who confesseth his errors, with a sincere admission of their magnitude."

"Have you come, father, to shrive a penitent?"

"Such is my errand. I lament the occasion, and if what I fear be true, still more must I regret that one so aged should have brought his devoted head beneath the arm of justice."

Antonio smiled, and again he bent his eyes along that dazzling streak of light, which had swallowed up the gondola and the person of the Bravo.

"Father," he said, when a long and earnest look was ended, "there can be little harm in speaking truth to one of thy holy office. They have told thee there was a criminal here in the lagunes, who hath provoked the anger of St. Mark?"

"Thou art right."

"It is not easy to know when St. Mark is pleased, or when he is not," continued Antonio, plying his line with indifference, "for the very man he now seeks has he long tolerated; aye, even in presence of the doge. The senate hath its reasons, which lie beyond the reach of the ignorant, but it would have been better for the soul of the poor youth, and more seemly for the republic, had it turned a discouraging countenance on his deeds from the first."

"Thou speakest of another!—thou art not, then, the criminal they seek?"

"I am a sinner, like all born of woman, reverend Carmelite, but my hand hath never held any other weapon than the good sword with which I struck the infidel. There was one lately here that, I grieve to add, cannot say this!"

"And he is gone?"

"Father, you have your eyes, and you can answer that question for yourself. He is gone; though he is not far; still is he beyond the reach of the swiftest gondola in Venice, praised be St. Mark!"

The Carmelite bowed his head, where he was seated, and his lips moved, either in prayer or in thanksgiving.

"Are you sorry, monk, that a sinner has escaped?"

"Son, I rejoice that this bitter office hath passed from me, while I mourn that there should be a spirit so depraved as to require it. Let us summon the servants of the republic, and inform them that their errand is useless."

"Be not of haste, good father. The night is gentle, and these hirelings sleep on their oars, like gulls on the lagunes. The youth will have more time for repentance, should he be undisturbed."

The Carmelite, who had arisen, instantly reseated himself, like one actuated by a strong impulse.

"I thought he had already been far beyond pursuit," he muttered, unconsciously apologizing for his apparent haste.

"He is over bold, and I fear he will row back to the canals, in which case you might meet nearer to the city—or there may be more gondolas of the state out—in short, father, thou wilt be more certain to escape hearing the confession of a Bravo, by listening to that of a fisherman who has long wanted an occasion to acknowledge his sins."

Men who ardently wish the same result, require few words to understand each other. The Carmelite took, intuitively, the meaning of his companion, and throwing back his cowl, a movement that exposed the countenance of Father Anselmo, he prepared to listen to the confession of the old man.

"Thou art a Christian; and one of thy years hath not to learn the state of mind that becometh a penitent," said the monk, when each was ready.

"I am a sinner, father; give me counsel and absolution, that I may have hope."

"Thy will be done—thy prayer is heard; approach and kneel."

Antonio, who had fastened his line to his seat, and disposed of his net with habitual care, now crossed himself devoutly, and took his station before the Carmelite. His acknowledgments of error then began. Much mental misery clothed the language and ideas of the fisherman with a dignity that his auditor had not been accustomed to find in men of his class. A spirit so long chastened by suffering had become elevated and noble. He related his hopes for the boy; the manner in which they had been blasted by the unjust and selfish policy of the state; of his different efforts to procure the release of his grandson; and his bold expedients at the regatta and the fancied nuptials with the Adriatic. When he had thus prepared the Carmelite to understand the origin of his sinful passions, which it was now his duty to expose, he spoke of those passions themselves, and of their influence on a mind that was ordinarily at peace with mankind. The tale was told simply, and without reserve, but in a manner to inspire respect, and to awaken powerful sympathy in him who heard it.

"And these feelings thou didst indulge against the honored and powerful of Venice?" demanded the monk, affecting a severity he could not feel.

"Before my God do I confess the sin! In bitterness of heart I cursed them; for to me they seemed men without feeling for the poor, and heartless as the marbles of their own palaces."

"Thou knowest that, to be forgiven, thou must forgive. Dost thou, at peace with all of earth, forget this wrong; and canst thou, in charity with thy fellows, pray to Him who died for the race, in behalf of those who have injured thee?"

Antonio bowed his head on his naked breast, and he seemed to commune with his soul.

"Father," he said, in a rebuked tone, "I hope I do."

"Thou must not trifle with thyself to thine own perdition. There is an eye in yon vault above us which pervades space, and which looks into the inmost secrets of the heart. Canst thou pardon the error of the patricians, in a contrite spirit for thine own sins?"

"Holy Maria, pray for them, as I now ask mercy in their behalf! Father, they are forgiven."

"Amen!"

The Carmelite arose and stood over the kneeling Antonio, with the whole of his benevolent countenance illuminated by the moon. Stretching his arms toward the stars, he pronounced the absolution, in a voice that was touched with pious fervor. The upward, expectant eye, with the withered lineaments of the fisherman, and the holy calm of the monk, formed a picture of resignation and hope, that angels would have loved to witness.

"Amen! amen!" exclaimed Antonio, as he arose, crossing himself; "St. Anthony and the Virgin aid me to keep these resolutions!"

"I will not forget thee, my son, in the offices of the holy church. Receive my benediction, that I may depart."

Antonio again bowed his knee, while the Carmelite firmly pronounced the words of peace. When this last office was performed, and a decent interval of mutual but silent prayer had passed, a signal was given to summon the gondola of the state. It came rowing down with great force, and was instantly at their side. Two men passed into the boat of Antonio, and with officious zeal assisted the monk to resume his place in that of the republic.

"Is the penitent shrived?" half whispered one, seemingly the superior of the two.

"Here is an error. He thou seekest has escaped. This aged man is a fisherman named Antonio, and one who cannot have gravely offended St. Mark. The Bravo hath passed toward the island of San Giorgio, and must be sought elsewhere."

The officer released the person of the monk, who passed quickly beneath the canopy, and he turned to cast a hasty glance at the features of the fisherman. The rubbing of a rope was audible, and the anchor of Antonio was lifted by a sudden jerk. A heavy plashing of the water followed, and the two boats shot away together, obedient to a violent effort of the crew. The gondola of the state exhibited its usual number of gondoliers bending to their toil, with its dark and hearse-like canopy, but that of the fisherman was empty!

The sweep of the oars and the plunge of the body of Antonio had been blended in a common wash of the surge. When the fisherman came to the surface, after his fall, he was alone in the centre of the vast but tranquil sheet of water. There might have been a glimmering of hope, as he arose from the darkness of the sea to the bright beauty of that moon-lit night. But the sleeping domes were too far for human strength, and the gondolas were sweeping madly toward the town. He turned, and swimming feebly, for hunger and previous exertion had undermined his strength, he bent his eye on the dark spot which he had constantly recognized as the boat of the Bravo.

Jacopo had not ceased to watch the interview with the utmost intentness of his faculties. Favored by position, he could see without being distinctly visible. He saw the Carmelite pronouncing the absolution, and he witnessed the approach of the larger boat. He heard a plunge heavier than that of falling oars, and he saw the gondola of Antonio towing away empty. The crew of the republic had scarcely swept the lagunes with their oar-blades before his own stirred the water.

" Jacopo !—Jacopo !" came fearfully and faintly to his ears.

The voice was known and the occasion thoroughly understood. The cry of distress was succeeded by the rush of the water, as it piled before the beak of the Bravo's gondola. The sound of the parted element was like the sighing of a breeze. Ripples and bubbles were left behind, as the driven scud floats past the stars, and all those muscles which had once before that day been so finely developed in the race of the gondoliers, were now expanded, seemingly in twofold volumes. Energy and skill were in every stroke, and the dark spot came down the streak of light like the swallow touching the water with its wing.

" Hither, Jacopo—thou steerest wide !"

The beak of the gondola turned, and the glaring eye of the Bravo caught a glimpse of the fisherman's head.

" Quickly, good Jacopo—I fail !"

The murmuring of the water again drowned the stifled words. The efforts of the oar were frenzied, and at each stroke the light gondola appeared to rise from its element.

" Jacopo—hither—dear Jacopo !"

" The mother of God aid thee, fisherman !—I come."

" Jacopo—the boy !—the boy !"

The water gurgled ; an arm was visible in the air, and it disappeared. The gondola drove upon the spot where the limb had just been visible, and a backward stroke, that caused the ashen blade to bend like a reed, laid the trembling boat motionless. The furious action threw the lagune into ebullition, but, when the foam subsided, it lay calm as the blue and peaceful vault it reflected.

" Antonio !" burst from the lips of the Bravo.

A frightful silence succeeded the call. There was neither answer nor human form.

Jacopo compressed the handle of his oar with fingers of iron, and his own breathing caused him to start. On every side he bent a frenzied eye, and on every side he beheld the profound repose of that treacherous element which is so terrible in its wrath. Like the human heart, it seemed to sympathize with the tranquil beauty of the midnight view; but, like the human heart, it kept its own fearful secrets.

XII.

THE HEADSMAN.

A SECOND excursion to Switzerland was made by the American author in the summer of 1832. The shores of the Lake of Geneva were on this occasion the selected goal:

"There lay the Leman, broad, blue, and tranquil, with its surface dotted by sails, or overshadowed by grand mountains; its shores varying from the impending precipice to the sloping and verdant lawn; the solemn, mysterious, and glen-like valley of the Rhone; the castles, towns, villages, hamlets, and towers, with all the smiling acclivities loaded with vines, villas, and churches; the remoter pastures, out of which rose the brown *châlets* like subdued *bas-reliefs*, and the background of *Dents*, peaks, and *glaciers*. Taking it all together, it is one of the most ravishing views of an earth that is only too lovely for its evil-minded tenants—a world that bears about it, in every lineament, the impression of its divine Creator!

"One of our friends used to tell an anecdote of the black servant of a visitor to Niagara, who could express his delight, on seeing the falls, in no other way than by peals of laughter; and—perhaps I ought to hesitate to confess it—I actually imitated the negro, as this glorious view broke suddenly upon me. Mine, however, was a laugh of triumph, for I discovered that it was still possible to awaken enthusiasm within me, by the sight of an admirable nature. Our first resolution was to pass a month in this beautiful region. Pointing to a building that stood a thousand feet below us, on a little grassy knoll, washed by the lake,

The Headsman: **The Travellers followed their leader
with more confidence, though blindly.**

and which had the quaint appearance of a tiny château of the middle ages, we claimed it at once as the very spot suited for the temporary residence of your scenery-hunters. Nothing could possibly suit us better; and we went down the descent amid vineyards and cottages, not building 'castles in the air,' but peopling one in a valley. That was to be the house, if it could be had for love or money—or if the thing, in other words, were practicable."

Unfortunately, the little château had degenerated into a mere coarse farm-house, scarcely habitable. "Finally, we were compelled to take refuge in a furnished house, *Mon Repos*, which stands quite near the lake, and in a retired corner of the place; and in less than twenty-four hours after entering Vevey, we had set up our household gods, and were to be reckoned among those who boiled their pot in the *commune*. One of the first measures, after taking possession of *Mon Repos*, was to secure a boat. This was soon done. Harbor, strictly speaking, Vevey has none, though it has the beginning of a mole, scarcely serving to shelter a skiff. The crafts in use on the lake are large, two-masted boats, having decks much broader than their true beam, and which carry most of their freight above-board. The sails are strictly neither latine nor lug, but sufficiently like the former to be picturesque, especially in the distance. These vessels are not required to make good weather, as they invariably run for the land when it blows, unless the wind happen to be fair, and sometimes even then. Nothing can be more primitive than the outfit of one of these barks, and yet they appear to meet the wants of the lake. * * * It is not easy to imagine a more charming acclivity than that which lies behind the town; the inclination is by no means so great as it is east or west, and admits of cultivation, and sites for hamlets, broken by inequalities and spacious natural terraces. I should think there is quite a league of this inclined plain in view from the town; it is covered with hamlets, châteaux, country houses, churches, and cottages, and in addition to its vineyards, of which there are many, it is highly beautiful from the verdure of its slopes, its orchards, and its groves of nut-trees. * * * We never tire of the Leman, but spend two or three hours every day in the boat. Sometimes we row in front of the town—which literally stands in the water in some places—musing on the quaint old walls, and listening to the lore of honest Jean Descloux, who moves two crooked oars as leisurely as a lady of the tropics utters words, but who has seen great events in his time. Sometimes even this lazy action is too much for the humor of the moment, and we are satisfied with drifting along the shore, for there is generally current enough to carry us the whole length of Vevey in half-an-hour. Occasionally we are tossed about like an egg-shell, the winds at a distance soon throwing this part of the sheet into commotion. Perhaps the greatest charm in the scenery of Vevey is the coast of Savoy; immediately opposite the town is a range of magnificent rocks, rising some four or five thousand feet above the surface of the water. In general these precipices are nearly perpendicular, though their surfaces are broken by huge ravines that may well be termed valleys. This is the region that impends over Meillerie, St. Gingoulph, and Evian—towns or hamlets that cling to the bases of the mountains, and form, of themselves, beautiful objects, from this side of the lake. The distance from Vevey to the opposite shore, agreeably to the authority of old John, our boatman, is about five miles, though the great purity of the atmosphere, and the height of the land, make it appear less. The summit of the rocks of Savoy are broken into the most fantastical forms, beautifully and clearly drawn, while they are quite irregular and without design. No description can give you an accurate idea of their beauty, for I know nothing else in nature to compare them to. As they lie nearly south of us, I cannot account for the unusual glow of the atmosphere beyond them, at every clear sunset, except from the reflection of the glaciers; Mont Blanc lying in that direction, at the distance of about fifty miles, though invisible. The effect of the outline of these rocks at, or after, sunset, relieved by a soft, golden sky, is not only one of the finest sights in Switzerland, but, in its way, it is just the most perfect spectacle I have ever beheld. It is not so apt to extort sudden admiration as the rosy tints and spectral hues of the High Alps at the same hour; but it wins on you, in the way the lovely shadows of the Apennines grow on the affections, and so far from tiring or becoming satisfied with their view, each successive evening would seem to bring greater delight than the last. You may get some idea of what I mean by imagining vast piles, outlined and drawn in a way that no art can equal, standing out huge, and dark, and grand, in high relief, blending sublimity with a bewitching softness, against a sky whose light is slowly passing from the glow of fiery gold to the mildest tints of evening. I scarcely know when this scene is most to be admired; when the rocks appear distinct and brown, showing their material, and the sky is burnished, or when the first are merely dark masses, on whose surface nothing is visible, and the void beyond is just pregnant with sufficient light to reveal their exquisite forms. Perhaps this is the perfection of the scene, for the gloom of the hour throws a noble mystery over all. No *dilettanti* were ever more punctual at the opening of the orchestra than we are punctual at this exhibition, which, very much like a fine and expressive harmony, grows upon us at each repetition. All this end of the lake—as we float lazily before the town, with the water like a mirror, the acclivity behind the town gradually darkening upward under the retiring light, the remote Alpine pastures just throwing out their *chalets*, the rocks of Savoy, the sublime and mysterious glen of the Rhone, with the glacier of Mont Velan in its depths, raising a white peak into the broad day long after evening has shadowed every object below—forms the most perfect natural picture I have ever beheld. You may easily imagine how greatly we enjoy all this. Jean and his boat have been put in requisition nearly every evening since our arrival, and the old fellow has dropped so readily into our humors, that his oars rise and fall in a way to produce a melancholy ripple, and little else. The sympathy between us is perfect, and I have almost fancied that his oars are growing daily more crooked and picturesque."

Gleaning, as all reading travellers do, many lesser historical details, which give something of a peculiar coloring to the annals of every town on old Europe's soil, Mr. Cooper's fancy was pleased with the account of a holiday festival, celebrated at Vevey in past ages, and still kept up, at intervals, by the good people of the borough. This is called the *Abbaye des Vignerons*—the great holiday of the vine-dressers—a gay and motley scene, partaking largely of the carnival spirit; blended, however, with something of the better feeling of the harvest-home. There were shepherds and shepherdesses, gaily costumed and garlanded, trooping onward with rustic dance and song—the last echoing many a wild sound heard amid Alpine pastures; there were your aproned gardeners, armed with rake and spade— their sweethearts bearing on the head baskets filled with fruits and flowers—all uniting in a dance, *à la ronde*, as they reached the principal point of the procession, singing, meanwhile, songs of their own; there were reapers, mowers, and gleaners, all in quaint and picturesque array, moving onward to rustic chant and pipe; there were your herdsmen and dairymaids, in Alpine costume, with blended garlands, from mount and meadow, timing their steps to horn and cowbell—singing in chorus the heart-stirring *Ranz des Vaches*, whose wild notes were first breathed amid Alpine echoes:

"Lé zermailli dè Colombetté
Dè bon matin, se san léhà—
  Ha, ah! Ha, ah!
    Liauba! Liauba!
    Por taria!

"Venidè toté
Bllantz et nairé
Rodz et motailé
Dzjouvan et etro
Dezò ou tzetiano
Io vo tario
Dezo ou triemblo
Io ïe triudzo,
    Liauba! Liauba!
    Por taria!"

"The cowherds of the Alps
At an early hour arose,
  Ha, ah! Ha, ah!
    Liauba! Liauba!
    In order to milk.

"Come all of you,
Black and white,
Red and dappled,
Old and young;
Under this oak
I will milk you;
Under this poplar
Let me press you.
    Liauba! Liauba!
    In order to milk!"

The concluding scene of the procession was always a rustic wedding; the bride being dowered—as was usual at many a great festival of olden time—by the lord and lady of the manor: the wedding-train, bride and groom, parents and friends, lord and lady, the wedding-gifts, the wardrobe and household gear—aye, the very broom and spindle, with a mimic cottage, all figuring in the long and quaint array.

This picturesque local festival the American author determined to introduce into a tale, whose scenes should be laid on the Lake of Geneva and the Pass of St. Bernard. The chief incident of the plot was taken from one of those oppressive laws of feudal times, which, from their inherent injustice, he held in abhorrence; in the canton of Berne, before the changes of the last century, the odious office of executioner, or headsman, was rendered obligatory upon one family, to be inherited, like a curse—not natural, but arbitrary—not for three or four generations only, but so long as that family should exist. Upon this fact the whole plot of the Swiss tale turns; the efforts of the hapless father and mother to save their innocent son from the life of ignominy impending over him by law, interwoven with other incidents connected with the holiday festival of the *Abbaye des Vignerons*, make up the pathetic and picturesque interest of the book. The opening pages of the narrative are given, the account of the festival itself being too long for insertion.

THE HEADSMAN.

THE year was in its fall, according to a poetical expression of our own, and the morning bright, as the fairest and swiftest bark that navigated the Leman lay at the quay of the ancient and historical town of Geneva, ready to depart for the country of Vaud. This vessel was called the Winkelried, in commemoration of Arnold of that name, who had so generously sacrificed life and hopes to the good of his country, and who deservedly ranks among the truest of those heroes of whom we have well-authenticated legends. She had been launched at the commencement of the summer, and still bore at the fore-top-mast-head a bunch of evergreens, profusely ornamented with knots and streamers of riband, the offerings of the patron's female friends, and the fancied gage of success. The use of steam, and the presence of unemployed seamen of various nations, in this idle season of the warlike, are slowly leading to innovations and improvements in the navigation of the lakes of Italy and Switzerland, it is true; but time, even at this hour, has done little toward changing the habits and opinions of those who ply on these inland waters for a subsistence. The Winkelried had the two low, diverging masts; the attenuated and picturesquely poised latine yards; the light, triangular sails; the sweeping and projecting gangways; the receding and falling stern; the high and peaked prow—with, in general, the classical and quaint air of those vessels that are seen in the older paintings and engravings. A gilded ball glittered on the summit of each mast—for no canvas was set higher than the slender and well-balanced yards—and it was above one of these that the wilted bush, with its gay appendages, trembled and fluttered in a fresh western wind. The hull was worthy of so much goodly apparel, being spacious, commodious, and, according to the wants of the navigation, of approved mould. The freight, which was sufficiently obvious— much the greatest part being piled on the ample deck—consisted of what our own watermen would term an assorted cargo.   It was, however, chiefly composed of those foreign luxuries—as they were then called, though use has now rendered them nearly indispensable to domestic economy—which were consumed, in singular moderation, by the more affluent of those who dwelt deeper among the mountains; and of the two principal products of the dairy; the latter being destined to a market in the less verdant countries of the south.   To these must be added the personal effects of an un- usual number of passengers, which were stowed on the top of the heavier part of the cargo, with an order and care that their value would scarcely seem to require.   The arrangement, however, was necessary to the convenience, and even to the security of the bark, having been made by the patron with a view to posting each individual by his particular wallet, in a manner to prevent confusion in the crowd, and to leave the crew space and opportunity to discharge the necessary duties of the navigation.

With a vessel stowed, sails ready to drop, the wind fair, and the day drawing on apace, the patron of the Winkelried, who was also her owner, felt a very natural wish to depart.   But an unlooked-for obstacle had just presented itself at the water-gate, where the officer charged with the duty of looking into the characters of all who went and came, was posted, and around whom some fifty representatives of half as many nations were now clustered in a clamorous throng, filling the air with a confusion of tongues that had some probable affinity to the noises which deranged the workmen of Babel.   It appeared, by parts of sentences, and broken remonstrances, equally ad- dressed to the patron, whose name was Baptiste, and to the guardian of the Genevese laws, a rumor was rife among these truculent travellers, that Balthazar, the headsman, or executioner, of the powerful and aristocratical canton of Berne, was about to be smuggled into their company by the cupidity of the former, contrary, not only to what was due to the feelings and rights of men of more creditable callings, but, as it was vehemently and plausibly insisted, to the very safety of those who were about to trust their fortunes to the vicissitudes of the elements.

Chance, and the ingenuity of Baptiste, had collected, on this occasion, as parti- colored and heterogeneous an assemblage of human passions, interests, dialects, wishes, and opinions, as any admirer of diversity of character could desire.   There were several small traders, some returning from adventures in Germany and France, and some bound southward, with their scanty stock of wares; a few poor scholars, bent on a literary pilgrimage to Rome; an artist or two, better provided with enthusiasm than with either knowledge or taste, journeying with poetical longings toward skies and tints of Italy; a *troupe* of street jugglers, who had been turning their Neapolitan buf- foonery to account among the duller and less sophisticated inhabitants of Swabia; divers lacqueys out of place; some six or eight capitalists who lived on their wits, and a nameless herd of that set which the French call bad " subjects;" a title that is just now, oddly enough, disputed between the dregs of society and a class that would fain become its exclusive leaders and lords.

These, with some slight qualifications that it is not yet necessary to particularize, composed that essential requisite of all fair representation—the majority. Those who remained were of a different caste. Near the noisy crowd of tossing heads and brandished arms in and around the gate, was a party containing the venerable and still fine figure of a man in the travelling dress of one of superior condition, and who did not need the testimony of the two or three liveried menials that stood near his person, to give an assurance of his belonging to the more fortunate of his fellow-creatures, as good and evil are usually estimated in calculating the chances of life. On his arm leaned a female, so young, and yet so lovely, as to cause regret in all who observed her fading color, the sweet but melancholy smile that occasionally lighted her mild and pleasing features at some of the more marked exuberances of folly among the crowd, and a form which, notwithstanding her lessened bloom, was nearly perfect. If these symptoms of delicate health did not prevent this fair girl from being amused at the volubility and arguments of the different orators, she oftener manifested apprehension at finding herself the companion of creatures so untrained, so violent, so exacting, and so grossly ignorant. A young man, wearing the roquelaure, and other similar appendages, of a Swiss in foreign military service, a character to excite neither observation nor comment in that age, stood at her elbow, answering the questions that from time to time were addressed to him by the others, in a manner to show he was an intimate acquaintance, though there were signs about his travelling equipage to prove he was not exactly of their ordinary society. Of all who were not immediately engaged in the boisterous discussion at the gate, this young soldier, who was commonly addressed by those near him as Monsieur Sigismund, was much the most interested in its progress. Though of herculean frame, and evidently of unusual physical force, he was singularly agitated. His cheek, which had not yet lost the freshness due to the mountain air, would, at times, become pale as that of the wilting flower near him; while at others, the blood rushed across his brow in a torrent that seemed to threaten a rupture of the starting vessels in which it so tumultuously flowed. Unless addressed, however, he said nothing; his distress gradually subsiding, until it was merely betrayed by the convulsive writhings of his fingers, which unconsciously grasped the hilt of his sword.

The uproar had now continued for some time: throats were getting sore, tongues clammy, voices hoarse, and words incoherent, when a sudden check was given to the useless clamor by an incident quite in unison with the disturbance itself. Two enormous dogs were in attendance hard by, apparently awaiting the movements of their respective masters, who were lost to view in the mass of heads and bodies that stopped the passage of the gate. One of these animals was covered with a short, thick coating of hair, whose prevailing color was a dingy yellow, but whose throat and legs, with most of the inferior parts of the body, were of a dull white. Nature, on the other hand, had given a dusky, brownish, shaggy dress to his rival, though his general hue was relieved by a few shades of a more decided black. As respects weight and force of body, the difference between the brutes was not very obvious; though perhaps it slightly inclined in favor of the former, who in length, if not in strength, of limb, however, had more manifestly the advantage.

It would much exceed the intelligence we have brought to this task to explain how far the instincts of the dogs sympathized in the savage passions of the human beings around them, or whether they were conscious that their masters had espoused opposite sides in the quarrel, and that it became them, as faithful esquires, to tilt together by way of supporting the honor of those they followed; but, after measuring each other for the usual period with the eye, they came violently together, body to body, in the manner of their species. The collision was fearful, and the struggle, being between two creatures of so great size and strength, of the fiercest kind. The roar resembled that of lions, effectually drowning the clamor of human voices. Every tongue was mute, and each head was turned in the direction of the combatants. The trembling girl recoiled with averted face, while the young man stepped eagerly forward to protect her, for the conflict was near the place they occupied; but powerful and active as was his frame, he hesitated about mingling in an affray so ferocious. At this critical moment, when it seemed that the furious brutes were on the point of tearing each other in pieces, the crowd was pushed violently open, and two men burst, side by side, out of the mass. One wore the black robes, the conical, Asiatic-looking, tufted cap, and the white belt of an Augustine monk; and the other had the attire of a man addicted to the seas, without, however, being so decidedly maritime as to leave his character a matter that was quite beyond dispute. The former was fair, ruddy, with an oval, happy face, of which internal peace and good-will to his fellows were the principal characteristics; while the latter had the swarthy hue, bold lineaments, and glittering eye of an Italian.

"Uberto!" said the monk, reproachfully, affecting the sort of offended manner that one would be apt to show to a more intelligent creature, willing, but at the same time afraid, to trust his person nearer to the furious conflict; "shame on thee, old Uberto! Hast forgotten thy schooling—hast no respect for thine own good name?"

On the other hand, the Italian did not stop to expostulate; but throwing himself with reckless hardihood on the dogs, by dint of kicks and blows, of which much the heaviest portion fell on the follower of the Augustine, he succeeded in separating the combatants.

"Ha, Nettuno!" he exclaimed, with the severity of one accustomed to exercise a stern and absolute authority, so soon as this daring exploit was achieved, and he had recovered a little of the breath lost in the violent exertion—"what dost mean? Canst find no better amusement than quarrelling with a dog of San Bernardo! Fie upon thee, foolish Nettuno! I am ashamed of thee, dog: thou, that hast discreetly navigated so many seas, to lose thy temper on a bit of fresh water!"

The dog, which was, in truth, no other than a noble animal of the well-known Newfoundland breed, hung his head, and made signs of contrition, by drawing nearer to his master, with a tail that swept the ground; while his late adversary quietly seated himself with a species of monastic dignity, looking from the speaker to his foe, as if endeavoring to comprehend the rebuke which his powerful and gallant antagonist took so meekly.

"Father," said the Italian, "our dogs are both too useful, in their several ways, and both of too good character to be enemies. I know Uberto of old, for the paths of St. Bernard and I are no strangers, and, if report does the animal no more than justice, he hath not been an idle cur among the snows."

"He hath been the instrument of saving seven Christians from death," answered the monk, beginning again to regard his mastiff with friendly looks, for at first there had been keen reproach and severe displeasure in his manner—"not to speak of the bodies that have been found by his activity, after the vital spark had fled."

"As for the latter, father, we can count little more in favor of the dog than a good intention. Valuing services on this scale, I might ere this have been the holy father himself, or at least a cardinal; but seven lives saved, for their owners to die quietly in their beds, and with opportunity to make their peace with Heaven, is no bad recommendation for a dog. Nettuno, here, is every way worthy to be the friend of old Uberto, for thirteen drowning men have I myself seen him draw from the greedy jaws of sharks and other monsters of deep water. What dost thou say, father; shall we make peace between the brutes?"

The Augustine expressed his readiness, as well as his desire, to aid in an effort so laudable, and by dint of commands and persuasion, the dogs, who were predisposed to peace from having had a mutual taste of the bitterness of war, and who now felt for each other the respect which courage and force are apt to create, were soon on the usual terms of animals of their kind that have no particular grounds for contention.

XIII.

THE MONIKINS.

ENJOYMENT of the humorous, a relish of the comical and ludicrous, were very strongly marked in Mr. Cooper's familiar life. At the table, by the fireside, his conversation was full of cheerful vivacity, of fun and pleasantry. He talked invariably with great freedom and fulness—often with an earnestness, a power, and an eloquence which riveted the attention of those about him. While touching upon some subject of a grave nature—especially when moral feeling was fully aroused—language, and manner, and countenance would appear severe and stern in the extreme. An hour later, perhaps, the same fine countenance would become beaming with kindliness, or glowing with merriment. He delighted in a humorous anecdote, in a witty remark. When, in the course of reading, any thing of this nature came in his way, he was never satisfied unless it was shared with others ; very frequently the laughable passage was carried immediately into the family circle, and read by him with infinite zest, and with a singularly hearty laugh—tears of merriment, meanwhile, rolling down his cheeks.

The idea of a satirical tale, in which the parts usually filled by men should be gravely carried out by monkeys, suggested itself to Mr. Cooper, while travelling in Europe. In the year 1835, the book was written, and published under the name of "The Monikins." The leading idea was certainly excellent ; two human

The Monikins: Dr. Reasono took a fid, and with its
end he traced all the desired objects with great readiness and skill.

beings, each particularly well sketched in his way—the English baronet, Sir John Goldencalf, and the Yankee skipper, Captain Noah Poke, of "Stunin'tun"—are made to travel in company through monkeyland, visiting regions which, under the names of Leaphigh, Leaplow, and Leapthrough, are intended to represent England, America, and France. There are pages full of wit, fun, the most clever satire, and strong truth. But, as a complete work, the book was scarcely successful; it was too long, the vein of irony was often too complicated, while the blending of the humorous story of Sir John and his lady-love, introduced to give the volumes something of the character of a regular novel, was clearly an error. The work was hastily written; had the author given himself time—which a task of this nature requires above all others; had he condensed his two volumes into one, rejected the love story, and thrown aside the more complicated passages of satire, the work would, no doubt, have come nearer to the idea he had conceived. But "The Monikins" is one of those books which prove that publishers may sometimes mistake their own interests. It would have been the author's wish to write a single volume, exclusively filled with his Monikin people—your Lord Chatterinos, your Lady Chatterissas, your Brigadiers Downright, your Judges, People's-Friends: something approaching to the regular novel in size and plot was required of him, in order to attract, if possible, the general reader. The attempt to combine both objects proved, as might have been foreseen, an error.

DR. REASONO AND HIS PARTY.

THE group which drew my attention was composed of six individuals, two of which were animals of the genus *homo*, or what is vulgarly termed *man;* and the remainder were of the order *primates*, and of the class *mammalia*, or what, in common parlance, are called *monkeys*.

The first were Savoyards, and may be generally described as being *unwashed, ragged*, and *carnivorous;* in color, *swarthy;* in lineaments and expression, *avaricious* and *shrewd;* and in appetites, *voracious*. The latter were of the common species, of the usual size, and of approved gravity. There were two of each sex; being very equally paired as to years and external advantages.

The monkeys were all habited with more or less of the ordinary attire of our modern European civilization; but peculiar care had been taken with the toilet of the senior of the two males. This individual had on the coat of a hussar—a cut that would have given a particular part of his body a more military *contour* than comported with his real character, were it not for a red petticoat, that was made shorter than common—less, however, with a view to show a pretty foot and ankle, than to leave the nether limbs at liberty to go through with certain extravagant efforts, which the Savoyards were unmercifully exacting from his natural agility. He wore a Spanish hat, decorated with a few bedraggled feathers; a white cockade, and a wooden sword. In addition to the latter, he carried in his hand a small broom.

Observing that my attention was strongly attracted to this party, the ill-favored Savoyards immediately commenced a series of experiments in saltation, with the sole view, beyond a question, to profit by my curiosity. The inoffensive victims of this act of brutal tyranny submitted with a patience worthy of the profoundest philosophy, meeting the wishes of their masters with a readiness and dexterity that was beyond all praise. One swept the earth, another leaped on the back of a dog, a third threw himself head-over-heels, again and again, without a murmur; and the fourth moved gracefully to and fro, like a young girl in a quadrille. All this might have passed without calling for particular remark (since, alas! the spectacle is only too common), were it not for certain eloquent appeals that were made to me, through the eyes, by the individual in the hussar jacket. His look was rarely averted from my face for a moment, and, in this way, a silent communion was soon established between us. I observed that his gravity was indomitable. Nothing could elicit a smile, or a change of countenance. Obedient to the whip of his brutal master, he never refused the required leap; for minutes at a time, his legs and petticoat described confused circles in the air, appearing to have taken a final leave of the earth; but, the effort ended, he invariably descended to the ground with a quiet dignity and composure, that showed how little the inward monkey partook of the antics of the outward animal. Drawing my companion a little aside, I ventured to suggest a few thoughts to him on the subject.

"Really, Captain Poke, it appears to me there is great injustice in the treatment of these poor creatures!" I said. "What right have these two foul-looking black-guards to seize upon beings much more interesting to the eye, and, I dare say, far more intellectual, than themselves, and cause them to throw their legs about in this extravagant manner, under the penalty of stripes, and without regard to their feelings, or to their convenience? I say, sir, the measure appears to me to be intolerably oppressive, and it calls for prompt redress."

"King!"

"King or subject, it does not alter the moral deformity of the act. What have these innocent beings done, that they should be subjected to this disgrace? Are they not flesh and blood, like ourselves—do they not approach nearer to our form, and, for aught we know to the contrary, to our reason, than any other animal? and is it tolerable that our nearest imitations, our very cousins, should be thus dealt by? Are they dogs, that they are treated like dogs?"

"Why, to my notion, Sir John, there isn't a dog on 'arth that can take such a summerset. Their flapjacks are quite extraor'nary!"

"Yes, sir, and more than extraordinary—they are oppressive. Place yourself, Mr. Poke, for a single instant, in the situation of one of these persons; fancy that you had a hussar jacket squeezed upon your brawny shoulders, a petticoat placed over your lower extremities, a Spanish hat with bedraggled feathers set upon your head, a wooden sword stuck at your side, and a broom put into your hand; and that these two Savoyards were to menace you with stripes unless you consented to throw summersets for the amusement of strangers—I only ask you to make the case your own, sir, and then say what course you would take, and what you would do?"

"I would lick both of these young blackguards, Sir John, without remorse, break the sword and the broom over their heads, kick their sensibilities till they couldn't see, and take my course for Stunin'tun, where I belong."

"Yes, sir, this might do with the Savoyards, who are young and feeble"—

"'Twouldn't alter the case much, if two of these Frenchmen were in their places," put in the Captain, glaring wolfishly about him. "To be plain with you, Sir John Goldencalf, being human, I'd submit to no such monkey tricks."

"Do not use the term reproachfully, Mr. Poke, I entreat of you. We call these animals monkeys, it is true; but we do not know what they call themselves. Man is merely an animal, and you must very well know"—

"Harkee, Sir John," interrupted the Captain, "I'm no botanist, and do not pretend to more schooling than a sealer has need of for finding his way about the 'arth; but, as for a man's being an animal, I just wish to ask you, now, if, in your judgment, a hog is also an animal?"

"Beyond a doubt—and fleas, and toads, and sea-serpents, and lizards, and water-devils—we are all neither more nor less than animals."

"Well, if a hog is an animal, I am willing to allow the relationship; for, in the course of my experunce, which is not small, I have met with men that you might have mistaken for hogs, in every thing but the bristles, the snout, and the tail. I'll never deny what I've seen with my own eyes, though I suffer for it; and therefore I admit that hogs being animals, it is more than likely that some men must be animals too."

"We call these interesting beings monkeys; but how do we know that they do not return the compliment, and call us, in their own particular dialect, something quite as offensive. It would become our species to manifest a more equitable and philosophi-cal spirit, and to consider these interesting strangers as an unfortunate family which has fallen into the hands of brutes, and which is, in every way, entitled to our com-miseration and our active interference. Hitherto, I have never sufficiently stimulated my sympathies for the animal world, by any investment in quadrupeds; but it is my intention to write to-morrow to my English agent to purchase a pack of hounds and a suitable stud of horses; and by way of quickening so laudable a resolution, I shall forthwith make propositions to the Savoyards for the speedy emancipation of this family of amiable foreigners. The slave-trade is an innocent pastime, compared to the cruel oppression that the gentleman in the Spanish hat, in particular, is compelled to endure."

"King!"

"He may be a king, sure enough, in his own country, Captain Poke; a fact that would add tenfold agony to his unmerited sufferings."

Hereupon I proceeded, without more ado, to open a negotiation with the Savoyards.

The judicious application of a few Napoleons soon brought about a happy understanding between the contracting parties, when the Savoyards transferred to my hands the strings which confined their vassals, as the formal and usual acknowledgment of the right of ownership. Committing the three others to the keeping of Mr. Poke, I led the individual in the hussar-jacket a little on one side; and, raising my hat, to show that I was superior to the vulgar feeling of feudal superiority, I addressed him, briefly, in the following words:

"Although I have ostensibly bought the right which these Savoyards professed to have in your persons and services, I seize an early occasion to inform you that, virtually, you are now free. As we are among a people accustomed to see your race in subjection, however, it may not be prudent to proclaim the nature of the present transaction, lest there might be some further conspiracies against your natural rights. We will retire to my hotel, forthwith, therefore, where your future happiness shall be the subject of our more mature, and of our united deliberations."

The respectable stranger in the hussar-jacket heard me with inimitable gravity and self-command, until, in the warmth of feeling, I raised an arm in earnest gesticulation, when, most probably overcome by the emotions of delight that were naturally awakened in his bosom by this sudden change of fortune, he threw three somersets—or flapjacks, as Captain Poke had quaintly designated his evolutions—in so rapid a succession, as to render it, for a moment, a matter of doubt whether nature had placed his head or his heels uppermost.

Making a sign for Captain Poke to follow, I now took my way directly to the Rue de Rivoli. We were attended by a constantly increasing crowd, until the gate of the hotel was fairly entered; and glad was I to see my charge safely housed, for there were abundant indications of another design upon their rights, in the taunts and ridicule of the living mass that rolled up, as it were, upon our heels.

*   *   *   *   *   *   *   *   *   *

"How, sir? are you not, then, of the same family as all the other monkeys that we see hopping and skipping about the streets?"

"No more, sir, than you are of the same family as the flat-nosed, thick-lipped, low-browed, ink-skinned negro, or the squalid, passionless, brutalized Esquimaux. I have said that nature delights in vagaries; and all these are no more than some of her mystifications. Of this class is the elephant, who, while verging nearest to pure materialism, makes a deceptive parade of the quality he is fast losing. Instances of this species of playing trumps, if I may so express it, are common in all classes of beings. How often, for instance, do men, just as they are about to fail, make a parade of wealth; women seem obdurate an hour before they capitulate; and diplomatists call Heaven to be a witness of their resolutions to the contrary, the day before they sign and seal? In the case of the elephant, however, there is a slight exception to the general rule, which is founded on an extraordinary struggle between mind and matter, the former making an effort that is unusual, and which may be said to form an exception to the ordinary warfare between these two principles, as it is commonly conducted in the retrogressive class of animals. The most infallible sign of the triumph of mind over matter is in the development of the tail"—

"King!"

"Of the tail, Dr. Reasono?"

"By all means, sir; that seat of reason, the tail! Pray, Sir John, what other portion of our frames did you imagine was indicative of intellect?"

"Among men, Dr. Reasono, it is commonly thought the head is the more honorable member, and, of late, we have made analytical maps of this part of our physical formation, by which it is pretended to know the breadth and length of a moral quality, no less than its boundaries."

"You have made the best use of your materials, such as they were, and I dare say the map in question, all things considered, is a very clever performance. But in the complication and abstruseness of this very moral chart (one of which I perceive standing on your mantel-piece), you may learn the confusion which still reigns over the human intellect. Now, in regarding us, you can understand the very converse of your dilemma. How much easier, for instance, it is to take a yard-stick, and, by a simple admeasurement of a tail, come to a sound, obvious, and incontrovertible conclusion as to the extent of the intellect of the specimen, than by the complicated, contradictory, self-balancing, and questionable process to which you are reduced! Were there only this fact, it would abundantly establish the higher moral condition of the monikin race, as it is compared with that of man."

"Dr. Reasono, am I to understand that the monikin family seriously entertain a position so extravagant as this: that a monkey is a creature more intellectual and more highly civilized than man?"

"Seriously, good Sir John! Why, you are the first respectable person it has been my fortune to meet, who has even affected to doubt the fact. It is well known that both belong to the *improvable* class of animals, and that monkeys, as you are pleased to term us, were once men, with all their passions, weaknesses, inconsistencies, modes of philosophy, unsound ethics, frailties, incongruities, and subserviency to matter; that they passed into the monikin state by degrees; and that large divisions of them are constantly evaporating into the immaterial world, completely spiritualized, and free from the dross of flesh. I do not mean in what is called death—for that is no more than an occasional deposit of matter, to be resumed in a new aspect, and with a nearer approach to the grand results (whether of the *improvable* or of the *retrogressive* classes)—but those final mutations which transfer us to another planet, to enjoy a higher state of being, and leaving us always on the high road toward final excellence."

"All this is very ingenious, sir; but, before you can persuade me into the belief that man is an animal inferior to a monkey, Dr. Reasono, you will allow me to say that you must prove it."

"Aye, aye; or me either," put in Captain Poke, waspishly.

"Were I to cite my proofs, gentlemen," continued the philosopher, whose spirit appeared to be much less moved by our doubts than ours were by his position—"I should, in the first place, refer you to history. All the monikin writers are agreed in recording the gradual translation of the species from the human family"—

"This may do very well, sir, for the latitude of Leaphigh, but permit me to say that no human historian, from Moses down to Buffon, has ever taken such a view of our respective races. There is not a word in any of all these writers on the subject."

"How should there be, sir? History is not a prediction, but a record of the past. Their silence is so much negative proof in our favor. Does Tacitus, for instance, speak of the French Revolution? Is not Herodotus silent on the subject of the independence of the American continent? Or do any of the Greek and Roman writers give us the annals of Stunin'tun—a city whose foundations were most probably laid some time after the commencement of the Christian era? It is morally impossible that men or monikins can faithfully relate events that have never happened; and, as it has never yet happened to any man, who is still a man, to be translated to the monikin state of being, it follows, as a necessary consequence, that he can know nothing about it. If you want historical proofs, therefore, of what I say, you must search the monikin annals for the evidence. There it is to be found, with an infinity of curious details; and I trust the time is not far distant, when I shall have great pleasure in pointing out to you some of the most approved chapters of our best writers on this subject. But we are not confined to the testimony of history, in establishing our condition to be of the secondary formation. The internal evidence is triumphant: we appeal to our simplicity, our philosophy, the state of the arts among us; in short, to all those concurrent proofs which are dependent on the highest possible state of civilization. In addition to this, we have the infallible testimony which is to be derived from the development of our tails. Our system of caudology is, in itself, a triumphant proof of the high improvement of the monikin reason."

"Do I comprehend you aright, Dr. Reasono, when I understand your system of caudology—or tailology, to render it into the vernacular—to dogmatize on the possibility that the seat of reason in a man, which to-day is certainly in his brains, can ever descend into a tail?"

"If you deem development, improvement, and simplification, a descent, beyond a question, sir. But your figure is a bad one, Sir John; for ocular demonstration is before you that a monikin can carry his tail as high as a man can possibly carry his head. Our species, in this sense, is morally nicked; and it costs us no effort to be on a level with human kings. We hold, with you, that the brain is the seat of reason while the animal is in what we call the human probation, but that it is a reason undeveloped, imperfect, and confused; cased, as it were, in an envelope unsuited to its functions; but that, as it gradually oozes out of this straitened receptacle, toward the base of the animal, it acquires solidity, lucidity, and, finally, by elongation and development, point. If you examine the human brain, you will find it, though capable of being stretched to a great length, compressed in a diminutive compass, involved and snarled; whereas the same physical portion of the genus gets simplicity, a beginning and an end, a directness and consecutiveness that are necessary to logic, and, as has just been mentioned, a point, in the monikin seat of reason, which, by all analogy, go to prove the superiority of the animal possessing advantages so great."

"Nay, sir, if you come to analogies, they will be found to prove more than you may wish. In vegetation, for instance, saps ascend for the purposes of fructification and usefulness; and, reasoning from the analogies of the vegetable world, it is far more probable that tails have ascended into brains, than that brains have descended into tails; and, consequently, that men are much more likely to be an improvement on monkeys, than monkeys an improvement on men."

I spoke with warmth, I know; for the doctrine of Dr. Reasono was new to me; and, by this time, my *esprit de corps* had pretty effectually blinded reflection.

"You gave him a red-hot shot that time, Sir John," whispered Captain Poke at my elbow; "now, if you are so disposed, I will wring the necks of all these little blackguards, and throw them out of the window."

I immediately intimated that any display of brute force would militate directly against our cause; as the object, just at that moment, was to be as immaterial as possible.

"Well, well, manage it in your own way, Sir John, and I'm quite as immaterial as you can wish; but should these cunning varments ra'ally get the better of us in the argument, I shall never dare look at Miss Poke, or show my face ag'in in Stunin'tun."

This little aside was secretly conducted, while Dr. Reasono was drinking a glass of *eau sucrée;* but he soon returned to the subject, with the dignified gravity that never forsook him.

"Your remark touching saps has the usual savor of human ingenuity, blended, however, with the proverbial short-sightedness of the species. It is very true that saps ascend for the purposes of fructification; but what is this fructification to which you allude? It is no more than a false demonstration of the energies of the plant. For all the purposes of growth, life, durability, and the final conversion of the vegetable matter into an element, the root is the seat of power and authority; and, in particular, the tap-root above, or rather below, all others. This tap-root may be termed the tail of vegetation. You may pluck fruits with impunity—nay, you may even top all the branches, and the tree shall survive; but, put the axe to the root, and the pride of the forest falls!"

All this was too evidently true to be denied, and I felt worried and badgered; for no man likes to be beaten in a discussion of this sort, and more especially by a monkey. I bethought me of the elephant, and determined to make one more thrust, by the aid of his powerful tusks, before I gave up the point.

"I am inclined to think, Dr. Reasono," I put in as soon as possible, "that your *savans* have not been very happy in illustrating their theory by means of the elephant. This animal, besides being a mass of flesh, is too well provided with intellect to be passed off for a dunce; and he not only has *one*, but he might almost be said to be provided with *two* tails."

"That has been his chief misfortune, sir. Matter, in the great warfare between itself and mind, has gone on the principle of divide and conquer. You are nearer the truth than you imagined, for the trunk of the elephant is merely the abortion of a tail; and yet, you see, it contains nearly all the intelligence that the animal possesses. On the subject of the fate of the elephant, however, theory is confirmed by actual experiment. Do not your geologists and naturalists speak of the remains of animals, which are no longer to be found among living things?"

"Certainly, sir; the mastodon—the megatherium, iguanodon; and the plesiosaurus"—

"And do you not also find unequivocal evidences of animal matter incorporated with rocks?"

"This fact must be admitted, too."

"These phenomena, as you call them, are no more than the final deposits which nature has made in the cases of those creatures in which matter has completely overcome its rival, mind. So soon as the will is entirely extinct, the being ceases to live; or it is no longer an animal. It falls and reverts altogether to the element of matter. The processes of decomposition and incorporation are longer, or shorter, according to circumstances; and these fossil remains of which your writers say so much, are merely cases that have met with accidental obstacles to their final decomposition. As respects our two species, a very cursory examination of their qualities ought to convince any candid mind of the truth of our philosophy. Thus, the physical part of man is much greater in proportion to the spiritual than it is in the monikin ; his habits are grosser and less intellectual ; he requires sauce and condiments in his food ; he is farther removed from simplicity, and, by necessary implication, from high civilization ; he eats flesh, a certain proof that the material principle is still strong in the ascendant ; he has no *cauda*"—

"On this point, Dr. Reasono, I would inquire if your scholars attach any weight to traditions ?"

"The greatest possible, sir. It is the monikin tradition that our species is composed of men refined, of diminished matter and augmented minds, with the seat of reason extricated from the confinement and confusion of the *caput*, and extended, unravelled, and rendered logical and consecutive, in the *cauda*."

"Well, sir, *we*, too, have our traditions ; and an eminent writer, at no great distance of time, has laid it down as incontrovertible, that men once *had caudæ*."

"A mere prophetic glance into the future, as coming events are known to cast their shadows before."

"Sir, the philosopher in question establishes his position by pointing to the stumps."

"He has unluckily mistaken a foundation-stone for a ruin ! Such errors are not unfrequent with the ardent and ingenious. That men *will* have tails, I make no doubt ; but that they *have* ever reached this point of perfection, I do most solemnly deny. There are many premonitory symptoms of their approaching this condition : the current opinions of the day, the dress, habits, fashions, and philosophy of the species, encourage the belief ; but hitherto you have never reached the enviable distinction. As to traditions, even your own are all in favor of our theory. Thus, for instance, you have a tradition that the earth was once peopled by giants. Now, this is owing to the fact that men were formerly more under the influence of matter, and less under that of mind, than to-day. You admit that you diminish in size, and improve in moral attainments ; all of which goes to establish the truth of the monikin philosophy. You begin to lay less stress on physical, and more on moral excellencies ; and, in short, many things show that the time for the final liberation and grand development of your brains is not far distant. This much I very gladly concede ; for, while the dogmas of our schools are not to be disregarded, I very cheerfully admit that you are our fellow-creatures, though in a more infant and less improved condition of society."

"King !"

Here Dr. Reasono announced the necessity of taking a short intermission, in order to refresh himself. I retired with Captain Poke, to have a little communication with my fellow-mortal, under the peculiar circumstances in which we were placed, and to ask his opinion of what had been said. Noah swore bitterly at some of the conclusions of the monikin philosopher, affirming he should like no better sport than to hear him lecture in the streets of Stunin'tun, where, he assured me, such doctrine would not be tolerated any longer than was necessary to sharpen a harpoon, or to load a gun.

Homeward Bound: On reaching the cabin, where
both immediately hastened, the two gentlemen found
the family party in the distress that the circumstances would naturally create.

XIV.

HOMEWARD BOUND.

Love of country was a feeling which, with the author of "The Bravo," had far more than common depth. There were many years of his life during which that feeling may be said to have partaken of the nature of a passion. Born with the country, the sympathies of his own ardent youth flowed naturally in the same current with the young life of the nation. The glow of an interest almost personal was felt in every important step of advancing civilization: the opening of broad forests, the tilling of great plains and valleys, the movement of busy fleets of shipping on river and coast, the building of manufactories and ware-houses, the progress of cities and villages, were all in turn followed with a closely-observant and animated eye, and appreciated with intelligent and practical insight into details. This sense of vigorous growth was, indeed, an unceasing source of enjoyment to him. In physical activity, in energy of spirit, he was most essentially American. The higher elements which make up national feeling were, of course, still more powerful in their influences: the early history of the country, its honorable origin, its healthful colonial progress, its independence so gallantly won, its achievements in arms by land and sea, its diffusion of education, and, above all, its political and religious constitution, wise, and just, and generous in spirit, were so many sources of honest pride. No man in the country bore about a heart more loyal in its allegiance than his own. And as years passed over, during a long period, they brought little change in the fervor of this feeling; the experience of maturity had no power of itself to chill the enthusiasm of his nature. At the moment when early manhood was passing away, a new career, wholly unforeseen, suddenly opened before him ; the first important step in that career gave to the world as noble a personification of the spirit of patriotism as literature can show.   And the young writer had scarcely made sure of his ground—had scarcely convinced himself of his ability to maintain this new position, to move onward in the same course—ere the hope arose of rendering service to his country in the field of letters.   With the power to act came simultaneously the resolution to work for good.   No writer could be more fully aware than himself of the importance of a healthful moral spirit pervading the lighter literature of a nation ; entirely free from puritanical tendencies alike in nature and in education, he believed the existence of a literature in that form to be a sort of necessity among every reading people—as much so as the existence of laugh or song, in every human household.   The importance of these lesser influences he rated highly ; he inclined to the opinion of him who said : " Let me make the songs of a people, and its laws you may shape as you please !" The power for good, or for evil, of this element in the education of a people, he held to be great—fearful in its facilities to excite, to pervert, to enervate, to corrupt, in the hands of the unprincipled and selfish, but capable, when worthily employed, of becoming an active agent for good in the sound, moral, and intellectual culture of a nation.   A just sense of responsibility, in a mind ever nobly conscientious, might have been sufficient to point out his course in this respect. But such an appeal to principle was scarcely needed.   Where there is strong feeling, there service is no longer a severe duty ; the task sits lightly, is performed almost unconsciously, when a labor of love.   It was no cold, abstract principle which made up patriotism in the heart which conceived the character of Harvey Birch ; nay, more, it was not only that local affection of soil and scene, which is the instinctive growth of every healthful nature ; it was human sympathy in one of its highest forms, it was a love of his kind, of his fellow-countrymen—ardent, generous, and active—which guided his pen.

Under influences of this character the first works of a long series were written. It required but brief reflection to show that in behalf of a young nation there was much especial mental work to be done.   There was fresh seed to be sown in the new soil.   The infusion of old and eternal principles into new forms was to be carried out.   The cultivation of a healthful national tone, blending the self-respect of a firm position with that spirit of mental growth, of moral amelioration, becoming the period of early youth—the cherishing of clear moral truth, of sound reasoning, of strong common sense, of pure feeling, of good taste—all this needed to be carried out into detail, amid institutions partially novel in form. To be one among those who should aid in this onward progress, this upward growth, of a high, free, Christian civilization, became his object as a writer; and he threw himself into the task with that ardor, that untiring spirit, and that buoyancy of a hopeful nature, which so strongly marked his course through life. "The Spy," "The Pioneers," "The Pilot," "The Mohicans," "The Prairie," were written. He sailed for Europe. And as he touched the shores of the old world, he felt that he had acquired a right to an honest pride in the name of an American; the pen in his hand had already given something toward an honorable fame for his country. He entered into European society, courted as literary men of reputation usually are in those countries. Here, to his surprise, he soon discovered that, while far more of personal homage than he could have anticipated—far more than he sought or wished for—was offered to himself as to other distinguished writers, his country was overlooked—as he conceived, undervalued and decried. This fact he attributed in a measure to political motives—to a dread of the influence of American institutions combined with American prosperity. Believing, as he conscientiously did, that those institutions were founded on principles true, just, and generous, he conceived it a duty to uphold them, in these assaults received in European society. And this course he steadfastly pursued; no amount of personal flattery offered at the expense of his country, her history, and her political institutions, could ever draw from him even the tacit rejection often sought for. The remark was frequently made to him that American travellers very generally abandoned the political principles of their country when thrown into European society. He was resolved that no such accusation should justly be made against himself.

It was during this period that "The Red Rover," "The Travelling Bachelor," "The Wish-ton-Wish," "The Water-Witch," "The Bravo," were written—unchanged in the general tone of almost enthusiastic fidelity to the country, and undiminished in mental power. After an absence of nearly eight years, the author returned home. With the exception of old personal friends, true as ever, his reception was chilling and repelling in the extreme. For this he was in some measure prepared; the reality, however, far surpassed what had been anticipated. With the publication of "The Bravo" had commenced a series of abuse in the public prints, which to an European must have appeared remarkable; that a man who had left his country some eight years earlier, one of the most popular of its public characters; should have passed those years in contributing to the literary reputation of his country, in upholding abroad her institutions and character; and then, as he again stepped on his native soil, be met with a burst of vulgar abuse only, may have seemed extraordinary to an intelligent observer from the old world. Let it be left to others—to those who take pleasure in analyzing the unworthy passions of human nature, what is weak, trivial, ignoble, cowardly—to search more closely into the motives by which too many of those abusive pens must have been guided. It has been said, and by those competent to judge, that a single sentence in the introduction to "The Heidenmauer" was the first and chief cause of all the gross personal abuse with which, for many years, Mr. Fenimore Cooper was assailed: "Each hour, as life advances, am I made to see how capricious and vulgar is the immortality conferred by a newspaper!" This sentence drew, at the time, from the editor of one of the leading papers in the country, a threat of lasting personal persecution: "The press has built him up—the press shall pull him down!" Which of these two remarks carried with it the larger share of truth, of justice, of uprightness of position, of honorable feeling, another generation is already deciding.

The nature of Mr. Cooper was one easily aroused by attack; while no man was more ready than he with heart, and hand, and lip, to reciprocate—nay, generously to go beyond, every friendly advance; yet assault instantly called out repelling power from him—and that, at times, perhaps, with a severity beyond what he was himself aware of. To criticism on his merits as a writer he always professed himself willing to allow the freest scope; to falsehood and prolonged personal abuse, where his moral character was concerned, he declared that he would not submit. The laws should protect that character—if need were, he would compel their protection, by the powers of truth and justice inherent in their spirit, however inert their daily action might have become where others were concerned. Those laws insuring to every citizen the rights of private character should for himself no longer be a dead letter. He chose at length, after a long period of vituperation, to assert his rights—he resolved to maintain them. The struggle lasted for years. The first step in such a course implied the necessity of others. Fresh assailants poured in upon him, until hundreds—aye, perhaps thousands—were openly arrayed against one. Single-handed, as it were, but supported by an upright conscience and a powerful intellect, truth and justice on his side, the laws of the land his only weapon, he went with his legal companions into one court-room after another, and drew from juries, often very strongly prejudiced against him, the conviction of his assailants. Seventeen different civil actions for libel were brought by him: of these, in nine cases the verdicts were in his favor; five cases were settled by the defendants publishing retractions; in one instance the case was not tried, owing to the death of the defendant; in one case a judgment in his favor was given by the Supreme Court, but afterward reversed by the Court of Errors on the ground that publication was not a libel; one cause was still pending at the time of the author's death. Two criminal indictments for libel were found, on his complaint. One of these cases was tried three times: on two occasions the juries disagreed, on the third occasion they acquitted the defendant; in this instance no evidence was introduced by the defendant beyond partially mutilated extracts from the book reviewed, and every reader could make up his own mind as to the value of the verdict by comparing—were he disposed to do so—the book itself with the charges contained in the pretended criticism. In the second criminal case the libel was retracted, and the prosecution dropped. It was Mr. Cooper's intention at first that the sums awarded as damages in these causes should be thrown into a common fund, and appropriated to some public object. But his pecuniary means were very limited, and he ultimately decided that the award of one cause should be made available in defraying the expenses of that which followed. An account was kept, and no more was received than was expended in the same way. At the close of these proceedings the sums were evenly balanced.

When the first attacks, full of personal abuse, were published at home, so clear was the author's conscience toward the country, that he was wholly unprepared for them. They took him entirely by surprise. When these attacks increased in number and in virulence—when he found the whole current of public feeling yielding with thoughtless indifference, with pitiful weakness, to such guidance, until at length it had turned into a flood of enmity against an absent man—he was amazed. He paused awhile; he stood awaiting and listening for some friendly voice to be raised in his favor—for some generous and indignant word to be heard above this low clamor, this prolonged unmanly iteration of the most vulgar abuse. For that voice—for that word—during years he listened in vain. There were, no doubt, many who, in private, spoke in his behalf. In public there was not one to defend him. This silence on the part of his friends may have been in a measure owing to the fact that all who knew him personally were well aware that his was not the timid, sensitive nature which sinks under attack; they knew him to be in every sense capable of self-defence. But if the power of his intellect was great; if he had physical vigor and nerve beyond most men; if in moral courage he was wholly dauntless—did they then believe the man who had conceived Harvey Birch—could they believe the man who created Natty—entirely without a heart! The country he had been striving to serve was casting him off; very many among those whom he had looked upon as friends were turning against him—nay, were now active in swelling the general outcry of the throng. His spirit was deeply wounded. The very enthusiasm of devotion which from boyhood had marked his love of country, its self-forgetful disinterestedness of character, gave greater force to the revulsion of feeling. Foul were the blasts which now poured about that noble head from every quarter of the land. No gallant ship of his own, storm and tempest raging fiercely about her ocean path, ever rode through gale of louder fury; none ever bore aloft more bravely the colors confided to her. Never was he known to quail. " He writes like a hero !" had been the language already applied to him by a great English critic, Christopher North. As he wrote, so he lived. He now aroused himself in the fulness of his strength, a very lion at bay. Had this been a mere personal struggle, the single arm stemming that fierce current might have been swept away; the result might have been different. He would himself have wearied of such work, in very disgust. But, in reality, there was something far beyond personal interest at stake; the struggle soon became one between principle and the spirit of tyranny, working under the form of a regular combination—a banded conspiracy, many against one ! " The King's name is a tower of strength," says the wise man. With habitual, firm trust in Providence, in the inherent and inalienable powers of Truth and Justice when worthily upheld and steadfastly adhered to, he moved onward in the course he had marked out for himself; gradually, as weeks and months passed over, what there was of personal feeling, on his side, yielded more and more to motives involving general principles. The public press was, in his view, a power for life, or for death, to this nation. On the healthful uses or the criminal abuses of this single element, he considered that the lasting good or the eventual corruption and fall of the country must inevitably depend, more than on any one other earthly influence. The poisons spread by the daily press—the spirit of error, of untruth, of dissension, of licentiousness—becomes blended with the daily life of every man, and woman, and child in the land—is necessarily infused into every vein of the body politic. No power for general corruption so great as that of the daily press; no tyranny more selfish, more reckless, more shameless, where individual interests are concerned, if left unchecked to work its own will ; nay, no power so truly inimical to the eventual freedom and healthful action of that press itself, as its own abuses. Laws, few, but clear and stringent, he believed absolutely necessary to counteract this tendency to corruption in the daily press—laws for the protection of public morals, for the protection of private rights. To see that these laws were carried into execution he held to be an obligation essentially connected with the very birthright of every citizen of a republic.

It has been said that silence under similar attacks should have been the author's course. It is to be hoped—nay, we may feel confident—that there are many in the country who could have borne in worthy silence obloquy even great and general as that with which the author of "The Prairie" was assailed; such might, perhaps, have been the course of the writer, and of the reader, of these lines. But let us turn our eyes abroad; let us inquire of each other if there was at the time in the whole republic one other nature so resolute, so untiring, so independent, so disinterested, so intrepid, as thus bravely to face single-handed the spirit of tyranny in that particular form most trying to American nerve—a form dangerous, insidious, intolerant, remorseless, manifold—a mob armed with a show of mental power! Upheld by principle, and unappalled by the vituperation of half the nation, the author moved steadily onward. As he advanced in his course, the bitterness of personal feeling, the disappointment which had chilled his warm heart when the fickleness of popular favor was first discovered in its fulness, lessened almost daily; reliance on Providence, the consciousness of innate integrity, the buoyancy of a naturally happy and joyous temper upheld him. His feeling toward the country underwent a change: the enthusiasm of that glowing devotion which he had carried with him for so many years had passed away, but not from the effects of time, which had no power of itself to chill affections strong, and generous, and deep as his own. It was now a sadder and a more sober feeling—still ready to give, still ready to serve, still gladly noting all of good—but it was the feeling which no longer looked for return of sympathy.

THE ARABS.

THE accidents of life could scarcely have brought together, in circumstances so peculiar, men whose characters were more completely the converse of each other than Mr. Monday and Mr. Dodge. They were perfect epitomes of two large classes in their respective nations, and so diametrically opposed to each other, that one could hardly recognize in them scions from a common stock. The first was dull, obstinate, straight-forward, hearty in his manners, and not without sincerity, though wily in a bargain, with all his seeming frankness; the last, distrustful, cunning, rather than quick of com-prehension, insincere, fawning when he thought his interests concerned, and jealous and detracting at all other times, with a coldness of exterior that had, at least, the merit of appearing to avoid deception. Both were violently prejudiced, though in Mr. Monday it was the prejudice of old dogmas in religion, politics, and morals; and, in the other, it was the vice of provincialism, and an education that was not entirely free from the fanaticism of the seventeenth century. One consequence of this discrepancy of char-acter was a perfectly opposite manner of viewing matters in this interview. While Mr. Monday was disposed to take things amicably, Mr. Dodge was all suspicion; and, had they then returned to the wreck, the last would have called to arms, while the first would have advised Captain Truck to go out and visit the sheik, in the manner one would visit a respectable and agreeable neighbor.

Things were in this state, the sheik and his guests communicating by signs, in such a way as completely to mystify each other, Mr. Monday drinking, Mr. Dodge conjec-turing, and parties quitting the camp and arriving every ten minutes, when an Arab pointed eagerly with his finger in the direction of the wreck. The head of the fore-mast was slowly rising, and the look-out in the top was clinging to the spar, which began to cant, in order to keep himself from falling. The sheik affected to smile; but he was evidently disturbed, and two or three messengers were sent out into the camp. In the meanwhile, the spar began to lower, and was soon entirely concealed beneath the bank.

It was now apparent that the Arabs thought the moment had arrived when it was their policy to interfere. The sheik, therefore, left his guests to be entertained by two or three others who had joined in the potations, and making the best assurances he could by means of signs, of his continued amity, he left the tent. Laying aside all his arms, attended by two or three old men like himself, he went boldly to the plank, and descended quietly to the sands, where he found Captain Truck busied in endeavoring to get the spar into the water. The top was already afloat, and the stick itself was cut round in the right position for rolling, when the foul, but grave-looking barbarians appeared among the workmen. As the latter had been apprised of their approach, and of the fact of their being unarmed, no one left his employment to receive them, with the exception of Captain Truck himself.

" Bear a hand with the spar, Mr. Leach," he said, " while I entertain these gentlemen. It is a good sign that they come to us without arms, and it shall never be said that we are behind them in civility. Half an hour will settle our affairs, when these gentry are welcome to what will be left of the Dane. Your servant, gentlemen; I am glad to see you, and beg the honor to shake hands with all of you, from the oldest to the youngest."

Although the Arabs understood nothing that was said, they permitted Captain Truck to give each of them a hearty shake of the hand, smiling, and muttering their own compliments with as much apparent good will as was manifested by the old seaman himself.

" God help the Danes, if they have fallen into servitude among these blackguards !" said the captain, aloud, while he was shaking the sheik a second time most cordially by the hand; "for a fouler set of thieves I never laid eyes on, Leach. Mr. Monday has tried the virtue of the *schnaps* on them, notwithstanding, for the odor of gin is mingled with that of grease about the old scoundrel. Roll away at the spar, boys! half a dozen more such heaves, and you will have him in his native element, as the newspapers call it. I'm glad to see you, gentlemen; we are badly off as to chairs, on this beach, but to such as we have you are heartily welcome. Mr. Leach, the Arab sheik; Arab sheik, Mr. Leach.—On the bank there ?"

" Sir ?"

" Any movement among the Arabs ?"

" About thirty have just ridden back into the desert, mounted on camels, sir; nothing more."

" No signs of our passengers ?"

"Aye, aye, sir. Here comes Mr. Dodge under full sail, heading for the bank, as straight as he can lay his course."

"Hah! Is he pursued?"

The men ceased their work, and glanced aside at their arms.

"Not at all, sir. Mr. Monday is calling after him, and the Arabs seem to be laughing. Mr. Monday is just splicing the main-brace with one of the rascals."

"Let the Atlantic ocean, then, look out for itself, for Mr. Dodge will be certain to run over it. Heave away, my hearties, and the stick will be afloat yet before that gentleman is fairly docked."

The men worked with good will, but their zeal was far less efficient than that of the editor of the "Active Inquirer," who now broke through the bushes, and plunged down the bank with a velocity which, if continued, would have carried him to Dodgeopolis itself within the month. The Arabs started at this sudden apparition, but, perceiving that those around them laughed, they were disposed to take the interruption in good part. The look-out now announced the approach of Mr. Monday, followed by fifty Arabs; the latter, however, being without arms, and the former without his hat. The moment was critical, but the steadiness of Captain Truck did not desert him. Issuing a rapid order to the second mate, with a small party previously selected for that duty, to stand by the arms, he urged the rest of the people to renewed exertions. Just as this was done, Mr. Monday appeared on the bank, with a bottle in one hand, and a glass in the other, calling aloud to Mr. Dodge to return and drink with the Arabs.

"Do not disgrace Christianity in this unmannerly way," he said; "but show these gentlemen of the desert that we know what propriety is. Captain Truck, I beg of you to urge Mr. Dodge to return. I was about to sing the Arabs 'God save the King,' and in a few more minutes we should have had 'Rule Britannia,' when we should have been the best friends and companions in the world. Captain Truck, I've the honor to drink your health."

But Captain Truck viewed the matter differently. Both his ambassadors were now safely back, for Mr. Monday came down upon the beach, followed, it is true, by all the Arabs, and the mast was afloat. He thought it better, therefore, that Mr. Dodge should remain, and that the two parties should be as quietly, but as speedily as possible, separated. He ordered the hauling-line to be fastened to the mast; and, as the stick was slowly going out through the surf, he issued the order for the men to collect their implements, take their arms, and to assemble in a body at the rocks, where the jolly-boat still lay.

"Be quick, men, but be steady; for there are a hundred of these rascals on the beach already, and all the last-comers are armed. We might pick up a few more useful things from the wreck, but the wind is coming in from the westward, and our principal concern now will be to save what we have got. Lead Mr. Monday along with you, Leach, for he is so full of diplomacy and *schnaps*, just now, that he forgets his safety. As for Mr. Dodge, I see he is stowed away in the boat already, as snug as the ground-tier in a ship loaded with molasses. Count the men off, sir, and see that no one is missing."

By this time, the state of things on the beach had undergone material changes. The wreck was full of Arabs—some of whom were armed, and some not; while mauls, crows, hand-spikes, purchases, coils of rigging, and marlin-spikes were scattered about on the sands, just where they had been dropped by the seamen. A party of fifty Arabs had collected around the rocks, where, by this time, all the mariners were assembled, intermingling with the latter, and apparently endeavoring to maintain the friendly relations which had been established by Mr. Monday. As a portion of these men were also armed, Captain Truck disliked their proceedings; but the inferiority of his numbers, and the disadvantage under which he was placed, compelled him to resort to management, rather than force, in order to extricate himself.

The Arabs now crowded around and intermingled with the seamen, thronged the ship, and lined the bank, to the number of more than two hundred. It became evident that their true force had been underrated, and that additions were constantly making to it, from those who lay behind the ridges of sand. All those who appeared last had arms of one kind or another, and several brought fire-arms, which they gave to the sheik, and to those who had first descended to the beach. Still, every face seemed amicable, and the men were scarcely permitted to execute their orders, from the frequent interruptions to exchange tokens of friendship.

But Captain Truck fully believed that hostilities were intended, and, although he had suffered himself in some measure to be surprised, he set about repairing his error with great judgment and admirable steadiness. His first step was to extricate his own people from those who pressed upon them—a thing that was effected by causing a few to take a position, that might be defended, higher among the rocks, as they afforded a good deal of cover, and which communicated directly with the place where they had landed; and then ordering the remainder of the men to fall back singly. To prevent an alarm, each man was called off by name, and in this manner the whole party had got within the prescribed limits, before the Arabs, who were vociferating and talking altogether, seemed to be aware of the movement. When some of the latter attempted to follow, they were gently repulsed by the sentinels. All this time Captain Truck maintained the utmost cordiality toward the sheik, keeping near him, and among the Arabs, himself. The work of plunder, in the meantime, had begun in earnest in the wreck, and this he thought a favorable symptom, as men thus employed would be less likely to make a hostile attack. Still, he knew that prisoners were of great account among these barbarians, and that an attempt to tow the raft off from the land, in open boats, where his people would be exposed to every shot from the wreck, would subject them to the greatest danger of defeat, were the former disposed to prevent it.

Having reflected a few minutes on his situation, Captain Truck issued his final orders. The jolly-boat might carry a dozen men at need, though they would be crowded and much exposed to fire; and he, therefore, caused eight to get into her, and to pull out to the launch. Mr. Leach went with this party, for the double purpose of directing its movements, and of being separated from his commander, in order that one of those who were of so much importance to the packet might at least stand a chance of being saved. This separation also was effected without alarming the Arabs, though Captain Truck observed that the sheik watched the proceeding narrowly.

As soon as Mr. Leach had reached the launch, he caused a light kedge to be put into the jolly-boat, and coils of the lightest rigging he had were laid on the top of it, or were made on the bows of the launch. As soon as this was done, the boat was pulled a long distance off from the land, paying out the ropes first from the launch, and then from the boat itself, until no more of the latter remained. The kedge was then dropped, and the men in the launch began to haul in upon the ropes that were attached to it. As the jolly-boat returned immediately, and her crew joined in the work, the line of boats, the kedge by which they had previously ridden having been first raised, began slowly to recede from the shore.

Captain Truck had rightly conjectured the effect of this movement. It was so unusual and so gradual, that the launch and the raft were warped up to the kedge before the Arabs fully comprehended its nature. The boats were now more than a quarter of a mile from the wreck, for Mr. Leach had run out quite two hundred fathoms of small rope, and of course so distant as greatly to diminish the danger from the muskets of the Arabs, though still within reach of their range. Near an hour was passed in effecting this point, which, as the sea and wind were both rising, could not probably have been effected in any other manner, half as soon, if at all.

The state of the weather, and the increasing turbulence of the barbarians, now rendered it extremely desirable to all on the rocks to be in their boats again. A very moderate blow would compel them to abandon their hard-earned advantages, and it began to be pretty evident, from the manners of those around them, that amity could not much longer be maintained. Even the old sheik retired, and, instead of going to the wreck, he joined the party on the beach, where he was seen in earnest conversation with several other old men, all of whom gesticulated vehemently, as they pointed toward the boats and to the party on the rocks.

Mr. Leach now pulled in toward the bar, with both the jolly-boats and the cutter, having only two oars each, half his men being left in the launch. This was done that the people might not be crowded at the critical moment, and that, at need, there might be room to fight as well as to row; all these precautions having been taken in consequence of Captain Truck's previous orders. When the boats reached the rocks, the people did not hurry into them; but a quarter of an hour was passed in preparations, as if they were indifferent about proceeding, and even then the jolly-boat alone took in a portion, and pulled leisurely without the bar. Here she lay on her oars, in order to cover the passage of the other boats, if necessary, with her fire. The cutter imitated this manœuvre, and the boat of the wreck went last. Captain Truck quitted the rock after all the others, though his embarkation was made rapidly by a prompt and sudden movement.

Not a shot was fired, however; and, contrary to his own most ardent hopes, the captain found himself at the launch, with all his people unhurt, and with all the spars he had so much desired to obtain. The forbearance of the Arabs was a mystery to him, for he had fully expected hostilities would commence, every moment, for the last two hours. Nor was he yet absolutely out of danger, though there was time to pause and look about him, and to take his succeeding measures more deliberately. The first report was a scarcity of both food and water. For both these essentials the men had depended on the wreck, and, in the eagerness to secure the fore-mast, and subsequently to take care of themselves, these important requisites had been overlooked—quite probably, too, as much from a knowledge that the Montauk was so near, as from hurry. Still, both were extremely desirable, if not indispensable, to men who had the prospect of many hours' hard work before them; and Captain Truck's first impulse was to despatch a boat to the ship for supplies. This intention was reluctantly abandoned, however, on account of the threatening appearance of the weather.

There was no danger of a gale, but a smart sea breeze was beginning to set in, and the surface of the ocean was, as usual, getting to be agitated. Changing all his plans, therefore, the captain turned his immediate attention to the safety of the all-important spars.

"We can eat to-morrow, men," he said; "but if we lose these sticks, our chance for getting any more will indeed be small. Take a gang on the raft, Mr. Leach, and double all the lashings, while I see that we get an offing. If the wind rises any more, we shall need it, and even then be worse off than we could wish."

The mate passed upon the raft, and set about securing all the spars by additional fastenings; for the working, occasioned by the sea, already rendered them loose, and liable to separate.

While this was in train, the two jolly-boats took in lines and kedges, of which, luckily, they had one that was brought from the packet, besides two found in the wreck, and pulled off into the ocean. As soon as one kedge was dropped, that by which the launch rode was tripped, and the boats were hauled up to it, the other jolly-boat proceeding on to renew the process. In this manner, in the course of two more hours, the whole, raft and all, were warped broad off from the land, and to windward, quite two miles, when the water became so deep that Captain Truck reluctantly gave the order to cease.

"I would gladly work our way into the offing in this mode, three or four leagues," he said, "by which means we might make a fair wind of it. As it is, we must get all clear, and do as well as we can.   Rig the masts in the launch, Mr. Leach, and we will see what can be done with this dull craft we have in tow."

While this order was in course of execution, the glass was used to ascertain the manner in which the Arabs were occupied.   To the surprise of all in the boats, every soul of them had disappeared.   The closest scrutiny could not detect one near the wreck, on the beach, nor even at the spot where the tents had so lately stood.

"They are all off, by George!" cried Captain Truck, when fully satisfied of the fact.   "Camels, tents, and Arabs!   The rascals have loaded their beasts already, and most probably have gone to hide their plunder, that they may be back and make sure of a second haul, before any of their precious brother vultures, up in the sands, get a scent of the carrion.   D——n the rogues ; I thought at one time they had me in a category!   Well, joy be with them!   Mr. Monday, I return you my hearty thanks for the manly, frank, and diplomatic manner in which you have discharged the duties of your mission.   Without you, we might not have succeeded in getting the fore-mast. Mr. Dodge, you have the high consolation of knowing that, throughout this trying occasion, you have conducted yourself in a way no other man of the party could have done."

Mr. Monday was sleeping off the fumes of the *schnaps*, but Mr. Dodge bowed to the compliment, and foresaw many capital things for the journal, and for the columns of the "Active Inquirer."   He even began to meditate a book.

SUSQUEHANNAH, WITH MOUNT VISION IN THE DISTANCE.

XV.

HOME AS FOUND.

AFTER a long absence, the writer, on returning from abroad, was struck with the fact that, in some important particulars, the country had lost ground. The progress hoped for in certain points of moral strength had not been attained. The timidity, the want of self-reliance, which had marked the first steps in the mental independence of the country, had passed away, and was now replaced by a vapid and sensitive public vanity, fostered by the fulsome flattery of selfish demagogues; a spirit different, in its very essence, from a manly, and honest, and generous love of country, and from which no healthful fruits, whatever, could be expected. To counteract this puerile spirit—to distinguish clearly between the strong and the weak points open to observation—he considered to be a duty on the part of every honest writer, who had the good of his country at heart. To aid in holding up a public standard, which should be at the same time high, and yet practical, he believed an especial duty in the citizen of a democracy, and of a nation isolated in position, immature in age; a standard high and rational on all points of principle, of judgment, and of culture. "*A une grande nation l'on peut tout dire!*" was his principle. There were two particulars, in the growth of national character, by which he was especially disappointed. One might have supposed that, among the citizens of a republic, frankness of speech, independence of action, would scarcely appear as individual virtues; we should have believed them natural consequences of that form of society. But far, indeed, was such from being the general state of the moral atmosphere which surrounded the writer on his return. He had not been at home a week, when, at an evening party, he had the ill luck carelessly to observe, that, on the evening of his arrival, he had been sadly jolted by the bad state of the pavement; and that he had also been surprised to find the town so poorly lighted. Anxious friends immediately gathered about him, cautiously making a diversion in his favor; and, at length, leading him aside, earnestly implored him to be more prudent. He had professed to enjoy exceedingly the bright November sunshine, the soft Indian-summer breezes, after the gloomy fogs and damp chills of the same season in London and Paris; this was very well; let him pursue that track, and all might yet be safe; but—by the shade of Washington! by the memory of John Jay!—of the pavement, not a word! of the lamps, not one syllable! He happened, at a dinner party, to allude to the fact that the Alps were some ten thousand feet higher than the White Mountains, and covered with perpetual snow. A severely reproving salutation, the next day, from those who had sat at table with him, was the consequence. He was heard, in answer to repeated inquiries, to affirm that the natural scenery, and the classical interest of the shores of the bay of Naples, far surpassed any claims of the bay of New York, beyond those of a maritime harbor; his fate was sealed. He was, clearly, devoid alike of taste and of patriotism! And again anxious friends gathered about him—imploring him, with increased earnestness, to avoid all such dangerous remarks; or, if it were really true that the Alps were fifteen thousand feet high, and that Baiæ and Pompeii actually lay on the shores of the Neapolitan waters, let him, at least, attest the fact in a corner, and lower his voice to a whisper! The effect of all this puerile weakness, this pusillanimity in the general tone of society, at that moment, on a nature frank as his own, may be conceived. At first, this Krähwinkel spirit made him laugh; when he met it continually, at every turn, it chafed and annoyed him; and when he found it actually carried into matters of grave importance, it produced indignation and disgust. This state of things—this want of frankness, this morbid public vanity in connection with trifles—led him, perhaps, to the opposite extreme of carelessness and freedom of speech and pen. But a point still more grave, even, than this puerile sensitiveness about pavements and lamps, took him by surprise, gave him pain. He was too often struck by the generally low and selfish vein of those

Home as Found: "You are bashfully silent, Miss Eve!
I make all due allowance for natural timidity, and
shall say no more at present – though, as silence
universally 'gives consent.'"

about him—the want of an elevated tone on points of taste, of morals, of practice. Among individuals, this tone was found as high and vigorous as in his own mind and life; yet, in general society, the aim openly sought, the object constantly avowed, seemed to him little beyond the acquirement of wealth, or the enjoyment of it in the way of wine and canvas-back ducks. Among the young men, especially, the lack of noble and generous impulse, the lethargy, the torpid inaction—both physical and mental—actually amazed him. Far different had been his own youth. And latterly, in Europe, he had been accustomed to hear men feign, at least, some honorable aim in life; utter just sentiments with their lips, even when they could not be supposed to feel them very deeply. But, with the low tone prevailing at the day, in American society, men seemed actually ashamed to adopt, or to avow, any object above those of the market. In connection with this subject, he frequently alluded to an observation made to him by a friend of his—a distinguished Englishwoman—that it gave her great pleasure to observe the marked improvement in tone, among her countrymen of the present generation, whose moral education, acquirements, and objects in life were far superior to what they had been half a century earlier. The author could but hope that some similar change for good might yet appear in American education—something to excite a higher spirit; to infuse motives more generous; to arouse to action more decided, among the men of the country. To aid, in some degree, in pointing out the evil, in holding up this higher standard, became his object in "Home as Found." That the principle was just and honorable, is clear. That he may have erred in some of the details of his task is very possible. Which, among the wisest of the sons of earth, has had, in pursuing a course just in itself, no error of detail to regret?

The shores of Lake Otsego were chosen for the scene of this book, solely from the fact that the same ground had been already described in an earlier stage of American society. The plot and characters of the book are, of course, entirely fictitious—repeatedly declared so by the author. One exception only must be made for a figure avowedly and minutely drawn from life—a figure long familiar to those living on the lake shores—a venerable figure, tall and upright, to be seen for some threescore years moving to and fro over the water, trolling for pickerel or angling for perch, almost any day in the year, excepting when the waters were ice-bound in winter.

THE COMMODORE.

The boat now came under a shore where the trees fringed the very water, frequently overhanging the element that mirrored their fantastic forms. At this point, a light skiff was moving leisurely along in their own direction, but a short distance in advance. On a hint from John Effingham, a few vigorous strokes of the oars brought the two boats near each other.

"This is the flag-ship," half whispered John Effingham, as they came near the other skiff, "containing no less a man than the 'commodore.' Formerly, the chief of the lake was an admiral, but that was in times when, living nearer to the monarchy, we retained some of the European terms; now, no man rises higher than a commodore in America, whether it be on the ocean or on the Otsego, whatever may be his merits or his services. A charming day, commodore; I rejoice to see you still afloat, in your glory."

The commodore—a tall, thin, athletic man of seventy, with a white head, and movements that were quick as those of a boy—had not glanced aside at the approaching boat until he was thus saluted in the well-known voice of John Effingham. He then turned his head, however, and scanning the whole party through his spectacles, he smiled good-naturedly, made a flourish with one hand, while he continued paddling with the other, for he stood erect and straight in the stern of his skiff, and answered heartily—

"A fine morning, Mr. John, and the right time of the moon for boating. This is not a real scientific day for the fish, perhaps; but I have just come out to see that all the points and bays are in their right places."

"How is it, commodore, that the water near the village is less limpid than common, and that even up here we see so many specks floating on its surface?"

"What a question for Mr. John Effingham to ask on his native water! So much for travelling in far countries, where a man forgets quite as much as he learns, I fear." Here the commodore turned entirely round, and, raising an open hand in an oratorical manner, he added, "You must know, ladies and gentlemen, that the lake is in blow."

"In blow, commodore! I did not know that the lake bore its blossoms."

"It does, sir, nevertheless. Aye, Mr. John, and its fruits, too; but the last must be dug for, like potatoes. There have been no miraculous draughts of the fishes, of late years, in the Otsego, ladies and gentlemen; but it needs the scientific touch, and the knowledge of baits, to get a fin of any of your true game above the water, now-a-days. Well, I have had the head of the sogdollager thrice in the open air, in my time; though I am told the admiral actually got hold of him once with his hand."

"The sogdollager," said Eve, much amused with the singularities of the man, whom she perfectly remembered to have been commander of the lake, even in her own infancy; "we must be indebted to you for an explanation of that term, as well as for the meaning of your allusion to the head and the open air."

"A sogdollager, young lady, is the perfection of a thing. I know Mr. Grant used to say there was no such word in the dictionary; but then there are many words that ought to be in the dictionaries that have been forgotten by the printers. In the way of salmon trout, the sogdollager is their commodore. Now, ladies and gentlemen, I should not like to tell you all I know about the patriarch of this lake, for you would scarcely believe me; but if he would not weigh a hundred when cleaned, there is not an ox in the county that will weigh a pound when slaughtered."

"You say you had his head above water?" said John Effingham.

"Thrice, Mr. John. The first time was thirty years ago; and I confess I lost him, on that occasion, by want of science; for the art is not learned in a day, and I had then followed the business but ten years. The second time was five years later; and I had then been fishing expressly for the old gentleman about a month. For near a minute, it was a matter of dispute between us, whether he should come out of the lake, or I go into it; but I actually got his gills in plain sight. That was a glorious haul! Washington did not feel better the night Cornwallis surrendered, than I felt on that great occasion!"

"One never knows the feelings of another, it seems. I should have thought disappointment at the loss would have been the prevailing sentiment on that great occasion, as you so justly term it."

"So it would have been, Mr. John, with an unscientific fisherman; but we experienced hands know better. Glory is to be measured by quality, and not by quantity, ladies and gentlemen; and I look on it as a greater feather in a man's cap, to see the sogdollager's head above water, for half a minute, than to bring home a skiff filled with pickerel. The last time I got a look at the old gentleman, I did not try to get him into the boat, but we sat and conversed for near two minutes; he in the water, and I in the skiff."

"Conversed!" exclaimed Eve, "and with a fish, too! What could the animal have to say?"

"Why, young lady, a fish can talk as well as one of ourselves; the only difficulty is to understand what he says. I have heard the old settlers affirm that the Leather-stocking used to talk for hours at a time with the animals of the forest."

"You knew the Leather-stocking, commodore?"

"No, young lady, I am sorry to say I never had the pleasure of looking on him even. He *was* a great man! They may talk of their Jeffersons and Jacksons, but I set down Washington and Natty Bumppo as the two only really great men of my time."

"What do you think of Bonaparte, commodore?" inquired Paul.

"Well, sir, Bonaparte had some strong points about him, I do really believe. But he could have been nothing to the Leather-stocking, in the woods! It's no great matter, young gentleman, to be a great man among your inhabitants of cities—what I call umbrella people. Why, Natty was almost as great with the spear as with the rifle; though I never heard that he got a sight of the sogdollager."

"We shall meet again this summer, commodore," said John Effingham; "the ladies wish to hear the echoes, and we must leave you."

"All very natural, Mr. John," returned the commodore, laughing, and again flourishing his hand in his own peculiar manner. "The women all love to hear the echoes, for they are not satisfied with what they have once said, but they like to hear it over again. I never knew a lady come on the Otsego, but one of the first things she did was to get paddled to the Speaking Rocks, to have a chat with herself. They come out in such numbers, sometimes, and then all talk at once, in a way quite to confuse the echo. I suppose you have heard, young lady, the opinion people have now got concerning these voices."

"I cannot say I have ever heard more than that they are some of the most perfect echoes known," answered Eve, turning her body so as to face the old man, as the skiff of the party passed that of the veteran fisherman.

"Some people maintain that there is no echo at all, and that the sounds we hear come from the spirit of the Leather-stocking, which keeps about its old haunts, and repeats every thing we say, in mockery of our invasion of the woods. I do not say this notion is true, or that it is my own; but we all know that Natty *did* dislike to see a new settler arrive in the mountains, and that he loved a tree as a muskrat loves water. They show a pine up here, on the side of the Vision, which he notched at every new-comer, until, reaching seventeen, his honest old heart could go no farther, and he gave the matter up in despair."

"This is so poetical, commodore, it is a pity it cannot be true. I like this explanation of the 'Speaking Rocks' much better than that implied by the name of 'Fairy Spring.' "

" You are quite right, young lady," called out the fisherman, as the boats separated still further; "there never was any fairy known in Otsego; but the time has been when we could boast of a Natty Bumppo."

Here the commodore flourished his hand again, and Eve nodded her adieus. The skiff of the party continued to pull slowly along the fringed shore, occasionally sheering more into the lake, to avoid some overhanging, and nearly horizontal tree, and then returning so closely to the land, as barely to clear the pebbles of the narrow strand with the oar.

Eve thought she had never beheld a more wild or beautifully variegated foliage than that which the whole leafy mountain-side presented. More than half of the forest of tall, solemn pines, that had veiled the earth when the country was first settled, had already disappeared; but, agreeably to one of the mysterious laws by which nature is governed, a rich second growth, that included nearly every variety of American wood, had shot up in their places. The rich, Rembrandt-like hemlocks, in particular, were perfectly beautiful, contrasting admirably with the livelier tints of the various deciduous trees. Here and there, some flowering shrub rendered the picture gay, while masses of the rich chestnut, in blossom, lay in clouds of natural glory among the dark tops of the pines.

The gentlemen pulled the light skiff fully a mile under the overhanging foliage, occasionally frightening some migratory bird from a branch, or a water-fowl from the narrow strand. At length, John Effingham desired them to cease rowing, and, managing the skiff for a minute or two with the paddle which he had used in steering, he desired the whole party to look up, announcing to them that they were beneath the " Silent Pine."

A common exclamation of pleasure succeeded the upward glance; for it is seldom that a tree is seen to more advantage than that which immediately attracted every eye. The pine stood on the bank, with its roots imbedded in the earth, a few feet higher than the level of the lake, but in such a situation as to bring the distance above the water into the apparent height of the tree. Like all of its kind that grow in the dense forests of America, its increase, for a thousand years, had been upward; and it now stood in solitary glory—a memorial of what the mountains, which were yet so rich in vegetation, had really been in their days of nature and pride. For near a hundred feet above the eye, the even round trunk was branchless, and then commenced the dark green masses of foliage, which clung around the stem like smoke ascending in wreaths. The tall, column-like tree had inclined toward the light, when struggling among its fellows, and it now so far overhung the lake, that its summit may have been some ten or fifteen feet without the base. A gentle, graceful curve added to the effect of this variation from the perpendicular, and infused enough of the fearful into the grand, to render the picture sublime.　Although there was not a breath of wind on the lake, the currents were strong enough above the forest to move this lofty object, and it was just possible to detect a slight, graceful yielding of the very uppermost boughs to the passing air.

"This pine is ill-named," cried Sir George Templemore; "for it is the most eloquent tree eye of mine has ever looked on!"

"It is, indeed, eloquent," answered Eve; "one hears it speak even now of the fierce storms that have whistled round its tops; of the seasons that have passed since it extricated that verdant cap from the throng of sisters that grew beneath it; and of all that has passed on the Otsego, when this limpid lake lay like a gem imbedded in the forest.　When the Conqueror first landed in England, this tree stood on the spot where it now stands!　Here, then, is, at last, an American antiquity!"

"A true and regulated taste, Miss Effingham," said Paul, "has pointed out to you one of the real charms of the country.　Were we to think less of the artificial, and more of our natural excellencies, we should render ourselves less liable to criticism."

Eve was never inattentive when Paul spoke; and her color heightened, as he paid this compliment to her taste; but still her soft blue eye was riveted on the pine.

"Silent it may be, in one respect, but it is, indeed, all eloquence in another," she resumed, with a fervor that was not lessened by Paul's remark.　"That crest of verdure, which resembles a plume of feathers, speaks of a thousand things to the imagination."

"I have never known a person of any poetry, who came under this tree," said John Effingham, "that did not fall into this very train of thought.　I once brought a man celebrated for his genius, here, and, after gazing for a minute or two at the high, green tuft that tops the tree, he exclaimed: 'That mass of green waved there in the fierce light when Columbus first ventured into the unknown sea.'　It is, indeed, eloquent; for it tells the same glowing tale to all who approach it—a tale fraught with feeling and recollections."

"And yet its silence is, after all, its eloquence," added Paul; "and the name is not so misplaced as one might at first think."

"It probably obtained its name from some fancied contrast to the garrulous rocks that lie up yonder, half-concealed by the forest.　If you will ply the oars, gentlemen, we will now hold a little communion with the spirit of the Leather-stocking."

The young men complied; and, in about five minutes, the skiff was off in the lake, at the distance of fifty rods from the shore, where the whole mountain-side came at one glance into the view.　Here they lay on their oars, and John Effingham called out to the rocks a "good morning," in a clear, distinct voice.　The mocking sounds were thrown back again, with a closeness of resemblance that actually startled the novice. Then followed other calls, and other repetitions of the echoes, which did not lose the minutest intonation of the voice.

"This actually surpasses the celebrated echoes of the Rhine," cried the delighted Eve; "for, though those do give the strains of the bugle so clearly, I do not think they answer to the voice with so much fidelity."

"You are very right, Eve," replied her kinsman; "for I can recall no place where so perfect and accurate an echo is to be heard as at these speaking rocks. By increasing our distance to half a mile, and using a bugle, as I well know, from actual experiment, we should get back entire passages of an air. The interval between the sound and the echo, too, would be distinct, and would give time for an undivided attention. Whatever may be said of the 'pine,' these rocks are most aptly named; and if the spirit of Leather-stocking has any concern with the matter, he is a mocking spirit."

John Effingham now looked at his watch, and then he explained to the party a pleasure he had in store for them. On a sort of small, public promenade, that lay at the point where the river flowed out of the lake, stood a rude shell of a building that was called the "gun-house." Here, a speaking picture of the entire security of the country, from foes within as well as from foes without, were kept two or three pieces of field artillery, with doors so open that any one might enter the building, and even use the guns at will, although they properly belonged to the organized corps of the state.

One of these guns had been sent a short distance down the valley; and John Effingham informed his companions that they might look momentarily for its reports to arouse the echoes of the mountains. He was still speaking when the gun was fired, its muzzle being turned eastward. The sound first reached the side of the Vision, abreast of the village, whence the reverberations reissued, and rolled along the range, from cave to cave, and cliff to cliff, and wood to wood, until they were lost, like distant thunder, two or three leagues to the northward. The experiment was thrice repeated, and always with the same magnificent effect, the western hills actually echoing the echoes of the eastern mountains, like the dying strains of some falling music.

XVI

THE PATHFINDER.

In the year 1808, several young officers of the navy, under the command of Lieutenant Woolsey, were ordered from New York to the shores of Lake Ontario, for the purpose of building a small vessel-of-war. Among these officers was Mr. Cooper, then a midshipman in the service. Their road beyond Utica lay for many a mile through the forest, the whole region to the northward of the Mohawk having scarcely yet thrown off the character of a wilderness. The mouth of the Oswego River was their destination; here they remained for some time, until the Oneida, a brig mounting sixteen guns, was built and launched. The whole party enjoyed extremely this marine campaign, with its wild coloring of frontier life, and none more so than the young midshipman from the Otsego Hills. During leisure hours, they roamed through the forest, or explored the shores of the lake. On one occasion they were ordered to Buffalo; they went by land through what is now the heart of a populous country, but was then a wilderness. They passed the site of future cities and towns, to be called into life from the depths of the forest only a very few years later. On one occasion they stopped for the night at a rude frontier inn. Mr. Cooper, who was acting as caterer for the party, inquired into the state of the larder. Mine host shook his

J. Hamilton pinxt   *J. Blythe sculpt*

The Pathfinder: In the Wilderness

head ruefully; he could promise very little; had they come a few weeks earlier, he could have set before them as good a meal as ought to be expected in the woods; but now matters were in a very bad way indeed. "Give us what you eat yourself; you must have food of some kind in the house!" Mine host looked melancholy; on his honor he assured the young officers he had absolutely nothing to set before them but grouse, venison steak, and brook trout; and maybe his wife could find cranberries for a tart! A month earlier they should have had a dish of fried pork fit for the President, with a pumpkin-pie after it, but in the present state of things, they must not expect such delicacies. "Game's plenty, but nothin' else!" added the publican with a sigh. Mine host was pining for pork!

On this expedition Mr. Cooper saw Niagara for the first time. He was struck with the grandeur of the cataract; but he felt its sublime character far more deeply at a later day, when visiting the same ground, after his return from Europe. When the brig was built and safely launched, the young officers gallantly resolved to give a ball. This was, in truth, an enterprise of a desperate character, under the circumstances; building a brig hundreds of miles from a ship-yard was a trifle compared to the attempt to give a ball in the wilderness. True, one fiddle, and half a dozen officers, were something to open the ball with; refreshments and a military ball-room might also be hoped for; but where, pray, were the ladies to come from? The officers declared they would not dance with each other. Ladies must be found. No recruiting officers ever made more vigorous efforts in behalf of the service, than Lieutenant Woolsey and his command on this occasion. At length, by dint of sending boats miles in one direction, and carts miles in another, the feat was accomplished; ladies were invited, and ladies accepted. A difficulty suggested itself, however; as the hour approached, a delicate point had to be decided, and that without the aid of any female counsellor. How, and by what rules, so many miles from a regular drawing-room, were the honors of the evening to be allotted among the different claimants? After a prolonged council of war, Mr. Woolsey took upon himself to decide the question; he issued his orders to the Master of Ceremonies: "All ladies, sir, provided with shoes and stockings, are to be led to the head of the Virginia reel; ladies with shoes, and without stockings, are considered in the second rank; ladies without either shoes or stockings, you will lead, gentlemen, to the foot of the country-dance!" Such was a grand military ball in Oswego county, at that date. It may have been on this occasion that the servant of the mess, a raw youth, fresh from Ireland, made an absurd exhibition of what Mr. Cooper called the bull practical: a tablecloth had taken fire, and was in full blaze; Paddy was at the moment filling a teapot from an ample kettle in his hand. "Pour the water on the table!" called out one of the officers. "Sure the wather is *hot*, your honor!" exclaimed Paddy, in great dismay, holding the kettle at a very safe distance from the blazing cloth, his face meanwhile exhibiting the most absurd expression of the *bull physiognomy* that could well be imagined. Mr. Cooper often laughed heartily at the very recollection of the poor fellow's countenance.

Cruises among the Thousand Isles were very frequent, and in great favor with the young officers; many were the fine fish caught in those waters, and many were the good chowders eaten there. The picturesque beauties of the region, the countless islands—all, then, in a wild condition—were greatly enjoyed, and never forgotten by one of the party at least. More than thirty years later, the young midshipman, now an experienced writer, determined that his next work of the imagination should be connected with that ground. The plan of the proposed book had been for some time in his mind; he had wished to lay the scene of a tale on one of the great lakes, and to bring sailors and Indians into the same picture. To sketch forest scenes, without Natty, seemed scarcely natural for his pen; the old Leather-stocking of "The Pioneers," Hawk-eye of "The Mohicans," the aged Trapper of "The Prairie," was again brought into view— the Pathfinder of the northern forests, and the shores of Lake Ontario. He now appears in the prime of life, and as a lover! A very daring experiment, indeed. But how perfect the success! Few are the books in the English language more beautiful than "The Pathfinder"—few, indeed, which are, at the same time, so purely natural, and so highly poetical in spirit. It is a singularly equal book— the most so, perhaps, of all the works from the same author; nor would it be easy to find the same number of pages from other pens, through which the current of feeling, of interest, of poetical imagination, flows so clearly, so easily, and so uninterruptedly. The glow of life, pervading the book, is that of nature her very self; we seem to hear the ripple of the lake waves—the rustling of the forest leaves; we seem actually to behold the islands, the schooner, and the skiff, with the human beings moving about them; we can fancy that we have really looked into Mabel's eyes—that we have heard the low, sweet tones of June's voice. The characters are all purely natural—whether sailor or soldier, savage or hunter, the warrior or the young girl—all are good in their way; nothing is overdrawn or labored, and yet many of the incidents are singularly striking and original. As for Natty— so simple, so tender, so true, so noble—what shall be said of him? We must all needs love him: it is not with words, but with tears, that we wring his hand, and part from him, on the lake shore.

NATTY A LOVER.

The party that was to land, consisted of Serjeant Dunham, his daughter, and the Pathfinder. Accustomed to the canoe, Mabel took her seat in the centre with great steadiness, her father was placed in the bows, while the guide assumed the office of conductor, by steering in the stern. There was little need of impelling the canoe by means of the paddle, for the rollers sent it forward, at moments, with a violence that set every effort to govern its movements at defiance. More than once, ere the shore was reached, Mabel repented of her temerity, but Pathfinder encouraged her, and really manifested so much self-possession, coolness, and strength of arm himself, that even a female might have hesitated about owning all her apprehensions. Our heroine was no coward, and while she felt the novelty of her situation, in landing through a surf, she also experienced a fair proportion of its wild delight. At moments, indeed, her heart was in her mouth, as the bubble of a boat floated on the very crest of a foaming breaker, appearing to skim the water like a swallow, and then she flushed and laughed, as, left by the glancing element, they appeared to linger behind, as if ashamed of having been outdone in the headlong race. A few minutes sufficed for this excitement, for, though the distance between the cutter and the land considerably exceeded a quarter of a mile, the intermediate space was passed in a very few minutes.

On landing, the serjeant kissed his daughter kindly, for he was so much of a soldier as always to feel more at home on terra-firma than when afloat, and taking his gun, he announced his intention to pass an hour in quest of game.

"Pathfinder will remain near you, girl, and no doubt he will tell you some of the traditions of this part of the world, or some of his own experiences with the Mingos."

The guide laughed, promised to have a care of Mabel, and in a few minutes the father had ascended a steep acclivity, and disappeared in the forest. The others took another direction, which, after a few minutes of a sharp ascent also, brought them to a small naked point on the promontory, where the eye overlooked an extensive and very peculiar panorama. Here Mabel seated herself on a fragment of fallen rock, to recover her breath and strength, while her companion, on whose sinews no personal exertion seemed to make any impression, stood at her side, leaning, in his own and not ungraceful manner, on his long rifle. Several minutes passed, and neither spoke; Mabel, in particular, being lost in admiration of the view.

The position the two had obtained was sufficiently elevated to command a wide reach of the lake, which stretched away toward the north-east, in a boundless sheet, glittering beneath the rays of an afternoon's sun, and yet betraying the remains of that agitation which it had endured while tossed by the late tempest. The land set bounds to its limits, in a huge crescent, disappearing in distance toward the south-east and the north. Far as the eye could reach, nothing but forest was visible—not even a solitary sign of civilization breaking in upon the uniform and grand magnificence of nature. The gale had driven the Scud beyond the line of those forts with which the French were then endeavoring to gird the English North American possessions; for, following the channels of communication between the great lakes, their posts were on the banks of the Niagara, while our adventurers had reached a point many leagues westward of that celebrated strait. The cutter rode at single anchor, without the breakers, resembling some well-imagined and accurately-executed toy, that was intended rather for a glass-case than for the struggles with the elements which she had so lately gone through, while the canoe lay on the narrow beach, just out of reach of the waves that came booming upon the land, a speck upon the shingles.

"We are very far, here, from human habitations!" exclaimed Mabel, when, after a long and musing survey of the scene, its principal peculiarities forced themselves on her active and ever-brilliant imagination; "this is, indeed, being on a frontier!"

"Have they more sightly scenes than this nearer the sea, and around their large towns?" demanded Pathfinder, with an interest he was apt to discover in such a subject.

"I will not say that; there is more to remind one of his fellow-beings there than here; less, perhaps, to remind one of God."

"Aye, Mabel, that is what my own feelings say. I am but a poor hunter, I know—untaught and unlarned—but God is as near me, in this my home, as he is near the king in his royal palace."

"Who can doubt it?" returned Mabel, looking from the view up into the hard-featured but honest face of her companion, though not without surprise at the energy of his manner—"One feels nearer to God, in such a spot, I think, than when the mind is distracted by the objects of the towns."

"You say all I wish to say myself, Mabel, but in so much plainer speech, that you make me ashamed of wishing to let others know what I feel on such matters. I have coasted this lake, in search of skins, afore the war, and have been here already; not at this very spot, for we landed yonder, where you may see the blasted oak that stands above the cluster of hemlocks"—

"How, Pathfinder, can you remember all these trifles so accurately?"

"These are our streets and houses—our churches and palaces. Remember them, indeed! I once made an appointment with the Big Sarpent, to meet at twelve o'clock at noon, near the foot of a certain pine, at the end of six months, when neither of us was within three hundred miles of the spot. The tree stood, and stands still, unless the judgment of Providence has lighted on that too, in the midst of the forest, fifty miles from any settlement, but in a most extraordinary neighborhood for beaver."

"And did you meet at that very spot and hour?"

"Does the sun rise and set? When I reached the tree, I found the Sarpent leaning against its trunk, with torn leggings and muddied moccasins. The Delaware had got into a swamp, and it worried him not a little to find his way out of it; but, as the sun which comes over the eastern hills in the morning goes down behind the western at night, so was he true to time and place. No fear of Chingachgook when there is either a friend or an enemy in the case. He is equally sartain with each."

"And where is the Delaware now?—why is he not with us to-day?"

"He is scouting on the Mingo trail, where I ought to have been, too, but for a great human infirmity."

"You seem above, beyond, superior to all infirmity, Pathfinder; I never yet met with a man who appeared to be so little liable to the weaknesses of nature."

"If you mean in the way of health and strength, Mabel, Providence has been kind to me; though I fancy the open air, long hunts, active scoutings, forest fare, and the sleep of a good conscience, may always keep the doctors at a distance. But I am human, after all; yes, I find I'm very human, in some of my feelings."

Mabel looked surprised, and it would be no more than delineating the character of her sex if we added that her sweet countenance expressed a good deal of curiosity, too, though her tongue was more discreet.

"There is something bewitching in this wild life of yours, Pathfinder," she exclaimed, a tinge of enthusiasm mantling her cheeks. "I find I'm fast getting to be a frontier girl, and am coming to love all this grand silence of the woods. The towns seem tame to me, and, as my father will probably pass the remainder of his days here, where he has already lived so long, I begin to feel that I should be happy to continue with him, and not to return to the sea-shore."

"The woods are never silent, Mabel, to such as understand their meaning. Days at a time have I travelled them alone, without feeling the want of company; and, as for conversation, for such as can comprehend their language, there is no want of rational and instructive discourse."

"I believe you are happier when alone, Pathfinder, than when mingling with your fellow-creatures."

"I will not say that—I will not say exactly that! I have seen the time when I have thought that God was sufficient for me in the forest, and that I craved no more than his bounty and his care. But other feelings have got uppermost, and I suppose natur' will have its way. All other creaturs mate, Mabel, and it was intended man should do so, too."

"And have you never bethought you of seeking a wife, Pathfinder, to share your fortunes?" inquired the girl, with the directness and simplicity that the pure of heart and the undesigning are the most apt to manifest, and with that feeling of affection which is inbred in her sex. "To me, it seems you only want a home to return to, from your wanderings, to render your life completely happy. Were I a man, it would be my delight to roam through these forests at will, or to sail over this beautiful lake."

"I understand you, Mabel; and God bless you for thinking of the welfare of men as humble as we are. We have our pleasures, it is true, as well as our gifts, but we might be happier; yes, I do think we might be happier."

"Happier! in what way, Pathfinder? In this pure air, with these cool and shaded forests to wander through, this lovely lake to gaze at and sail upon, with clear consciences, and abundance for all the real wants, men ought to be nothing less than as perfectly happy as their infirmities will allow."

"Every creatur' has its gifts, Mabel, and men have theirs," answered the guide, looking stealthily at his beautiful companion, whose cheeks had flushed and eyes brightened under the ardor of feelings excited by the novelty of her striking situation; "and all must obey them. Do you see yonder pigeon that is just alightin' on the beach— here in a line with the fallen chestnut?"

"Certainly; it is the only thing stirring, with life in it, besides ourselves, that is to be seen in this vast solitude."

"Not so, Mabel, not so; Providence makes nothing that lives, to live quite alone. Here is its mate, just rising on the wing; it has been feeding near the other beech, but it will not long be separated from its companion."

"I understand you, Pathfinder," returned Mabel, smiling sweetly, though as calmly as if the discourse was with her father. "But a hunter may find a mate, even in this wild region. The Indian girls are affectionate and true, I know, for such was the wife of Arrowhead to a husband who oftener frowned than smiled."

"That would never do, Mabel, and good would never come of it. Kind must cling to kind, and country to country, if one would find happiness. If, indeed, I could meet with one like you, who would consent to be a hunter's wife, and who would not scorn my ignorance and rudeness, then, indeed, would all the toil of the past appear like the sporting of the young deer, and all the future like sunshine!"

The Pathfinder: Then the body of Serjeant Danham,
which was propped against it, fell partly within the
block. To draw in the legs and secure the fastenings
occupied the Pathfinder but a moment.

"One like me! A girl of my years and indiscretion would hardly make a fit companion for the boldest scout and surest hunter on the lines!"

"Ah, Mabel! I fear me, that I have been improving a redskin's gifts with a paleface's natur'! Such a character would insure a wife in an Indian village."

"Surely, surely, Pathfinder, you would not think of choosing one as ignorant, as frivolous, as vain, and as inexperienced as I, for your wife!" Mabel would have added, "and as young," but an instinctive feeling of delicacy repressed the words.

"And why not, Mabel? If you are ignorant of frontier usages, you know more than all of us of pleasant anecdotes and town customs; as for frivolous, I know not what it means, but if it signifies beauty, ah's me! I fear it is no fault in my eyes. Vain you are not, as is seen by the kind manner in which you listen to all my idle tales about scoutings and trails; and as for experience, that will come with years. Besides, Mabel, I fear men think little of these matters when they are about to take wives; I do."

"Pathfinder—your words—your looks—surely all this is meant in trifling—you speak in pleasantry!"

"To me it is always agreeable to be near you, Mabel, and I should sleep sounder this blessed night than I have done for a week past, could I think that you find such discourse as pleasant as I do."

We shall not say that Mabel Dunham had not believed herself a favorite with the guide. This, her quick, feminine sagacity had early discovered, and perhaps she had occasionally thought there had mingled with his regard and friendship, some of that manly tenderness which the ruder sex must be coarse indeed not to show, on occasions, to the gentler; but the idea that he seriously sought her for his wife had never before crossed the mind of the spirited and ingenuous girl. Now, however, a gleam of something like the truth broke in upon her imagination, less induced by the words of her companion, perhaps, than by his manner. Looking earnestly into the rugged, honest countenance of the scout, Mabel's own features became concerned and grave, and when she spoke again, it was with a gentleness of manner that attracted him to her, even more powerfully than the words themselves were calculated to repel.

"You and I should understand each other, Pathfinder," she said, with an earnest sincerity; "nor should there be any cloud between us. You are too upright and frank to meet with any thing but sincerity and frankness in return. Surely—surely, all this means nothing—has no other connection with your feelings than such a friendship as one of your wisdom and character would naturally feel for a girl like me."

"I believe it's all nat'ral, Mabel; yes, I do; the sarjeant tells me he had such feelings toward your own mother, and I think I've seen something like it in the young people I have, from time to time, guided through the wilderness. Yes, yes—I dare say it's all nat'ral enough, and that makes it come so easy, and is a great comfort to me."

"Pathfinder, your words make me uneasy! Speak plainer, or change the subject forever. You do not—cannot mean that—you—cannot wish me to understand"—

even the tongue of the spirited Mabel faltered, and she shrunk, with maiden shame, from adding what she wished so earnestly to say. Rallying her courage, however, and determined to know all as soon and as plainly as possible, after a moment's hesitation, she continued—"I mean, Pathfinder, that you do not wish me to understand that you seriously think of me as a wife?"

"I do, Mabel; that's it—that's just it, and you have put the matter in a much better point of view than I, with my forest gifts and frontier ways, would ever be able to do. The sarjeant and I have concluded on the matter, if it is agreeable to you, as he thinks is likely to be the case, though I doubt my own power to please one who deserves the best husband America can produce."

Mabel's countenance changed from uneasiness to surprise, and then, by a transition still quicker, from surprise to pain.

"My father!" she exclaimed. "My dear father has thought of my becoming your wife, Pathfinder!"

"Yes, he has, Mabel; he has, indeed. He has even thought such a thing might be agreeable to you, and has almost encouraged me to fancy it might be true."

"But you, yourself—you certainly can care nothing whether this singular expectation shall ever be realized or not?"

"Anan?"

"I mean, Pathfinder, that you have talked of this match more to oblige my father than any thing else; that your feelings are no way concerned, let my answer be what it may."

The scout looked earnestly into the beautiful face of Mabel, which had flushed with the ardor and novelty of her sensations, and it was not possible to mistake the intense feeling that betrayed itself in every lineament of his ingenuous countenance.

"I have often thought myself happy, Mabel, when ranging the woods on a success-ful hunt, breathing the pure air of the hills, and filled with vigor and health; but I now know that it has all been idleness and vanity compared with the delight it would give me to know that you thought better of me than you think of most others."

"Better of you! I do indeed think better of you, Pathfinder, than of most others; I am not certain that I do not think better of you than of any other—for your truth, honesty, simplicity, justice, and courage, are scarcely equalled by any of earth."

"Ah! Mabel! these are sweet and encouraging words from you, and the sarjeant, after all, was not as near wrong as I feared."

"Nay, Pathfinder—in the name of all that is sacred and just, do not let us misun-derstand each other, in a matter of so much importance. While I esteem, respect—nay, reverence you almost as much as I reverence my own dear father, it is impossible that I should ever become your wife—that I "—

The change in her companion's countenance was so sudden and so great, that the moment the effect of what she had uttered became visible in the face of the Pathfinder, Mabel arrested her own words, notwithstanding her strong desire to be explicit; the reluctance with which she could at any time cause pain being sufficient of itself to induce the pause. Neither spoke for some time, the shade of disappointment that crossed the rugged lineaments of the hunter, amounting so nearly to anguish as to frighten his companion, while the sensation of choking became so strong in the Pathfinder, that he fairly griped his throat, like one who sought physical relief for physical suffering. The convulsive manner in which his fingers worked actually struck the alarmed girl with a feeling of awe.

"Nay, Pathfinder," Mabel eagerly added, the instant she could command her voice—"I may have said more than I mean, for all things of this nature are possible, and women, they say, are never sure of their own minds. What I wish you to understand is, that it is not likely that you and I should ever think of each other as man and wife ought to think of each other."

"I do not—I shall never think in that way again, Mabel," gasped forth the Pathfinder, who appeared to utter his words like one just raised above the pressure of some suffocating substance. "No—no—I shall never think of you, or any one else, again in that way."

"Pathfinder—dear Pathfinder—understand me—do not attach more meaning to my words than I do myself—a match like that would be unwise—unnatural, perhaps."

"Yes, unnat'ral—ag'in natur'; and so I told the sarjeant, but he *would* have it otherwise."

"Pathfinder!—Oh! this is worse than I could have imagined—take my hand, excellent Pathfinder, and let me see that you do not hate me. For God's sake smile upon me again!"

"Hate you, Mabel! Smile upon you! Ah's me!"

"Nay, give me your hand; your hardy, true, and manly hand—both, both, Pathfinder, for I shall not be easy until I feel certain that we are friends again, and that all this has been a mistake."

"Mabel," said the guide, looking wistfully into the face of the generous and impetuous girl, as she held his two hard and sunburnt hands in her own pretty and delicate fingers, and laughing in his own silent and peculiar manner, while anguish gleamed over lineaments which seemed incapable of deception, even while agitated with emotions so conflicting—"Mabel, the sarjeant was wrong!"

The pent-up feelings could endure no more, and the tears rolled down the cheeks of the scout like rain. His fingers again worked convulsively at his throat, and his breast heaved, as if it possessed a tenant of which it would be rid, by any effort, however desperate.

"Pathfinder!—Pathfinder!" Mabel almost shrieked—"any thing but this—any thing but this. Speak to me, Pathfinder—smile again—say one kind word—any thing to prove you can forgive me."

" The sarjeant was wrong," exclaimed the guide, laughing amid his agony, in a way to terrify his companion by the unnatural mixture of anguish and light-heartedness. " I knew it—I knew it, and said it ; yes, the sarjeant was wrong, after all."

" We can be friends, though we cannot be man and wife," continued Mabel, almost as much disturbed as her companion, scarce knowing what she said ; " we can always be friends, and always will."

" I thought the sarjeant was mistaken," resumed the Pathfinder, when a great effort had enabled him to command himself, " for I did not think my gifts were such as would please the fancy of a town-bred girl. It would have been better, Mabel, had he not over-persuaded me into a different notion ; and it might have been better, too, had you not been so pleasant and confiding, like ; yes, it would."

" If I thought any error of mine had raised false expectations in you, Pathfinder, however unintentionally on my part, I should never forgive myself ; for, believe me, I would rather endure pain in my own feelings, than you should suffer."

" That's just it, Mabel ; that's just it. These speeches and opinions, spoken in so soft a voice, and in a way I'm so unused to in the woods, have done the mischief. But I now see plainly, and begin to understand the difference between us better, and will strive to keep down thought, and to go abroad again as I used to do, looking for the game and the inimy. Ah's me ! Mabel, I have, indeed, been on a false trail, since we met !"

" But you will now travel on the true one. In a little while you will forget all this, and think of me as a friend, who owes you her life."

" This may be the way in the towns, but I doubt if it's nat'ral to the woods. With us, when the eye sees a lovely sight, it is apt to keep it long in view ; or when the mind takes in an upright and proper feeling, it is loth to part with it."

" But it is not a proper feeling that you should love me, nor am I a lovely sight. You will forget it all, when you come seriously to recollect that I am altogether unsuited to be your wife."

" So I told the sarjeant—but he would have it otherwise. I knew you was too young and beautiful for one of middle age, like myself, and who never was comely to look at, even in youth ; and then your ways have not been my ways, nor would a hunter's cabin be a fitting place for one who was edicated among chiefs, as it were. If I were younger and comelier, though, like Jasper Eau-douce"—

" Never mind Jasper Eau-douce," interrupted Mabel, impatiently ; " we can talk of something else."

" Jasper is a worthy lad, Mabel ; aye, and a comely," returned the guileless guide, looking earnestly at the girl, as if he distrusted her judgment in speaking slightingly of his friend. " Were I only half as comely as Jasper Western, my misgivings in this affair would not have been so great, and they might not have been so true."

" We will not talk of Jasper Western," repeated Mabel, the color mounting to her temples—" he may be good enough in a gale, or on the lake, but he is not good enough to talk of here."

" I fear me, Mabel, he is better than the man who is likely to be your husband, though the sarjeant says that never can take place. But the sarjeant was wrong once, and he may be wrong twice."

" And who is likely to be my husband, Pathfinder? This is scarcely less strange than what has just passed between us!"

" I know it is nat'ral for like to seek like, and for them that have consorted much with officers' ladies, to wish to be officers' ladies themselves. But, Mabel, I may speak plainly to you, I know, and I hope my words will not give you pain, for, now I understand what it is to be disappointed in such feelings, I wouldn't wish to cause even a Mingo sorrow, on this head. But happiness is not always to be found in a marquee, any more than in a tent, and though the officers' quarters may look more tempting than the rest of the barracks, there is often great misery, between husband and wife, inside of their doors."

" I do not doubt it, in the least, Pathfinder; and did it rest with me to decide, I would sooner follow you to some cabin in the woods, and share your fortune, whether it might be better or worse, than go inside the door of any officer I know, with an intention of remaining there as its master's wife!"

" Mabel, this is not what Lundie hopes, or Lundie thinks!"

" And what care I for Lundie? He is major of the 55th, and may command his men to wheel and march about as he pleases, but he cannot compel me to wed the greatest or the meanest of his mess; besides, what can you know of Lundie's wishes on such a subject?"

" From Lundie's own mouth. The sarjeant had told him that he wished me for a son-in-law; and the major, being an old and a true friend, conversed with me on the subject; he put it to me, plainly, whether it would not be more ginerous in me to let an officer succeed, than to strive to make you share a hunter's fortune. I owned the truth, I did; and that was, that I thought it might; but when he told me that the quarter-master would be his choice, I would not abide by the conditions. No—no—Mabel; I know Davy Muir well, and though he may make you a lady, he can never make you a happy woman, or himself a gentleman. I say this honestly, I do; for I now plainly see that the sarjeant has been wrong."

" My father has been very wrong if he has said or done aught to cause you sorrow, Pathfinder; and so great is my respect for you, so sincere my friendship, that were it not for one—I mean that no person need fear Lieutenant Muir's influence with me. I would rather remain as I am, to my dying day, than become a lady at the cost of being his wife."

" I do not think you would say that which you do not feel, Mabel," returned Pathfinder, earnestly.

"Not at such a moment, on such a subject, and least of all to you. No ; Lieutenant Muir may find wives where he can—my name shall never be on his catalogue."

"Thank you—thank you for that, Mabel; for, though there is no longer any hope for me, I could never be happy were you to take to the quarter-master. I feared the commission might count for something, I did, and I know the man. It is not jealousy that makes me speak in this manner, but truth, for I know the man. Now, were you to fancy a desarving youth, one like Jasper Western, for instance"—

"Why always mention Jasper Eau-douce, Pathfinder ? he can have no concern with our friendship; let us talk of yourself, and of the manner in which you intend to pass the winter."

"Ah's me !—I'm little worth at the best, Mabel, unless it may be on a trail, or with the rifle ; and less worth now that I've discovered the sarjeant's mistake. There is no need, therefore, of talking of me. It has been very pleasant to me to be near you so long, and even to fancy that the sarjeant was right; but that is all over now. I shall go down the lake with Jasper, and then there will be business to occupy us, and that will keep useless thoughts out of the mind."

"And you will forget this—forget me—no, not forget me, either, Pathfinder; but you will resume your old pursuits, and cease to think a girl of sufficient importance to disturb your peace ?"

"I never know'd it afore, Mabel, but girls, as you call them, though gals is the name I've been taught to use, are of more account in this life than I could have believed. Now, afore I know'd you, the new-born babe did not sleep more sweetly than I used to could ; my head was no sooner on the root, or the stone, or mayhap on the skin, than all was lost to the senses, unless it might be to go over, in the night, the business of the day, in a dream, like ; and there I lay till the moment came to be stirring, and the swallows were not more certain to be on the wing, with the light, than I to be afoot, at the moment I wished to be. All this seemed a gift, and might be calculated on, even in the midst of a Mingo camp; for I've been outlying, in my time, in the very villages of the vagabonds."

"And all this will return to you, Pathfinder; for one so upright and sincere will never waste his happiness on a mere fancy. You will dream again of your hunts, of the deer you have slain, and of the beaver you have taken."

"Ah's me, Mabel, I wish never to dream again ! Before we met, I had a sort of pleasure in following up the hounds, in fancy, as it might be ; and even in striking a trail of the Iroquois—nay, I've been in skrimmages and ambushments, in thought, like, and found satisfaction in it, according to my gifts ; but all those things have lost their charms since I've made acquaintance with you. Now, I think no longer of any thing rude in my dreams, but the very last night we staid in the garrison, I imagined I had a cabin in a grove of sugar-maples, and at the root of every tree was a Mabel Dunham, while the birds that were among the branches sung ballads, instead of the notes that natur' gave, and even the deer stopped to listen. I tried to shoot a fa'an, but Killdeer missed fire, and the creatur' laughed in my face, as pleasantly as a young girl laughs in her merriment, and then it bounded away, looking back, as if it expected me to follow."

"No more of this, Pathfinder—we'll talk no more of these things," said Mabel, dashing the tears from her eyes; for the simple, earnest manner in which this hardy woodsman betrayed the deep hold she had taken of his feelings, nearly proved too much for her own generous heart. "Now, let us look for my father; he cannot be distant, as I heard his gun quite near."

"The sarjeant was wrong—yes, he was wrong, and it's of no avail to attempt to make the dove consort with the wolf."

"Here comes my dear father," interrupted Mabel; "let us look cheerful and happy, Pathfinder, as such good friends ought to look, and keep each other's secrets."

A pause succeeded; the serjeant's foot was heard crushing the dried twigs hard by, and then his form appeared, shoving aside the bushes of a copse, quite near. As he issued into the open ground, the old soldier scrutinized his daughter and her companion, and, speaking good-naturedly, he said—

"Mabel, child, you are young and light of foot—look for a bird I've shot, that fell just beyond the thicket of young hemlocks, on the shore; and, as Jasper is showing signs of an intention of getting under way, you need not take the trouble to clamber up this hill again, but we will meet you on the beach in a few minutes."

Mabel obeyed, bounding down the hill with the elastic step of youth and health. But, notwithstanding the lightness of her steps, the heart of the girl was heavy, and no sooner was she hid from observation by the thicket, than she threw herself on the root of a tree, and wept as if her heart would break.

LAKE OTSEGO FROM WITCHHAZEL POINT.

XVII.

THE DEERSLAYER.

One pleasant summer evening the author of the Pathfinder was driving along the lake shore in his farm wagon, singing cheerily, as he passed over that quiet, shady road, as he frequently did. Though no musician, he often sang—when in a gay mood—snatches of familiar songs which had struck his fancy; and many a time, when driving along the quiet, shady road leading to his mountain-farm, the squirrel at play, or the sleepy teamster, dozing on his seat, has been surprised by some sudden burst of Burns' "Scots wha ha' wi' Wallace bled!" or Moore's "Love's Young Dream"—always especial favorites with him. On the present occasion, however, it was a political song that he was singing; and, shall we avow the act of infidelity, an electioneering song of the party opposed to his own! Suddenly he paused, as an opening in the wood revealed a sweet view of the lake. His spirited gray eye rested a moment on the water, with that expression of abstracted, poetical thought, ever familiar to those who lived with him; then, turning to the companion at his side—the daughter now writing these lines—he exclaimed: "I must write one more book, dearie, about our little lake!" Again his eye rested on the water and the banks, with the far-seeing look of one evoking

The Deerslayer: **Death of the Indian**

imaginary figures to fill the beautiful scene. A moment of silence followed—his daughter being unwilling to interrupt the train of thought opening before him; a few minutes passed—again he cracked his whip, resumed his song, with some careless chat on little incidents of the hour, and drove homeward. A few days later the first pages of the Deerslayer were written.

During many a long year had Natty now been, as it were, a constant companion of the writer: in four different works the Leather-stocking had been brought before the public; and very many were the hours, no doubt, in which the author held communion with this creature of his imagination in scenes never recorded. Reversing the usual order, when himself a young man, he had first brought the hunter into view at the age of threescore and ten; now, when his own head was growing hoary, he brings Natty before the reader as a youth—he leads us over the first war-path of his hero. And the same lake shores on which that striking figure had first appeared, are again chosen for the closing work of the series, as the scene of Natty's earlier prowess in the hunt and in war. We are made to look backward at the highland lake; to behold it in its native aspect, when, a hundred years earlier, no building of the white man was yet reflected from its banks; when, girt to the very water's edge with forests, the growth of ages, the eye of the savage and the hunter had alone beheld its sylvan beauty. With singular fertility of invention, a train of appropriate and very original incident—full of spirit, of feeling, of interest—is woven about the shores, and over the very bosom of the little lake. Muskrat Castle, and the Ark of Floating Tom, with the Indian canoe, give a strange, wild interest to the picture; while the well-drawn characters of Judith, beautiful, but designing—of simple-hearted Hetty, touchingly innocent and artless—give the lighter and sweeter touches to scenes which were otherwise wholly wild.

WILD ROSE POINT.

THE RESCUE OF HIST.

CHINGACHGOOK and his pale-face friend set forth on their hazardous and delicate enterprise with a coolness and method that would have done credit to men who were on their twentieth, instead of being on their first war-path. As suited his relation to the pretty fugitive in whose service they were engaged, the Indian took his place in the head of the canoe; while Deerslayer guided its movements in the stern. By this arrangement, the former would be the first to land, and, of course, the first to meet his mistress. The latter had taken his post without comment, but in secret influenced by the reflection that one who had so much at stake as the Indian, might not possibly guide the canoe with the same steadiness and intelligence as another who had more command of his feelings. From the instant they left the side of the ark, the movements of the two adventurers were like the manœuvres of highly-drilled soldiers, who, for the first time, were called on to meet the enemy in the field. As yet, Chingachgook had never fired a shot in anger, and the *début* of his companion in warfare is known to the reader. It is true, the Indian had been hanging about his enemy's camp for a few hours, on his first arrival, and he had even once entered it, as related in the last chapter, but no consequences had followed either experiment. Now, it was certain that an important result was to be effected, or a mortifying failure was to ensue. The rescue, or the continued captivity of Hist, depended on the enterprise. In a word, it was virtually the maiden expedition of these two ambitious young forest soldiers; and, while one of them set forth, impelled by sentiments that usually carry men so far, both had all their feelings of pride and manhood enlisted in their success.

Instead of steering in a direct line to the point, then distant from the ark less than a quarter of a mile, Deerslayer laid the head of his canoe diagonally toward the centre of the lake, with a view to obtain a position, from which he might approach the shore, having his enemies in his front only. The spot where Hetty had landed, and where Hist had promised to meet them, moreover, was on the upper side of the projection, rather than on the lower; and, to reach it, would have required the adventurers to double nearly the whole point close in with the shore, had not this preliminary step been taken. So well was the necessity for this measure understood, that Chingachgook quietly paddled on, although it was adopted without consulting him, and apparently was taking him in a direction nearly opposite to that in which, one might think, he most wished to go. A few minutes sufficed, however, to carry the canoe the necessary distance, when both the young men ceased paddling, as it were, by instinctive consent, and the boat became stationary.

The darkness increased rather than diminished; but it was still possible, from the place where the adventurers lay, to distinguish the outlines of the mountains. In vain did the Delaware turn his head eastward, to catch a glimpse of the promised star; for, notwithstanding the clouds broke a little near the horizon, in that quarter of the heavens, the curtain continued so far drawn as effectually to conceal all behind it. In front, as was known by the formation of land above and behind it, lay the point, at a distance of about a thousand feet. No signs of the castle could be seen, nor could any movement in that quarter of the lake reach the ear. The latter circumstance might have been equally owing to the distance, which was several miles, or to the fact that nothing was in motion. As for the ark, though scarcely further from the canoe than the point, it lay so completely buried in the shadows of the shore, that it would not have been visible even had there been many degrees more of light than actually existed.

The adventurers now held a conference in low voices, consulting together as to the probable time. Deerslayer thought it wanted yet some minutes to the rising of the star, while the impatience of the chief caused him to fancy the night further advanced, and to believe that his betrothed was already awaiting his appearance on the shore. As might have been expected, the opinion of the latter prevailed, and his friend disposed himself to steer for the place of rendezvous. The utmost skill and precaution now became necessary in the management of the canoe. The paddles were lifted and returned to the water in a noiseless manner; and when within a hundred yards of the beach, Chingachgook took in his altogether, laying his hand on his rifle instead. As they got still more within the belt of darkness that girded the woods, it was seen that they were steering too far north, and the course was altered accordingly. The canoe now seemed to move by instinct, so cautious and deliberate were all its motions. Still it continued to advance, until its bows grated on the gravel of the beach, at the precise spot where Hetty had landed, and whence her voice had issued, the previous night, as the ark was passing. There was, as usual, a narrow strand, but bushes fringed the woods, and in most places overhung the water.

Chingachgook stepped upon the beach, and cautiously examined it for some distance on each side of the canoe. In order to do this he was often obliged to wade to his knees in the lake, but no Hist rewarded his search. When he returned he found his friend also on the shore. They next conferred in whispers, the Indian apprehending that they must have mistaken the place of rendezvous. But Deerslayer thought it was probable they had mistaken the hour. While he was yet speaking, he grasped the arm of the Delaware, caused him to turn his head in the direction of the lake, and pointed toward the summits of the eastern mountains. The clouds had broken a little, apparently behind rather than above the hills, and the selected star was glittering among the branches of a pine. This was every way a flattering omen, and the young men leaned on their rifles, listening intently for the sound of approaching footsteps. Voices they often heard, and mingled with them were the suppressed cries of children, and the low but sweet laugh of Indian women. As the native Americans are habitually cautious, and seldom break out in loud conversation, the adventurers knew by these facts, that they must be very near the encampment. It was easy to perceive that there was a fire within the woods, by the manner in which some of the upper branches of the trees were illuminated; but it was not possible, where they stood, to ascertain exactly how near it was to themselves. Once or twice it seemed as if stragglers from around the fire were approaching the place of rendezvous; but these sounds were either altogether illusion, or those who had drawn near returned again without coming to the shore. A quarter of an hour was passed in this state of intense expectation and anxiety, when Deerslayer proposed that they should circle the point in the canoe; and, by getting a position close in, where the camp could be seen, reconnoitre the Indians, and thus enable themselves to form some plausible conjectures for the non-appearance of Hist. The Delaware, however, resolutely refused to quit the spot, reasonably enough offering as a reason the disappointment of the girl should she arrive in his absence. Deerslayer felt for his friend's concern, and offered to make the circuit of the point by himself, leaving the latter concealed in the bushes to await the occurrence of any fortunate event that might favor his views. With this understanding, then, the parties separated.

As soon as Deerslayer was at his post again, in the stern of the canoe, he left the shore with the same precautions, and in the same noiseless manner, as he had approached it. On this occasion he did not go far from the land, the bushes affording a sufficient cover, by keeping as close in as possible. Indeed, it would not have been easy to devise any means more favorable to reconnoitring round an Indian camp than those afforded by the actual state of things. The formation of the point permitted the place to be circled on three of its sides, and the progress of the boat was so noiseless as to remove any apprehensions from an alarm through sound. The most practiced and guarded foot might stir a bunch of leaves, or snap a dried stick in the dark, but a bark canoe could be made to float over the surface of smooth water, almost with the instinctive readiness, and certainly with the noiseless movements of an aquatic bird.

Deerslayer had got nearly in a line between the camp and the ark before he caught a glimpse of the fire. This came upon him suddenly, and a little unexpectedly, at first causing an alarm, lest he had incautiously ventured within the circle of light it cast. But, perceiving at a second glance, that he was certainly safe from detection so long as the Indians kept near the centre of the illumination, he brought the canoe to a state of rest, in the most favorable position he could find, and commenced his observations.

We have written much, but in vain, concerning this extraordinary being, if the reader requires now to be told, that, untutored as he was in the learning of the world, and simple as he ever showed himself to be in all matters touching the subtleties of conventional taste, he was a man of strong, native, poetical feeling. He loved the woods for their freshness, their sublime solitudes, their vastness, and the impress that they everywhere bore of the divine hand of their Creator. He seldom moved through them without pausing to dwell on some peculiar beauty that gave him pleasure, though rarely attempting to investigate the causes; and never did a day pass without his communing in spirit—and this, too, without the aid of forms or language—with the infinite source of all he saw, felt, and beheld. Thus constituted in a moral sense, and of a steadiness that no danger could appal, or any crisis disturb, it is not surprising that the hunter felt a pleasure in looking on the scene he now beheld, that momentarily caused him to forget the object of his visit. This will more fully appear when we describe the scene.

The canoe lay in front of a natural vista, not only through the bushes that lined the shore, but of the trees, also, that afforded a clear view of the camp. It was by means of this same opening that the light had been first seen from the ark. In consequence of their recent change of ground, the Indians had not yet retired to their huts, but had been delayed by their preparations, which included lodging as well as food. A large fire had been made, as much to answer the purpose of torches, as for the use of their simple cookery; and at this precise moment it was blazing high and bright, having recently received a large supply of dried brush. The effect was to illuminate the arches of the forest, and to render the whole area occupied by the camp as light as if hundreds of tapers were burning. Most of the toil had ceased, and even the hungriest child had satisfied its appetite. In a word, the time was that moment of relaxation and general indolence which is apt to succeed a hearty meal, and when the labors of the day have ended. The hunters and the fishermen had been equally successful; and food—that one great requisite of savage life—being abundant, every other care appeared to have subsided in the sense of enjoyment dependent on this all-important fact.

Deerslayer saw at a glance that many of the warriors were absent.   His acquaintance, Rivenoak, however, was present, being seated in the foreground of a picture that
Salvator Rosa would have delighted to draw, his swarthy features illuminated as much
by pleasure, as by the torch-like flame, while he showed another of the tribe one of
the elephants that had caused so much sensation among his people. A boy was looking
over his shoulder, in dull curiosity, completing the group.   More in the background,
eight or ten warriors lay half recumbent on the ground, or sat with their backs
inclining against trees, so many types of indolent repose.   Their arms were near them
all, sometimes leaning against the same trees as themselves, or were lying across their
bodies, in careless preparation.   But the group that most attracted the attention of
Deerslayer was that composed of the women and children.   All the females appeared
to be collected together, and, almost as a matter of course, their young were near
them.   The former laughed and chatted, in their rebuked and quiet manner, though
one who knew the habits of the people might have detected that every thing was
not going on in its usual train.   Most of the young women seemed to be light-
hearted enough ; but one old hag was seated apart, with a watchful, soured aspect,
which, the hunter at once knew, betokened that some duty of an unpleasant character
had been assigned her by the chiefs.   What that duty was, he had no means of knowing ; but he felt satisfied it must be, in some measure, connected with her own sex, the
aged among the women generally being chosen for such offices, and no other.

As a matter of course, Deerslayer looked eagerly and anxiously for the form of
Hist.   She was nowhere visible, though the light penetrated to considerable distances,
in all directions around the fire.   Once, or twice, he started, as he thought he recognized her laugh ; but his ears were deceived by the soft melody that is so common to
the Indian female voice.   At length the old woman spoke loud and angrily, and then
he caught a glimpse of one or two dark figures, in the background of trees, which
turned as if obedient to the rebuke, and walked more within the circle of the light.
A young warrior's form first came fairly into view ; then followed two youthful
females, one of whom proved to be the Delaware girl.   Deerslayer now comprehended
it all.   Hist was watched, possibly by her young companion, certainly by the old
woman.   The youth was probably some suitor of either her or her companion ; but
even his discretion was distrusted under the influence of his admiration.   The known
vicinity of those who might be supposed to be her friends, and the arrival of a
strange red-man on the lake, had induced more than the usual care, and the girl had
not been able to slip away from those who watched her, in order to keep her appointment.   Deerslayer traced her uneasiness, by her attempting, once or twice, to look up
through the branches of the trees, as if endeavoring to get glimpses of the star she
had herself named, as the sign for meeting.   All was vain, however, and after strolling
about the camp a little longer, in affected indifference, the two girls quitted their male
escort, and took seats among their own sex.   As soon as this was done, the old

sentinel changed her place to one more agreeable to herself—a certain proof that she had hitherto been exclusively on the watch.

Deerslayer now felt greatly at a loss how to proceed. He well knew that Chingachgook could never be persuaded to return to the ark, without making some desperate effort for the recovery of his mistress, and his own generous feelings well disposed him to aid in such an undertaking. He thought he saw the signs of an intention among the females to retire for the night; and should he remain, and the fire continue to give out its light, he might discover the particular hut, or arbor, under which Hist reposed —a circumstance that would be of infinite use, in their future proceedings. Should he remain, however, much longer where he was, there was great danger that the impatience of his friend would drive him into some act of imprudence. At each instant, indeed, he expected to see the swarthy form of the Delaware appearing in the background, like the tiger prowling around the fold. Taking all things into consideration, therefore, he came to the conclusion it would be better to rejoin his friend, and endeavor to temper his impetuosity by some of his own coolness and discretion. It required but a minute or two to put this plan in execution—the canoe returning to the strand some ten or fifteen minutes after it had left it.

Contrary to his expectations, perhaps, Deerslayer found the Indian at his post, from which he had not stirred, fearful that his betrothed might arrive during his absence. A conference followed, in which Chingachgook was made acquainted with the state of things in the camp. When Hist named the point as the place of meeting, it was with the expectation of making her escape from the old position, and of repairing to a spot that she expected to find without any occupants; but the sudden change of localities had disconcerted all her plans. A much greater degree of vigilance than had been previously required, was now necessary; and the circumstance that an aged woman was on watch, also denoted some special grounds of alarm. All these considerations, and many more that will readily suggest themselves to the reader, were briefly discussed before the young men came to any decision. The occasion, however, being one that required acts instead of words, the course to be pursued was soon chosen.

Disposing of the canoe in such a manner that Hist must see it, should she come to the place of meeting previously to their return, the young men looked to their arms, and prepared to enter the wood. The whole projection into the lake contained about two acres of land; and the part that formed the point, and on which the camp was placed, did not compose a surface of more than half that size. It was principally covered with oaks, which, as is usual in the American forests, grew to a great height without throwing out a branch, and then arched in a dense and rich foliage. Beneath, except the fringe of thick bushes along the shore, there was very little underbrush; though, in consequence of their shape, the trees were closer together than is common in regions where the axe has been freely used, resembling tall, straight, rustic columns, upholding the usual canopy of leaves. The surface of the land was tolerably

even, but it had a small rise near its centre, which divided it into a northern and
southern half. On the latter the Hurons had built their fire, profiting by the formation to conceal it from their enemies, who, it will be remembered, were supposed to
be in the castle, which bore northerly. A brook also came brawling down the sides
of the adjacent hills, and found its way into the lake, on the southern side of the point.
It had cut for itself a deep passage through some of the higher portions of the ground,
and, in later days, when this spot has become subjected to the uses of civilization, by
its windings and shaded banks, it has become no mean accessory in contributing to the
beauty of the place. This brook lay west of the encampment, and its waters found
their way into the great reservoir of that region on the same side, and quite near to
the spot chosen for the fire. All these peculiarities, so far as circumstances allowed,
had been noted by Deerslayer, and explained to his friend.

The reader will understand that the little rise in the ground, that lay behind the
Indian encampment, greatly favored the secret advance of the two adventurers. It
prevented the light of the fire diffusing itself on the ground directly in the rear,
although the land fell away toward the water, so as to leave what might be termed the
left, or eastern flank of the position, unprotected by this covering. We have said
" unprotected," though that is not properly the word, since the knoll behind the huts
and the fire offered a cover for those who were now stealthily approaching, rather than
any protection to the Indians. Deerslayer did not break through the fringe of bushes
immediately abreast of the canoe, which might have brought him too suddenly within
the influence of the light, since the hillock did not extend to the water; but he followed
the beach northerly until he had got nearly on the opposite side of the tongue of land,
which brought him under the shelter of the low acclivity, and, consequently, more in
shadow.

As soon as the friends emerged from the bushes, they stopped to reconnoitre. The
fire was still blazing behind the little ridge, casting its light upward, into the tops of
the trees, producing an effect that was more pleasing than advantageous. Still the
glare had its uses; for, while the background was in obscurity, the foreground was
in strong light; exposing the savages and concealing their foes. Profiting by the
latter circumstance, the young men advanced cautiously toward the ridge, Deerslayer
in front, for he insisted on this arrangement, lest the Delaware should be led by his
feelings into some indiscretion. It required but a moment to reach the foot of the little
ascent, and then commenced the most critical part of the enterprise. Moving with exceeding caution, and trailing his rifle, both to keep its barrel out of view and in
readiness for service, the hunter put foot before foot, until he had got sufficiently high
to overlook the summit, his own head being alone brought into the light. Chingachgook
was at his side, and both paused to take another close examination of the camp. In
order, however, to protect themselves against any straggler in the rear, they placed
their bodies against the trunk of an oak, standing on the side next the fire.

J. Hamilton fecit.   J. Mc Goffin sculp.

The Deerslayer: Burial of Hetty Hutter

The view that Deerslayer now obtained of the camp, was exactly the reverse of that he had perceived from the water. The dim figures which he had formerly discovered, must have been on the summit of the ridge, a few feet in advance of the spot where he was now posted. The fire was still blazing brightly, and around it were seated, on logs, thirteen warriors, which accounted for all whom he had seen from the canoe. They were conversing, with much earnestness, among themselves, the image of the elephant passing from hand to hand. The first burst of savage wonder had abated, and the question now under discussion was the probable existence, the history, and the habits of so extraordinary an animal. We have not leisure to record the opinions of these rude men on a subject so consonant to their lives and experience; but little is hazarded in saying that they were quite as plausible, and far more ingenious, than half the conjectures that precede the demonstrations of science. However much they may have been at fault, as to their conclusions and inferences, it is certain that they discussed the questions with a zealous and most undivided attention. For the time being, all else was forgotten, and our adventurers could not have approached at a more fortunate instant.

The females were collected near each other, much as Deerslayer had last seen them, nearly in a line between the place where he now stood and the fire. The distance from the oak against which the young man leaned, and the warriors, was about thirty yards; the women may have been half that number of yards nigher. The latter, indeed, were so near as to make the utmost circumspection, as to motion and noise, indispensable. Although they conversed in their low, soft voices, it was possible, in the profound stillness of the woods, even to catch passages of the discourse; and the light-hearted laugh that escaped the girls, might occasionally have reached the canoe. Deerslayer felt the tremor that passed through the frame of his friend, when the latter first caught the sweet sounds that issued from the plump, pretty lips of Hist. He even laid a hand on the shoulder of the Indian, as a sort of admonition to command himself. As the conversation grew more earnest, each leaned forward to listen.

"The Hurons have more curious beasts than that," said one of the girls, contemptuously; for, like the men, they conversed of the elephant and his qualities. "The Delawares will think this creature wonderful, but, to-morrow, no Huron tongue will talk of it. Our young men will find him, if the animal dares to come near our wigwams!"

This was, in fact, addressed to Wah-tah-Wah, though she who spoke uttered her words with an assumed diffidence and humility, that prevented her looking at the other.

"The Delawares are so far from letting such creatures come into their country," returned Hist, "that no one has even seen their images there! Their young men would frighten away the *images* as well as the *beasts.*"

"The Delaware young men! The nation is women; even the deer walk when they hear their hunters coming! Who has ever heard the name of a young Delaware warrior?"

This was said in good humor, and with a laugh; but it was also said bitingly. That Hist so felt it was apparent by the spirit betrayed in her answer.

"Who has ever heard the name of a young Delaware?" she repeated, earnestly. "Tamenund himself, though now as old as the pines on the hill, or as the eagles in the air, was once young; his name was heard from the great salt lake to the sweet waters of the west. What is the family of Uncas? Where is another as great, though the pale-faces have ploughed up its graves, and trodden on its bones? Do the eagles fly as high, is the deer as swift, or the panther as brave? Is there no young warrior of that race? Let the Huron maidens open their eyes wider, and they may see one called Chingachgook, who is as stately as the young ash, and as tough as the hickory."

As the girl used her figurative language, and told her companions to "open their eyes, and they would see" the Delaware, Deerslayer thrust his fingers into the sides of his friend, and indulged in a fit of his hearty, benevolent laughter. The other smiled; but the language of the speaker was too flattering, and the tones of her voice too sweet, for him to be led away by any accidental coincidence, however ludicrous. The speech of Hist produced a retort, and the dispute, though conducted in good humor, and without any of the coarse violence of tone and gesture that often impairs the charms of the sex in what is called civilized life, grew warm and slightly clamorous. In the midst of this scene, the Delaware caused his friend to stoop, so as completely to conceal himself, and then he made a noise so closely resembling the little chirrup of the smallest species of the American squirrel, that Deerslayer himself, though he had heard the imitation a hundred times, actually thought it came from one of the little animals, skipping about over his head. The sound is so familiar in the woods, that none of the Hurons paid it the least attention. Hist, however, instantly ceased talking, and sat motionless. Still she had sufficient self-command to abstain from turning her head. She had heard the signal by which her lover so often called her from the wigwam to the stolen interview, and it came over her senses and her heart as the serenade affects the maiden in the land of song.

From that moment Chingachgook felt certain that his presence was known. This was effecting much, and he could now hope for a bolder line of conduct on the part of his mistress than she might dare to adopt under an uncertainty of his situation. It left no doubt of her endeavoring to aid him in his effort to release her. Deerslayer arose as soon as the signal was given, and though he had never held that sweet communion which is known only to lovers, he was not slow to detect the great change that had come over the manner of the girl. She still affected to dispute, though it was no longer with spirit and ingenuity; but what she said was uttered more as a lure to draw her antagonists on to an easy conquest, than with any hopes of succeeding herself. Once or twice, it is true, her native readiness suggested a retort, or an argument, that raised a laugh, and gave her a momentary advantage; but these little sallies, the offspring of mother-wit, served the better to conceal her real feelings, and to give to the triumph of the other party a more natural air than it might have possessed without them. At length the disputants became wearied, and they rose in a body, as if about to separate. It was now that Hist, for the first time, ventured to turn her face in the direction whence the signal had come. In doing this, her movements were natural but guarded, and she stretched her arm and yawned, as if overcome with a desire to sleep. The chirrup was again heard, and the girl felt satisfied as to the position of her lover, though the strong light in which she herself was placed, and the comparative darkness in which the adventurers stood, prevented her from seeing their heads, the only portions of their forms that appeared above the ridge at all. The tree against which they were posted had a dark shadow cast upon it by the intervention of an enormous pine that grew between it and the fire; a circumstance which, alone, would have rendered objects within its cloud invisible at any distance. This Deerslayer well knew, and it was one of the reasons why he had selected this particular tree.

The moment was near when it became necessary for Hist to act. She was to sleep in a small hut, or bower, that had been built near the spot where she stood, and her companion was the aged hag, already mentioned. Once within the hut, with this sleepless old woman stretched across the entrance, as was her nightly practice, the hope of escape was nearly destroyed, and she might, at any moment, be summoned to her bed. Luckily, at this instant, one of the warriors called to the old woman by name, and bade her bring him water to drink. There was a delicious spring on the northern side of the point, and the hag took a gourd from a branch, and summoning Hist to her side, she moved toward the summit of the ridge, intending to descend and cross the point to the natural fountain. All this was seen and understood by the adventurers, and they fell back into the obscurity, concealing their persons by trees, until the two females had passed them. In walking, Hist was held tightly by the hand. As she moved by the tree that hid Chingachgook and his friend, the former felt for his tomahawk, with the intention to bury it in the brain of the woman. But the other saw the hazard of such a measure, since a single scream might bring all the warriors upon them, and he was averse to the act on considerations of humanity. His hand, therefore, prevented the blow. Still, as the two moved past, the chirrup was repeated, and the Huron woman stopped and faced the tree whence the sounds seemed to proceed, standing, at the moment, within six feet of her enemies. She expressed her surprise that a squirrel should be in motion at so late an hour, and said it boded evil. Hist answered that she had heard the same squirrel three times within the last twenty minutes, and that she supposed it was waiting to obtain some of the crumbs left from the late supper. This explanation appeared satisfactory, and they moved toward the spring, the men following stealthily and closely. The gourd was filled, and the old woman was hurrying back, her hand still grasping the wrist of the girl, when she was suddenly seized so violently by the throat, as to cause her to release her captive, and to prevent her making any other sound than a sort of gurgling, suffocating noise. The Serpent passed his arm round the waist of his mistress, and dashed through the bushes with her, on the north side of the point. Here he immediately turned along the beach, and ran toward the canoe. A more direct course could have been taken, but it might have led to a discovery of the place of embarking.

Deerslayer kept playing on the throat of the old woman, like the keys of an organ, occasionally allowing her to breathe, and then compressing his fingers again, nearly to strangling. The brief intervals for breath, however, were well improved, and the hag succeeded in letting out a screech or two that served to alarm the camp. The tramp of the warriors, as they sprang from the fire, was plainly audible ; and, at the next moment, three or four of them appeared on the top of the ridge, drawn against the background of light, resembling the dim shadows of the phantasmagoria. It was now quite time for the hunter to retreat. Tripping up the heels of his captive, and giving her throat a parting squeeze, quite as much in resentment at her indomitable efforts to sound the alarm, as from any policy, he left her on her back, and moved toward the bushes, his rifle at a poise, and his head over his shoulders, like a lion at bay.

PRIMEVAL PINES.

XVIII.

WING-AND-WING.

WHILE in Italy, the American writer had made a short cruise, in a Genoese felucca, along the coast of Tuscany, Romagna, and Naples. He often recalled the excursion, with great pleasure, at a later day, when sitting at his own fireside among the Otsego Hills; and a marine tale connected with the waters of the blue Mediterranean, the islands and coasts explored on that occasion, was now planned. Passages from his original record of the little cruise are given to the reader:

"With this outfit, then, the little 'Belle Genovese'—a felucca of thirty tons—got her anchor, with a light wind at north-west, about five in the afternoon, and began to turn out of the harbor. In half an hour we had made three or four stretches, which enabled us to weather the head of the mole, when we stood to the southward with flowing sheets. Our course lay between a succession of islands and the main, in a south-easterly direction. Gorgona and Capraja were in sight on quitting the port—Leghorn; and our first object was to run through what is here called the *canal* of Elba, a strait between that island and the headland of Piombino. The wind was so light that our progress was slow, and when we took to our mattresses, Leghorn was but two or three leagues behind us. On turning out the next morning, I found the felucca close hauled, beating up for the channel with a fresh breeze from the southward. The brown mountains of Elba formed the background to windward; Porto Ferrajo lying about two leagues from us directly on our weather beam. We fetched in just beneath the cliff or promontory that forms the north-eastern extremity of the town of Porto Ferrajo, a rocky eminence of some elevation. The bay is several miles deep, and at its mouth nearly a league wide; the land being chiefly mountain and *côtes*. The promontory on which stands the town makes a bend on its inner side, like the curve of a hook; and this, aided a little by some artificial works, forms a beautiful and secure little harbor, the water being everywhere deep, with bold shores. I had called a boat to put us ashore, when the *padrone* announced the appalling news of there being a quarantine of fifteen days between Elba and Naples! We immediately hauled out of the harbor; but while discussing breakfast the padrone came to us, to say he had just learned that while there was a quarantine of fifteen days between Elba and Naples, there was none at all between the Roman states and Naples; and thus, by running into Civita Vecchia, we might get clean bills of health, and all would be plain sailing—so much for a Mediterranean quarantine! I accepted the terms, and we landed. Porto Ferrajo is a small, crowded town, containing five thousand souls, and lying on the acclivity on the inner side of the promontory. It is pretty well fortified, though the works are old; it is walled, and has two little forts or citadels on the heights. It was garrisoned by five hundred men, they told me, and there were two hundred galley-slaves kept in the place. The town was clean enough, the streets having steps, or narrow terraces, by which we ascended the hills. The arrival of a party of strangers created quite a sensation, for there are few more retired spots in Europe than this. We went to the best inn, which bears the imposing title of the *Quattro Nazioni*. It was far from bad, and gave us a reasonably good dinner, promising four beds and a sofa should we pass the night there. The art of coloring brick floors has not reached this inn; the room in which we dined had *seven* mirrors, while the floor was of coarse, dirt-colored bricks, full of holes. I had some conversation with the people of the house concerning their late sovereign. Napoleon arrived in the evening, and remained in the frigate until the next day. One of his first acts was to send for the oldest known flag used by Elba, and this he caused to be hoisted on the forts—a sign of independency. After dinner, we walked to the home of Napoleon; it stands conspicuously; is low and small, composed of a main body and two wings, showing a front in all of ten windows. The entire length may have been ninety feet, but the other dimensions were not on a proportionate scale. The house of Madame Mère has a better air, as to comfort; it has but one story, showing fifteen windows in a row. At the inn I saw what the Italians call a *tarantula*—it is not a spider, but a lizard; perhaps nine-tenths of the Italians fancy the bite of this animal mortal; but it is a perfectly inoffensive lizard, living on insects, and is

Wing-and-Wing: He moved toward the edge of his narrow scaffolding, endeavored to stretch forth his arms, and blessed her, again, aloud. The poor girl dropped on her knees, in the bottom of the boat, bowed her head, and in that humble attitude did she remain until all was over.

found in America, where no one ever heard of its poison. It is, however, a most disgusting-looking object, which is probably the reason it bears so bad a name. * * * After a good deal of difficulty, I got our padrone out of the port just as the sun was setting. We found the wind fresh outside, but as fair as could be wished. Our course was to double the eastern end of the island, where there was a narrow passage between it and a small rocky islet—the spot of which Napoleon is said to have taken possession with a corporal's guard as soon as he landed. It was a dependency of the new empire. This act of his has been laughed at, and is cited as a proof of his passion for conquest; but it strikes me as more probable that he did it to prevent an unpleasant neighborhood. * * * At daylight next day, we stood to the southward, the wind being fair, but light. At ten it fell calm. There was a small rocky islet, about a mile from us, and we swept the felucca up to it, and anchored in a little sandy bay. The padrone said the island was called Troja; it contained about thirty acres, a high rock, with a little shrubbery, and was surmounted by an ancient and ruined watch-tower. We landed, and explored the country; our arrival gave the alarm to some thousands of gulls, and other marine birds, who had probably not been disturbed for years. W—— undertook to ascend to the tower—an exploit more easily achieved than the descent; he found it the remains of a watch-tower, of which this coast has hundreds, erected as a protection against the invasions of the Barbary corsairs. With one coast peopled by those who were at the head of civilization, and the other by those who were just civilized enough to be formidable, constant warfare, the habits of slavery, and the harem, one can understand the uses of all these towers. At noon we embarked; we had a good run for the rest of the day, at the distance of a league or two from the coast, which was low, with many islets and sand-banks visible. Just before sunset we came up with a high headland that looked like an island—Monte Argentaro, a peninsula connected with the mainland by a low spit of sand. Behind it lies one of the best harbors for small craft in Italy, at the town of Orbitello. Directly abreast of it are several small islands, and we took our course among them; this was delightful navigation at the close of a fine day in August, with a cool north wind, and in such a sea. We ran so near the mountain as to discern the smallest objects, and were constantly changing the scene. On this headland I counted seven watch-towers, and all within the space of a league or two. Including Elba, we must have seen and passed this day, in a run of about twenty miles, some twenty islands. The Roman coast commenced as soon as we were clear of Argentaro; it was low, and the watch-towers, better constructed than common—a sort of martello tower—were so near each other as completely to sweep the beach with

their guns. Civita Vecchia lies around a shallow cove, with an artificial basin
within it, and a mole stretching athwart the mouth of the cove. The town is
small, but not dirty; there is an ancient mole, and a basin that once contained
Roman gallies; the bronze rings by which they were made fast to the quays still
remain! *   *   *   The run the following evening was delightful; we glided
along, in perfectly smooth water, at the rate of seven knots, and so near the
shore as to discern every thing of moment. As the day declined, the land
melted away until it got to be a low waste, the water margin of the Campagna
of Rome. About nine the padrone pointed out the position of Ostia and the
mouths of the Tiber. He kept the vessel well off the shore, pretending that the
malaria at this season was so penetrating as to render it dangerous to be closer in,
with the wind off the land. I was singularly struck with the existence of this
subtle and secret danger in the midst of a scene otherwise so lovely. The night
was as brilliant a star-light as I remember to have seen. Nothing could surpass the
diamond-like lustre of the placid and thoughtful stars; and the blue waters
through which we were gliding betrayed our passage by a track of molten silver.
While we were gazing at this beautiful spectacle, a meteor crossed the heavens,
illuminating every thing to the brightness of a clear moonlight. It was much
the finest meteor I have ever seen, and its course included more than half the
arch above us.   *   *   *   *   *   *

"We hauled up to the windward of Procida, sailing through an element so
limpid that we saw every rock and stone on the bottom, in five fathoms water.
Having opened the channel between the two islands, we bore up for Ischia, where
we arrived a little before sunset. There a scene presented itself which more resembled a fairy picture than one of the realities of this every-day world of ours.
I think it was the most ravishing spectacle, in its way, eye of mine ever looked
upon. We had the black, volcanic peaks of the island for a background, with
the ravine-like valleys and mountain faces—covered with villas and groves—in
front. The town is near the southern extremity of the island, and lies along the
shore for more than a mile on a bit of level formation; but, after passing a sort
of bridge or terrace—which I took to be a public promenade—the rocks rose suddenly, and terminated in two or three lofty, fantastic, broken, fragment-like crags,
which make the south-eastern end of the island. On these rocks are perched
several old castles, so beautifully wild and picturesque, that they seemed placed
there for no other purpose than to adorn the landscape. By a curvature of the
land, these rocks sheltered the roadstead, and the quaint old structures were
brought almost to impend over our heads. The whole population seemed to be
out enjoying themselves after the heat of the day; and a scene in which a move-

ment of life was so mingled with a superb, but most lovely nature, it is, indeed, rare to witness. Until that moment, I was not fully sensible of the vast superiority of the Italian landscapes over all others. Switzerland astonishes, often delights, by its union of the pastoral with the sublime; but Italian nature wins upon you, until you come to love it as a friend. I can only liken the effect of the scene we gazed upon this evening, to a feeling allied to transport; to the manner in which we dwell upon the serene expression of a beloved and lovely countenance. Other scenes have the tints, the hues, the outlines, the proportions, the grandeur, and even the softness of beauty; but these have the character that mark the existence of a soul. The effect is to pour a flood of sensations upon the mind, wholly distinct from the common feeling of wonder excited by vastness and magnificence. The refinement of Italian nature appears to distinguish it as much from that of other countries, as the same quality distinguishes the man of sentiment and intellect from the man of mere impulses. In sublimity of a certain sort—more especially in its sublimity of desolation—Switzerland, probably, has no equal on earth; and to this is to be added a certain unearthly aspect which the upper glaciers assume in particular conditions of the atmosphere. But these Italian scenes rise to a sublimity of a different kind, which, though it does not awe, leaves behind it a tender sensation allied to that of love. I can conceive of even an ardent admirer of nature wearying, in time, of the grandeur of the Alps; but I can scarcely imagine one who would ever tire of the witchery of Italy. * * * The lower classes of Italy, with the exception of those who live on travellers, appear to me to be unsophisticated, kind, and well-principled. There is a native activity of mind about them that renders their rogues great rogues; but I question if the mass here be not quite as honest as the mass in any other country under the same social pressure. An American should always remember the comparative exemption from temptation existing in his own country. Common crimes are certainly not as general with us as in Europe, and precisely for the reason named; but *uncommon meannesses* abound in a large circle of our population. The vices of an American origin are necessarily influenced by the condition of American society; and, as a principle, the same is true here. It may be questioned if examination, taking into view all the circumstances, would give a result so much in our favor as some pretend. Once removed from the towns and other haunts of travellers, I have found the Italians of the lower classes endued with quite as many good qualities as most of their neighbors, and with more than some of them. They are more generous than the English, more sincere than the French, and more refined than the Germans. Certainly they are quicker-witted, and, physically, they are altogether a finer race, though short, than I had imagined.

"Shades of difference exist in Italian character, as between the different states; the preference being usually given to the inhabitants of Upper Italy. I have not found the difference so manifestly clear against the South; though I do believe that the Piedmontese, in a physical sense, are the finest race of the entire country. Foreigners would better appreciate the Italian character if they better understood the usages of the country. A nation divided like this—conquered, as this has been, and lying, as it now does, notoriously at the mercy of any powerful invader—loses the estimation that is due to numbers. The stranger regards the people as unworthy of possessing distinctive traits, and obtrudes his own habits on them, coarsely, and, too often, insolently. This, in part, is submitted to from necessity; but mutual ill-will and distrust are the consequences. The vulgar-minded Englishman talks of the "damned Italians," and the vulgar-minded American imitates his great model, though neither has, probably, any knowledge of the people, beyond that which he has obtained in inns, and in the carriages of the *vetturini*. In grace of mind—in a love, and even a knowledge of the arts—a large portion of the common Italians are as much superior to the Anglo-Saxon race as civilization is superior to barbarism. We deride their religious super-stitions; but we overlook the exaggerations, uncharitableness, and severity of our own fanaticism. I do not know any peasantry in which there is more ingenuous-ness, with less of rusticity and vulgarity, than that of Tuscany. The society of Italy—which is but another word for the nobles of the country—so far as I have seen it, has the general European character, modified a little by position. They have a general acquaintance with literature, without being often learned; and there is a grace about their minds, derived from the constant practice of contem-plating the miracles of art, that is rather peculiar to them. An Italian gentleman is more gracious than an Englishman, and less artificial than a Frenchman. Indeed, I have often thought that, in these particulars, he is the nearest to a true standard of any gentleman of Europe. There is a sincerity in this class, also, that took me by surprise—a simplicity of mind and manner, not common on the other side of the Alps.

"Nature appears to have intended Italy for a single country. With a people speaking the same language; a territory almost surrounded by water, or separated from the rest of Europe by a barrier of great mountains; its actual ancient history, relative position, and interests—would all seem to have a direct tendency toward bringing about this great end. The —— of —— assured me that such was the intention of Napoleon, who looked forward to the time when he might convert the whole peninsula into a single state. Had he continued to reign, and had he been the father of two or more sons, it is quite probable that he would have distributed his kingdoms among them at his death; but, while he lived, no man would have got any thing back from Napoleon Bonaparte with his own consent. Italy, instead of being the consolidated country one could wish it were, is now divided into ten states, including little Monaco. The study of Italy is profitable to an American. One of the greatest—indeed, the only serious obstacle to consolidation of all the Italian states, arises from the hereditary hatreds and distrusts of the people of one portion of the country to those of another. Such is it to separate the family tie; and such would soon be our own condition, were the bond of union that now unites us severed. By playing off one portion of the country against another, the common enemy would plunder all. The Italians, while they are sensible that Napoleon did them good by introducing the vigor and improvements of France, do not extol his reign. They justly deem him a selfish conqueror; and, I make no doubt, joyfully threw off his yoke. The conscription appears to have been the most oppressive of his measures; and well it might be, for, even admitting that his ultimate ends were to be beneficial, the means were next to intolerable. He improved the roads, invigorated the police, reformed many abuses, and gave new impulses to society, it is true; but in the place of the old grievances he substituted King Stork for King Log.

"The laws and customs of the Italian states have so many minute points of difference, that the wishes of some of the patriots of this region point toward a confederated republic, something like that of Switzerland. Sooner or later, Italy will, inevitably, become a single state; this is a result which I hold to be certain, though the means by which it is to be effected are still hidden. In the absence of great political events, to weaken the authority of the present government, education is the surest process, though a slow one."   *   *   *   *   *

The leading idea of "Wing-and-Wing" consists in bringing together sailors of different nations—English, French, Yankee, and Italian—throwing them into the same scenes, on the blue waters of the Mediterranean. The name "Wing-and-Wing" refers, as the reader may be already aware, to the peculiar Italian rig, the lateen sails, which hover about every gulf and bay of that beautiful sea, like white-winged birds, in picturesque flight. The craft, however, in which the reader becomes especially interested, is French, and, like her captain, the gallant Raoul Yvard, bears a French name, "Le Feu Follet"—The Jack-o'-Lanthorn, or Will-o'-the-Wisp—whichever translation the reader may prefer. And, by-the-by, is it not true that those idle, mocking, dancing flames—which, we are told, delight in beguiling the solitary wayfarer in Europe—are more common in the old hemisphere than in the new? Which of us has ever had the pleasure of meeting Jack-o'-Lanthorn, even in the darkest of nights, and over the most marshy of roads?   Nay, which of us can even boast of the collateral honors of a wonder-monger—which of us can say that this or that kinsman, or neighbor, ever had the good luck to be led astray, into marsh or mire, by Will-o'-the-Wisp? Like Puck, and Robin Goodfellow, Will seems to have little fancy for a Yankee marsh.   Ghita, the Italian diminutive of Margarita, the heroine of the narrative, is a very sweet character, and the reader soon learns to share in her deep anxiety regarding her lover, the brave young Frenchman, who is represented as being, like too many of his nation at that period, a sceptic on religious subjects.   The death of Raoul is very impressive, and, like the heart-stricken Ghita, kneeling on the rock at his side, when the young man expires with his eyes riveted in dawning conviction on the glorious heavens above, the reader is left with the hope that, even in that last solemn hour, something of the light of sacred Truth, and assent to its influences, may have reached his spirit.

"Wing-and-Wing," though not one of Mr. Cooper's most brilliant tales of the sea, is yet assuredly a work of very decided merit.   A brief extract, the death of Carraccioli, is all that is allowed us as a picture from its pages.

CARACCIOLI.

VITO VITI muttered an answer; for, by this time, he had discovered that he was a very different personage, on board the Proserpine, from what the other had appeared to consider him, while in his native island. He might have expressed himself aloud, indeed; but, at that instant, a column of smoke glanced out of the bow port of the Minerva—a yellow flag was shown aloft—and then came the report of the signal-gun.

It has been said that vessels of war, of four different nations, were, at that time, lying in the bay of Naples. Nelson had come in, but a short time previously, with seventeen ships of the line; and he found several more of his countrymen lying there. This large force had been assembled to repel an expected attack on the island of Minorca; and it was still kept together in an uncertainty of the future movements of the enemy. A Russian force had come out of the Black Sea, to act against the French, bringing with it a squadron of the Grand Signor; thus presenting to the world the singular spectacle of the followers of Luther, devotees of the Greek church, and disciples of Mahomet, uniting in defence of " our rights, our firesides, and our altars!" To these vessels must be added a small squadron of ships of the country; making a mixed force of four different ensigns that was to witness the melancholy scene we are about to relate.

The yellow flag, and the signal-gun, brought every thing, in the shape of duty, to a stand-still, in all the fleets. The hoarse commands ceased—the boatswains and their mates laid aside their calls, and the echoing midshipmen no longer found orders to repeat. The seamen gathered to the sides of their respective vessels; every part glistened with expectant eyes; the booms resembled clusters of bees, suspended from the boughs of a forest; and the knight-heads, taffrails, gangways, and stretchers of the rigging, were garnished with those whose bright buttons, glazed hats, epaulettes, and dark blue dresses, denoted them to belong to the privileged classes of a ship. Notwithstanding all this curiosity, nothing like the feeling which is apt to be manifested at an exhibition of merited punishment was visible in a single countenance. An expression resembling a sombre gloom appeared to have settled on all those grim warriors of the deep; English, Russian, Neapolitan, or Turk, apparently reserving all his sympathies for the sufferer, rather than for the majesty of justice. Still, no murmur arose; no sign of resistance was made; no look of remonstrance given. The unseen mantle of authority covered all; and these masses of discontented men submitted, as we bow to what is believed to be the fiat of fate. The deep-seated and unresisting habit of discipline, suppressed complaint; but there was a general conviction that some act was about to be committed, that it were better for humanity and justice should not be done; or, if done at all, that it needed more of form, greater deliberation, and a fairer trial, to be so done as to obtain the commendation of men. The Turks, alone, showed apathy; though all showed submission. These subjects of destiny looked on coldly; though even among them a low rumor had passed that a malign influence prevailed in the fleet; and that a great and proud spirit had gotten to be mastered by the passion that so often deprives heroes of their self-command and independence.

Ghita ceased her prayers, as the report of the gun broke rudely on her ears, and, with streaming eyes, she even dared to look toward the frigate. Raoul, and all the rest, bent their gaze in the same direction. The sailors among them saw the rope at the fore-yard-arm move, and then heads rose slowly above the hammock-cloths; when the prisoner and his attendant priest were visible even to their feet. The unfortunate Caraccioli, as has been said, had nearly numbered his threescore and ten years in the regular course of nature; and his bare head now showed the traces of time. He wore no coat; and his arms were bound behind his back, at the elbows, leaving just motion enough to the hands to aid him in the slighter offices about his own person. His neck was bare, and the fatal cord was tightened sufficiently around it to prevent accidents, constantly admonishing its victim of its revolting office.

A low murmur arose among the people in the boats, as this spectacle presented itself to their eyes; and many bowed their faces in prayer. The condemned man caught a ray of consolation from this expression of sympathy; and he looked around him, an instant, with something like a return of those feelings of the world which it had been his effort and his desire totally to eradicate, since he had taken leave of Ghita, and learned that his last request—that of changing his mode of punishment— had been denied. That was a fearful moment, for one like Don Francesco Caraccioli, who had passed a long life in the midst of the scene that surrounded him—illustrious by birth, affluent, honored for his services, and accustomed to respect and deference.

Never had the glorious panorama of the bay appeared more lovely than it did at that instant, when he was about to quit it forever, and this by means of a violent and disgraceful death. From the purple mountains—the cerulean void above him—the blue waters over which he seemed already to be suspended—and the basking shores, rich in their towns, villas, and vines, his eye turned toward the world of ships, each alive with its masses of living men. A glance of melancholy reproach was cast upon the little flag that was just waving at the mizzen-mast-head of the Foudroyant; and then it fell on the carpet of faces beneath, that seemed fairly to change the surface of the smooth sea into an arena of human countenances. His look was steady, though his soul was in a tumult. Ghita was recognized by her companion, and by her dress. He moved toward the edge of his narrow scaffolding, endeavored to stretch forth his arms, and blessed her again aloud. The poor girl dropped on her knees, in the bottom of the boat, bowed her head, and in that humble attitude did she remain until all was over; not daring once to look upward again.

"Son," said the priest, "this is a moment when the earth, and its feelings, must be forgotten."

"I know it, father," answered the old man, his voice trembling with emotion, for his sensations were too powerful—too sublime, even—for the degrading passion of fear; "but never before did this fair piece of the creation seem so lovely in my eyes as now, when I am about to quit it for the last time."

"Look beyond this scene, into the long vista of eternity, son; there thou wilt behold that which mocks at all human, all earthly means to equal. I fear that our time is but short—hast thou aught yet to say, in the flesh?"

"Let it be known, holy priest, that in my dying moment I prayed for Nelson, and for all who have been active in bringing me to this end. It is easy for the fortunate, and the untempted, to condemn; but he is wiser, as he is safer, who puts more reliance on the goodness of God than on his own merits."

A ray of satisfaction gleamed athwart the pale countenance of the priest—a sincerely pious man, or fear of personal consequences might have kept aloof from such a scene—and he closed his eyes, while he expressed his gratitude to God in the secret recesses of his own spirit. Then he turned to the prince, and spoke cheeringly.

"Son," he said, "if thou quittest life with a due dependence on the Son of God, and in this temper toward thy fellow-creatures, of all this living throng, thou art he who is most to be envied! Address thy soul in prayer, once more, to Him whom thou feelest can alone serve thee."

Caraccioli, aided by the priest, knelt on the scaffold—for the rope hung loose enough to permit that act of humiliation—and the other bent at his side.

"I wish to God Nelson had nothing to do with this!" muttered Cuffe, as he turned away his face, inadvertently bending his eyes on the Foudroyant, nearly under the stern of which ship his gig lay. There, in the stern-walk, stood the lady, already mentioned in this chapter, a keen spectator of the awful scene. No one, but a maid, was near her, however, the men of her companionship not being of moods stern enough to be at her side. Cuffe turned away from this sight, in still stronger disgust; and just at that moment a common cry arose from the boats. Looking round, he was just in time to see the unfortunate Caraccioli dragged from his knees, by the neck, until he rose, by a steady, man-of-war pull, to the end of the yard; leaving his companion alone on the scaffold, still lost in prayer. There was a horrible minute, of the struggles between life and death, when the body, so late the tenement of an immortal spirit, hung, like one of the jewel-blocks of the ship, dangling passively at the end of the spar, as insensible as the wood which sustained it.

XIX.

WYANDOTTE.

THE author of "The Deerslayer" was most thoroughly a pioneer in spirit. He delighted in the peculiarly American process of "clearing;" not in its ruder forms, of course, where the chief object of the colonist often appears to consist in felling a noble wood, and leaving the unsightly wreck—a lifeless array of half-charred stumps—to moulder slowly away, under the storm and sunshine of half a life-time. It was the work of improvement, in all its different stages, in which he took pleasure, from the first opening of the soil to the sunlight, through all the long course of removing the wood, burning the brush, the first tilling, and the first crop. About a mile and a half from the village, on the eastern bank of the lake, lay a small farm, belted on all sides by the forest, and which he had taken great pleasure in improving, from the first stages of clearing the ground by means of that ingenious Yankee contrivance, the stump-extractor, to the neat drain and finished stone wall. To this little farm, lying on the eastern mountain-side, he drove daily, to overlook his laborers and direct the work. It was one of the most beautiful natural positions in the neighborhood, commanding charming views over lake and shore, field and wood. It was here, while looking down on the lake, that he planned the minute movements of Floating Tom, and the rude "ark," so prominent in "The Deerslayer." Almost every morning, writing hours over, he drove to the *châlet*, looking after the stock and the dairy, the pigs and the poultry.   It was a frequent remark of the workmen, that the animals all soon learned to know, and to follow him, from his invariable kindness to dumb creatures.   Farming, in all its forms, had given him pleasure through life; but he chiefly delighted in taking a fresh piece of land, and, commencing with the very first stages of cultivation, bringing it into shape and fruitfulness.

"Wyandotte; or, The Hutted Knoll," is a tale of border life, planned and written wholly in this spirit.   A family of the colonial period of our brief annals, is led into the wilderness to take possession of a new tract of land ; and the reader is made to follow their steps through the work of the first generation.   The narrative itself is original, and very pleasing ; the book would, no doubt, have been considered a very agreeable addition to American literature, if the same pen had given us nothing more.   The principal Indian character is admirably well drawn under a form different from any yet sketched by the same hand ; throughout the book he is seen in a double light—two distinct characters, as it were, blended into one peculiar whole, which is, in itself, perfectly true to nature and American life. As "Sassy Nick," he is the common idle vagrant, a mere hanger-on of the whites, in that degraded condition to which too many of his race have been reduced by the first contact with civilization ; as "Wyandotte," he is the warrior of his people, wily in plot, brave in fight, fierce in revenge, with outbreaks of savage wisdom, and eloquence, and dignity, peculiar to the council-fire and the war-post of his people. The long struggle in the heart and mind of this wild creature, between gratitude for the kindness of Mrs. Willoughby, and the spirit of hatred and revenge against her husband, Colonel Willoughby, are admirably kept up and worked out through the whole tale, until its fatal close.   Wyandotte is one of those books to which an extract cannot do justice ; to appreciate the merit of the work we must follow the history of the little colony, and trace the course of the Indian, alike the savage friend and foe, of the border household.

Wyandotte: This was enough. Nick passed out of the forest on a swift walk – but for the female, it would have been his customary loping trot, followed by Willoughby, his arm again cir'cling the waist of Maud.

SAUCY NICK.

OUR present tale now leads us to the description of one of those early, personal, or family settlements, that had grown up in what was, then, a very remote part of the territory in question, under the care and supervision of an ancient officer of the name of Willoughby. Captain Willoughby, after serving many years, had married an American wife, and, continuing his services until a son and daughter were born, he sold his commission, procured a grant of land, and determined to retire to his new possessions, in order to pass the close of his life in the tranquil pursuits of agriculture, and in the bosom of his family. An adopted child was also added to his cares. Being an educated as well as a provident man, Captain Willoughby had set about the execution of this scheme with deliberation, prudence, and intelligence. On the frontiers, or lines, as it is the custom to term the American boundaries, he had become acquainted with a Tuscarora, known by the English *soubriquet* of "Saucy Nick." This fellow—a sort of half-outcast from his own people—had early attached himself to the whites, had acquired their language, and, owing to a singular mixture of good and bad qualities, blended with great native shrewdness, he had wormed himself into the confidence of several commanders of small garrisons, among whom was our captain. No sooner was the mind of the latter made up, concerning his future course, than he sent for Nick, who was then in the fort; when the following conversation took place:

"Nick," commenced the captain, passing his hand over his brow, as was his wont when in a reflecting mood; "Nick, I have an important movement in view, in which you can be of some service to me."

The Tuscarora, fastening his dark, basilisk-eyes on the soldier, gazed a moment, as if to read his soul; then he jerked a thumb backward, over his own shoulder, and said, with a grave smile—

"Nick understand.   Want six, two, scalp off Frenchman's head; wife and child; out yonder, over dere, up in Canada.   Nick do him—what you give?"

"No, you red rascal, I want nothing of the sort; it is peace now (this conversation took place in 1764), and you know I never bought a scalp in time of war.   Let me hear no more of this."

"What you want, *den?*" asked Nick, like one who was a good deal puzzled.

"I want land—*good* land—little, but *good*.   I am about to get a grant—a patent —

"Yes," interrupted Nick, nodding; "I know *him*—paper to take away Indian's hunting-ground."

"Why, I have no wish to do that; I am willing to pay the red men reasonably for their right, first."

"Buy Nick's land, den; better dan any oder."

"Your land, knave!   You own no land; belong to no tribe; have no rights to sell."

"What for ask Nick help, den?"

"What for?   Why, because you *know* a good deal, though you own literally nothing.   That's what for."

"Buy Nick *know*, den.   Better dan he great fader *know*, down at York."

"That is just what I do wish to purchase.   I will pay you well, Nick, if you will start to-morrow, with your rifle, and a pocket-compass, off here toward the head-waters of the Susquehanna and Delaware, where the streams run rapidly, and where there are no fevers, and bring me an account of three or four thousand acres of rich bottom-land, in such a way as a surveyor can find it, and I can get a patent for it.   What say you, Nick—will you go?"

"He not wanted.   Nick sell 'e captain his own land, here in 'e fort."

"Knave, do you not know me well enough not to trifle when I am serious?"

"Nick ser'ous too—Moravian priest no ser'ouser more dan Nick at dis moment. Got land to sell."

Captain Willoughby had found occasion to punish the Tuscarora, in the course of his services; and, as the parties understood each other perfectly well, the former saw the improbability of the latter's daring to trifle with him.

"Where is this land of yours, Nick?" he inquired, after studying the Indian's countenance for a moment.   "Where does it lie, what is it like, how much is there of it, and how came you to own it?"

"Ask him just so, ag'in," said Nick, taking up four twigs, to note down the questions *seriatim*.

The captain repeated his inquiries, the Tuscarora laying down a stick at each separate interrogatory.

"Where he be?" answered Nick, taking up a twig, as a memorandum. "He out dere, where he want him, where he say. One day's march from Susquehanna."

"Well, proceed."

"What he like? Like land, to be sure. T'ink he like water! Got *some* water—no too much; got some land—got no tree—got some tree. Got good sugar-bush—got place for wheat and corn."

"Proceed."

"How much of him?" continued Nick, taking up another twig; "much as he want: want little, got him—want more, got him. Want none at all, got none at all; got what he want."

"Go on."

"To be sure. How came to own him? How a pale-face come to own America? *Discover* him—ha! Well, Nick discover land down yonder, up dere, over here."

"Nick, what the devil do you mean by all this?"

"No mean devil at all; mean land—*good* land. *Discover* him—know where he is—catch beaver dere, three, two year. All Nick say true as word of honor; much more too."

"Do you mean it is an old beaver-dam destroyed?" asked the captain, pricking up his ears; for he was too familiar with the woods not to understand the value of such a thing.

"No destroy—stand up yet—good as ever. Nick dere last season."

"Why, then, do you tell of it? Are not the beaver of more value to you than any price you may receive for the land?"

"Cotch him all, four, two year ago—rest run away. No find beaver to stay long, when Indian once know, two time, where to set he trap. Beaver cunninger 'an pale-face—cunning as bear."

"I begin to comprehend you, Nick. How large do you suppose this pond to be?"

"He'm not as big as Lake Ontario. S'pose him smaller—what den? Big enough for farm."

"Does it cover one or two hundred acres, think you? Is it as large as the clearing around the fort?"

"Big as two, six, four of him. Take forty skin dere, one season. Little lake; all 'e tree gone."

"And the land around it—is it mountainous and rough, or will it be good for corn?"

"All sugar-bush—what you want better? S'pose you want corn, *plant* him. S'pose you want sugar, *make* him."

Captain Willoughby was struck with this description, and he returned to the subject again and again. At length, after extracting all the information he could get from Nick, he struck a bargain with the fellow. A surveyor was engaged, and he started for the place, under the guidance of the Tuscarora. The result showed that

Nick had not exaggerated. The pond was found, as he had described it to be, covering at least four hundred acres of low bottom-land; while near three thousand acres of higher river-flat, covered with beech and maple, spread around it for a considerable distance. The adjacent mountains, too, were arable, though bold, and promised, in time, to become a fertile and manageable district. Calculating his distances with judgment, the surveyor laid out his metes and bounds in such a manner as to include the pond, all the low-land, and about three thousand acres of hill, or mountain, making the materials for a very pretty little "patent" of somewhat more than six thousand acres of capital land. He then collected a few chiefs of the nearest tribe, dealt out his rum, tobacco, blankets, wampum, and gunpowder, got twelve Indians to make their marks on a bit of deer-skin, and returned to his employer with a map, a field-book, and a deed, by which the Indian title was "extinguished." The surveyor received his compensation, and set off on a similar excursion, for a different employer, and in another direction. Nick got his reward, too, and was well satisfied with the transaction. This he afterward called "sellin' beaver, when he all run away."

Furnished with the necessary means, Captain Willoughby now "sued out his patent," as it was termed, in due form. Having some influence, the affair was soon arranged; the grant was made by the governor in council, a massive seal was annexed to a famous sheet of parchment, the signatures were obtained, and "Willoughby's Patent" took its place on the records of the colony, as well as on its maps. We are wrong as respects the latter particular; it did not take *its* place on the maps of the colony, though it took *a* place; the location given for many years afterward being some forty or fifty miles too far west. In this peculiarity there was nothing novel, the surveys of all new regions being liable to similar trifling mistakes. Thus it was that an estate lying within five-and-twenty miles of the city of New York, and in which we happen to have a small interest at this hour, was clipped of its fair proportions, in consequence of losing some miles that run over obtrusively into another colony; and, within a short distance of the spot where we are writing, a "patent" has been squeezed entirely out of existence, between the claims of two older grants.

No such calamity befell "Willoughby's Patent," however. The land was found, with all its "marked or *blazed* trees," its "heaps of stones," "large butternut corners," and "dead oaks." In a word, every thing was as it should be; even to the quality of the soil, the beaver-pond, and the quantity. As respects the last, the colony never gave "struck measure;" a thousand acres on paper seldom falling short of eleven or twelve hundred in soil. In the present instance, the six thousand two hundred and forty-six acres of "Willoughby's Patent," were subsequently ascertained to contain just seven thousand and ninety-two acres of solid ground.

Satanstoe: Cross it we did, my delicate companion
being as much sustained by my supporting arm, as by
her own resolution.

XX.

SATANSTOE.

In the year 1845 appeared "Satanstoe," a very pleasant book, giving us pictures of society in the colony of New York, some hundred years earlier. The narrative takes the form of an autobiography, purporting to have been written by a member of the Littlepage family, living on one of the "Necks" of West Chester, on the shores of the Sound, but the proprietor of extensive lands in the interior of the province. The reader follows the steps of Cornelius Little-page in his visits to New York, his quiet but amusing accounts of the state of things in the great capital of the province at that time, in his glimpses of Albany and our Dutch ancestors, and goes with him into the wilderness, to Mooseridge, the tract of ground to be peopled and worked by the proprietor. In reading the book, at the first glance we should deem it simply a pleasant look backward at town and country, among our forefathers, while the quiet interest thrown about the different characters leads us onward, without effort, through some striking scenes. The latent object of the writer scarcely appears in this, the first work of a connected series of three, relating to the same family and the same tract of lands. We are made to see clearly, however, that the task of redeeming Moose-ridge from the wilderness, and taking the first steps toward cultivation, was one requiring money, forethought, and effort. In the second work of the series we shall find the plot thickening, the cloud of disturbance drawing nearer. The name of "Satanstoe" was given to this book in a fit of intense disgust at the unmeaning absurdity of the newly-coined word of "Hurl-Gate," which he often stigmatized as a piece of "canting corruption." He maintained that the name of Hell-Gate should either be left in its original form or entirely abandoned for something new; and Hurl-Gate he conceived a flagrant absurdity, quite unworthy of people of common sense.

DIRCK AND CORNY.

The spring of the year I was twenty, Dirck and myself paid our first visit to town, in the characters of young men. Although Satanstoe was not more than five-and-twenty miles from New York by the way of King's Bridge, the road we always travelled in order to avoid the ferry, it was by no means as common to visit the capital as it has since got to be. I know gentlemen who pass in and out from our neighborhood, now, as often as once a fortnight, or even once a week; but thirty years since this was a thing very seldom done. My dear mother always went to town twice a year: in the spring to pass Easter week, and in the autumn to make her winter purchases. My father usually went down four times, in the course of the twelve months, but he had the reputation of a gadabout, and was thought by many people to leave home quite as much as he ought to do. As for my grandfather, old age coming on, he seldom left home now, unless it were to pay stated visits to certain old brother campaigners who lived within moderate distances, and with whom he invariably passed weeks each summer.

The visit I have mentioned occurred some time after Easter, a season of the year that many of our country families were in the habit of passing in town, to have the benefit of the daily services of Old Trinity, as the Hebrews resorted to Jerusalem to keep the feast of the Passover. My mother did not go to town this year, on account of my father's gout, and I was sent to supply her place with my Aunt Legge, who had been so long accustomed to have one of the family with her at that season, that I was substituted.   Dirck had relatives of his own, with whom he staid, and thus every thing was rendered smooth.   In order to make a fair start, my friend crossed the Hudson the week before, and, after taking breath at Satanstoe for three days, we left the Neck for the capital, mounted on a pair of as good roadsters as were to be found in the county; and that is saying a good deal: for the Morrises, and De Lanceys, and Van Cortlandts all kept racers, and sometimes gave us good sport, in the autumn, over the county course.   West Chester, to say no more than she deserved, was a county with a spirited gentry, and one of which no colony need be ashamed.

My mother was a tender-hearted parent, and full of anxiety in behalf of an only child.   She knew that travelling always has more or less of hazard, and was desirous we should be off betimes, in order to make certain of our reaching town before the night set in.   Highway robbers, Heaven be praised! were then, and are still, unknown to the colonies; but there were other dangers that gave my excellent parent much concern.   All the bridges were not considered safe; the roads were, and are yet, very circuitous, and it was possible to lose one's way; while it was said persons had been known to pass the night on Harlem common—an uninhabited waste that lies some seven or eight miles on our side of the city.   My mother's first care, therefore, was to get Dirck and myself off early in the morning; in order to do which she rose with the light, gave us our breakfasts immediately afterward, and thus enabled us to quit Satanstoe just as the sun had burnished the eastern sky with its tints of flame-color.

Dirck was in high good-humor that morning, and, to own the truth, Corny did not feel the depression of spirits which, according to the laws of propriety, possibly ought to have attended the first really free departure of so youthful an adventurer from beneath the shadows of the paternal roof.   We went on our way laughing and chatting like two girls just broke loose from boarding-school.   I had never known Dirck more communi-cative, and I got certain new insights into his feelings, expectations, and prospects, as we rode along the colony's highway that morning, that afterward proved to be matters of much interest with us both.   We had not got a mile from the chimney-tops of Satanstoe, ere my friend broke forth as follows:

"I suppose you have heard, Corny, what the two old gentlemen have been at, lately?"

"Your father and mine?   I have not heard a syllable of any thing new."

"They have been suing out, before the Governor and Council, a joint claim to that tract of land they bought of the Mohawks, the last time they were out together on service, in the colony militia."

I ought to mention, here, that though my predecessors had made but few campaigns in the regular army, each had made several in the more humble capacity of a militia officer.

"This is news to me, Dirck," I answered.   "Why should the old gentlemen have been so sly about such a thing?"

"I cannot tell you, lest they thought silence the best way to keep off the Yankees. You know my father has a great dread of a Yankee's getting a finger into any of his bargains. He says the Yankees are the locusts of the west."

"But how came you to know any thing about it, Dirck?"

"I am no Yankee, Corny."

"And your father told *you*, on the strength of this recommendation?"

"He told me, as he tells me most things that he thinks it best I should know. We smoke together, and then we talk together."

"I would learn to smoke, too, if I thought I should get any useful information by so doing."

"Dere is much to be l'arnt from ter pipe!" said Dirck, dropping into a slightly Dutch accent, as frequently happened with him, when his mind took a secret direction toward Holland, though in general he spoke English quite as well as I did myself, and vastly better than that miracle of taste, and learning, and virtue, and piety, Mr. Jason Newcome, A.B., of Yale, and prospective president of that or some other institution.

"So it would seem, if your father is telling you secrets all the time you are smoking together. But where is this land, Dirck?"

"It is in the Mohawk country—or, rather, it is in the country near the Hampshire Grants, and at no great distance from the Mohawk country."

"And how much may there be of it?"

"Forty thousand acres; and some of it of good, rich flats, they say, such as a Dutchman loves."

"And your father and mine have purchased all this land in company, you say— share and share alike, as the lawyers call it."

"Just so."

"Pray how much did they pay for so large a tract of land?"

Dirck took time to answer this question. He first drew from his breast a pocket-book, which he opened as well as he could under the motion of his roadster, for neither of us abated his speed, it being indispensable to reach town before dark. My friend succeeded at length in putting his hand on the paper he wanted, which he gave to me.

"There," he said, "that is a list of the articles paid to the Indians, which I have copied, and then there have been several hundred pounds of fees paid to the Governor and his officers."

I read from the list as follows, the words coming out by jerks, as the trotting of my horse permitted: "Fifty blankets, each with yellow strings and yellow trimmings; ten iron pots, four gallons each; forty pounds of gunpowder; seven muskets; twelve pounds of small beads; ten strings of wampum; fifty gallons of rum, pure Jamaica, and of high proof; a score of jews-harps, and three dozen first quality English-made tomahawks."

"Well, Dirck," I cried, as soon as through reading, "this is no great matter to give for forty thousand acres of land, in the colony of New York. I dare say a hundred pounds currency ($250) would buy every thing here, even to the rum and the first quality of English-made tomahawks."

"Ninety-six pounds, thirteen shillings, seven pence 't'ree fart'in's' was the footing of the whole bill," answered Dirk deliberately, preparing to light his pipe; for he could smoke very conveniently while trotting no faster than at the rate of six miles the hour.

"I do not find that dear for forty thousand acres; I suppose the muskets, and rum, and other things, were manufactured expressly for the Indian trade."

"Not they, Corny: you know how it is with the old gentlemen; they are as honest as the day."

"So much the better for them, and so much the better for us! But what is to be done with this land, now they own it?"

Dirck did not answer, until we had trotted twenty rods; for by this time the pipe was at work, and the moment the smoke was seen he kept his eye on it, until he saw a bright light in front of his nose.

"The first thing will be to find it, Corny. When a patent is signed and delivered, then you must send forth some proper person to find the land it covers. I have heard of a gentleman who got a grant of ten thousand acres, five years since; and though he has had a hunt for it every summer since, he has not been able to find it yet. To be sure, ten thousand acres is a small object to look for, in the woods."

"And our fathers intend to find this land as soon as the season opens?"

"Not so fast, Corny; not so fast! That was the scheme of your father's Welsh blood, but mine takes matters more deliberately. 'Let us wait until next year,' he said, 'and then we can send the boys. By that time, too, the war will take some sort of a shape, and we shall know better how to care for the children.' The subject has been fairly talked over between the two patentees, and we are to go early *next* spring, not this."

The idea of land-hunting was not in the least disagreeable to me; nor was it unpleasant to think that I stood in reversion, or as heir, to twenty thousand acres of land, in addition to those of Satanstoe. Dirck and I talked the matter over, as we trotted on, until both of us began to regret that the expedition was so far in perspective.

The war to which Dirck alluded had broken out a few months before our visit to town: a Mr. Washington, of Virginia—the same who has since become so celebrated as the Colonel Washington of Braddock's defeat, and other events at the south—having been captured, with a party of his men, in a small work thrown up in the neighborhood of the French, somewhere on the tributaries of the Ohio—a river that is known to run into the Mississippi, a vast distance to the west. I knew very little then, nor do I know much now, of these remote regions, beyond the fact that there are such places, and that they are sometimes visited by detachments, war-parties, hunters, and other adventurers from the colonies. To me, it seems scarce worth fighting about such distant and wild territory; for ages and ages must elapse before it can be of any service for the purposes of civilization. Both Dirck and myself regretted that the summer would be likely to go by without our seeing the enemy; for we came of families that were commonly employed on such occasions. We thought both our fathers might be out; though even that was a point that still remained under discussion.

We dined and baited at Kingsbridge, intending to sup in town. While the dinner was cooking, Dirck and I walked out on the heights that overlook the Hudson; for I knew less of this noble river than I wished to know of it. We conversed as we walked; and my companion—who knew the river much better than myself, having many occasions to pass up and down it, between the village of Haverstraw and town, in his frequent visits to his relatives below—gave me some useful information.

"Look here, Corny," said Dirck, after betraying a good deal of desire to obtain a view of some object in the distance, along the river-side—"Look here, Corny, do you see yonder house, in the little bay below us, with the lawn that extends down to the water, and that noble orchard behind it?"

I saw the object to which Dirck alluded. It was a house that stood near the river, but sheltered and secluded, with the lawn and orchard as described; though at the distance of some two or three miles all the beauties of the spot could not be discovered, and many of them had to be received on the faith of my companion's admiration. Still I saw very plainly all the principal objects named; and, among others, the house, the orchard, and the lawn. The building was of stone—as is common with most of the better sort of houses in the country—was long, irregular, and had that air of solid comfort about it which it is usual to see in buildings of that description. The walls were not whitewashed, according to the lively tastes of our Dutch fellow-colonists, who appear to expend all their vivacity in the pipe and the brush, but were left in their native gray—a circumstance that rendered the form and dimensions of the structure a little less distinct, at a first glance, than they might otherwise have proved. As I gazed at the spot, however, I began to fancy it a charm, to find the picture thus sobered down; and found a pleasure in drawing the different angles, and walls, and chimneys, and roofs, from this background, by means of the organ of sight. On the whole, I thought the little sequestered bay, the wooded and rocky shores, the small but well-distributed lawn, the orchard, with all the other similar accessories, formed together one of the prettiest places of the sort I had ever seen. Thinking so, I was not slow in saying as much to my companion. I was thought to have some taste in these matters, and had been consulted on the subject of laying out grounds by one or two neighbors in the county.

"Whose house is it, Dirck?" I inquired; "and how came you to know any thing about it?"

"That is Lilacsbush," answered my friend.

The Chainbearer: "Mordaunt is what you call my
'given name,'" I answered, disdaining deception, "and
Littlepage"—The hand of the Indian was suddenly
placed on my mouth stopping further utterance.

XXI.

THE CHAINBEARER.

A few months after the publication of "Satanstoe," appeared "The Chainbearer," an autobiography like the first work, and purporting to be written by the son of Cornelius and Anneke. The history of the tract of land at Mooseridge is continued, and in following the steps of Mordaunt Littlepage, the son of the proprietor, who goes there for the purpose of carrying on the improvements of the border colony, we find "Squatters" already in possession, and in the lawless proceedings of Thousandacres and his party are made to note the first working of the disorderly spirit of "Anti-Rent."

"Every chronicle of manners has a certain value," says the writer. "When customs are connected with principles, in their origin, development, or end, such records have a double importance, and it is because we think we see such a connection between the facts and incidents of the Littlepage Manuscripts, and certain theories of our own time, that we give the former to the world. It is, perhaps, a fault of your professed historian to refer too much to philosophical agencies, and too little to those which are more humble. * * * 'Satanstoe' and 'The Chainbearer' relate directly to the great New York question of the day, Anti-Rentism, which question will be found to be pretty fully laid bare in the third and last book of the series.   We conceive that no apology is necessary for treating the subject of Anti-Rentism with the utmost frankness.   Agreeably to our view of the matter, the existence of true liberty among us, the perpetuity of the institutions, and the safety of public morals, are all dependent on putting down wholly and absolutely the false and dishonest theories and statements that have been boldly advanced in connection with this subject.   In our view, New York is at this moment a disgraced state; and her disgrace arises from the fact that her laws are trampled under foot, without any efforts—at all commensurate with the object—being made to enforce them.   If words and professions can save the character of a community, all may yet be well; but if states, like individuals, are to be judged by their actions, and the 'tree is to be known by its fruit,' God help us!   For ourselves, we conceive that true patriotism consists in laying bare every thing like public vice, and in calling such things by their right names. It is time that they who have not been afraid to praise, when praise was merited, should not shrink from the office of censuring, when the want of timely warnings may be one cause of the most fatal evils.   The great practical defect of institutions like ours, is the circumstance that 'what is everybody's business is nobody's business'—a neglect that gives to the activity of the rogue a very dangerous ascendancy over the more dilatory correctives of the honest man."

The narrative of "The Chainbearer" is decidedly interesting, while the characters are all well drawn; honest Andries Coejemans, the Chainbearer, is excellent in his way, and Ursula, his pretty niece, is quite charming, so warm-hearted, and natural, and womanly; the wily Newcome, and the rude Thousandacres, with his brood, also receive full justice at the writer's hands, and that without the least exaggeration.

THE CHAINBEARER.

DAY came as usual, but it did not find these squatters in their beds. They appeared with the dawn, and most of them were at work ere the broad light of the sun was shed on the forest. Most of the men went down into the river, and busied themselves, as we supposed, for we could not see them, in the water, with the apples of their eyes, their boards. Old Thousandacres, however, chose to remain near his habitation, keeping two or three well-grown lads about him; probably adverting in his mind to the vast importance it was to all of his race to make sure of his prisoners. I could see, by the thoughtful manner of the old squatter, as he lounged around his mill, among his swine, and walked through his potatoes, that his mind wavered greatly as to the course he ought to pursue, and that he was sorely troubled. How long this perplexity of feeling would have continued, and to what it might have led, it is hard to say, had it not been cut short by an incident of a very unexpected nature, and one that called for more immediate decision and action. I shall relate the occurrence a little in detail.

The day was considerably advanced, and, Thousandacres and the girl who then watched the store-house excepted, everybody was occupied. Even Susquesus had picked up a piece of birch, and, with a melancholy countenance, that I fancied was shadowing forth the future life of a half-civilized red man, was attempting to make a broom with a part of a knife that he had found in the building; while I was sketching, on a leaf of my pocket-book, the mill and a bit of mountain-land that served it for a background. Thousandacres, for the first time that morning, drew near our prison, and spoke to me. His countenance was severe, yet I could see he was much troubled. As I afterward ascertained, Tobit had been urging on him the necessity of putting both myself and the Indian to death, as the only probable means that offered to save the lumber.

"Young man," said Thousandacres, "you have stolen on me and mine like a thief at night, and you ought to expect the fate of one. How in natur' can you expect men will give up their hard 'arnin's without a struggle and a fight for 'em? You tempt me more than I can bear."

I felt the fearful import of these words; but human nature revolted at the thought of being cowed into any submission, or terms unworthy of my character or late profession. I was on the point of making an answer in entire consonance with this feeling, when, in looking through the chinks of my prison to fasten an eye on my old tyrant, I saw Chainbearer advancing directly toward the store-house, and already within a hundred yards of us. The manner in which I gazed at this apparition, attracted the attention of the squatter, who turned and first saw the unexpected visitor who approached. At the next minute Andries was at his side.

"So, T'ousantacres, I fint you here," exclaimed Chainbearer. "It's a good many years since you and I met, and I'm sorry we meet now on such pusiness as t'is!"

"The meetin's of your own seekin', Chainbearer. I've neither invited nor wished for your company."

"I p'lieve you wit' all my heart. No, no; you wish for no chains and no chainpearers, no surfeyors and no compasses, no lots and no owners, too, put a squatter. You and I haf not to make an acquaintance for t'e first time, Thousandacres, after knowin' each other for fifty years."

"Yes, we *do* know each other for fifty years; and seein' that them years haven't sarved to bring us of a mind on any one thing, we should have done better to keep apart than to come together now."

"I haf come for my poy, squatter—my nople poy, whom you haf illegally arrestet, and mate a prisoner, in the teet' of all law and justice. Gif me pack Mortaunt Littlepage, and you'll soon be rit of my company."

"And how do you know that I've ever seen your 'Mortaunt Littlepage?' What have I to do with your boy, that you seek him of me? Go your ways, go your ways, old Chainbearer, and let me and mine alone. The world's wide enough for us both, I tell you; and why should you be set on to your own ondoin', by runnin' ag'in a breed like that which comes of Aaron and Prudence Timberman?"

"I care not for you or your preet," answered old Andries, sternly. "You've darest to arrest my frient, against law and right, and I come to demant his liberty, or to warn you of the consequences."

"Don't press me too far, Chainbearer; don't press me too far. There's desp'rate crittur's in this clearin', and them that isn't to be driven from their righteous 'arnin's by any that carry chains or p'int compasses. Go your way, I tell ye, and leave us to gather the harvest that comes of the seed of our own sowin' and plantin'."

"Ye'll gat'er it, ye'll gat'er it all, T'ousantacres—you and yours. Ye've sown t'e wint, and ye'll reap t'e whirlwints, as my niece, Dus Malpone, has reat to me often, of late. Ye'll gat'er in all your harvest, tares ant all, ye will; and t'at sooner t'an ye t'ink for."

"I wish I'd never seen the face of the man! Go away, I tell you, Chainbearer, and leave me to my hard 'arnin's."

"Earnin's! Do you call it earnin's to chop and pillage on anot'er's lants, and to cut his trees into logs, and to saw his logs into poarts, and sell his poarts to speculators, and gif no account of your profits to t'e rightful owner of it all? Call you such t'ievin' righteous earnin's?"

"Thief back ag'in, old measurer! Do not the sweat of the brow, long and hard days of toil, and achin' bones, and hungry bellies, give a man a claim to the fruit of his labors?"

"T'at always hast peen your failin', T'ousantacres; t'at's t'e very p'int on which you've proken town, man. You pegin wit' your morals, at t'e startin' place t'at's most convenient to yourself and your plunterin' crew, instead of going pack to t'e laws of your Lort ant Master. Reat what t'e Almighty Got of heaven ant 'art' sait unto Moses, and you'll find t'at you've not turnet over leafs enough of your piple. You may chop ant you may hew, you may haul ant you may saw, from t'is tay to t'e ent of time, ant you'll nefer pe any nearer to t'e right t'an you are at t'is moment. T'e man t'at starts on his journey wit' his face in t'e wrong tirection, olt T'ousantacres, will nefer reach its ent; t'ough he trafel till t'e sweat rolls from his poty like water. You pegin wrong, olt man, and you must ent wrong."

I saw the cloud gathering in the countenance of the squatter, and anticipated the outbreaking of the tempest that followed. Two fiery tempers had met, and, divided as they were in opinions and practice, by the vast chasm that separates principles from expediency, right from wrong, honesty from dishonesty, and a generous sacrifice of self to support the integrity of a noble spirit, from a homage to self that confounded and overshadowed all sense of right, it was not possible that they should separate without a collision. Unable to answer Chainbearer's reasoning, the squatter resorted to the argument of force. He seized my old friend by the throat, and made a violent effort to hurl him to the earth. I must do this man of violence and evil the justice to say, that I do not think it was his wish at that moment to have assistance; but the instant the struggle commenced the conch blew, and it was easy to predict that many minutes would not elapse before the sons of Thousandacres would be pouring in to the rescue. I would have given a world to be able to throw down the walls of my prison, and rush to the aid of my sterling old friend. As for Susquesus, he must have felt a lively interest in what was going on, but he remained as immovable, and seemingly as unmoved, as a rock.

Andries Coejemans, old as he was—and it will be remembered he, too, had seen his threescore years and ten, was not a man to be taken by the throat with impunity. Thousandacres met with a similar assault, and a struggle followed that was surprisingly fierce and well contested, considering that both the combatants had completed the ordinary limits of the time of man. The squatter gained a slight advantage in the suddenness and vigor of his assault; but Chainbearer was still a man of formidable physical power. In his prime, few had been his equals; and Thousandacres soon had reason to know that he had met more than his match. For a single instant Chainbearer gave ground, then he rallied, made a desperate effort, and his adversary was hurled to the ground with a violence that rendered him, for a short time, insensible; old Andries, himself, continuing erect as one of the neighboring pines, red in the face, frowning, and more severe in aspect than I remembered ever to have seen him before, even in battle.

Instead of pushing his advantage, Chainbearer did not stir a foot after he had thrown off his assailant. There he remained, lofty in bearing, proud, and stern. He had reason to believe no one was a witness of his prowess, but I could see that the old man had a soldier's feeling at his victory. At this instant I first let him know my close proximity by speaking.

"Fly—for your life take to the woods, Chainbearer," I called to him through the chinks. "That conch will bring all the tribe of the squatters upon you in two or three minutes; the young men are close at hand, in the stream below the mill, at work on the logs, and have only the banks to climb."

"Got be praiset! Mortaunt, my tear poy, you are not injuret, t'en! I will open t'e toor of your prison, and we will retreat toget'er."

My remonstrances were vain. Andries came round to the door of the store-house, and made an effort to force it open. That was not easy, however, for, opening outward, it was barred with iron, and secured by a stout lock. Chainbearer would not listen to my remonstrances, but he looked around him for some instrument by means of which he could either break the lock or draw the staple. As the mill was at no great distance, away he went in that direction, in quest of what he wanted, leaving me in despair at his persevering friendship. Remonstrance was useless, however, and I was compelled to await the result in silence.

Chainbearer was still a very active man. Nature, early training, sobriety of life in the main, and a good constitution, had done this much for him. It was but a moment before I saw him in the mill, looking for the crow-bar. This he soon found, and he was on his way to the store-house, in order to apply this powerful lever, when Tobit came in sight, followed by all the brethren, rushing up the bank like a pack of hounds in close pursuit. I shouted to my friend again to fly, but he came on steadily toward my prison, bent on the single object of setting me free. All this time Thousandacres was senseless, his head having fallen against a corner of the building. Chainbearer was so intent on his purpose that, though he must have seen the crowd of young men, no less than six in number, including well-grown lads, that was swiftly advancing toward him, he did not bestow the least attention on them. He was actually busied with endeavoring to force the bar in between the hasp and the post, when his arms were seized behind, and he was made a prisoner.

Chainbearer was no sooner apprised of the uselessness of resistance than he ceased to make any. As I afterward learned from himself, he had determined to become a captive with me, if he could not succeed in setting me free. Tobit was the first to lay hands on the Chainbearer; and so rapidly were things conducted, for it happened this man had the key, that the door was unbarred, opened, and old Andries was thrust into the cage, almost in the twinkling of an eye. The rapidity of the movement was doubtless aided by the acquiescent feeling that happened to be uppermost in the mind of Chainbearer, at that precise moment.

No sooner was this new prisoner secured, than the sons of Thousandacres raised their father's body, and bore it to his own residence, which was but a few yards distant. Old and young, both sexes and all ages, collected in that building, and there was an hour during which we appeared to be forgotten. The sentinel, who was a son of Tobit's, deserted his post; and even Lowiny, who had been hovering in sight of the store-house the whole morning, seemed to have lost her interest in us. I was too much engaged with my old friend, and had too many questions to ask and to answer, however, to care much for this desertion; which, moreover, was natural enough for the circumstances.

XXII.

THE REDSKINS.

In "The Redskins" we have the third and last work of the Anti-Rent series, in which the crisis is reached, and the cupidity and lawless spirit of the disorderly faction appear in their true light. "You well know that I am no advocate for any government but that which is founded on popular right, protected from popular abuses," were words which Mr. Fenimore Cooper had written many years earlier. And now, in the hour of danger, to aid in protecting these rights of the people, against their abuse by the evil-minded among themselves, he held to be a high duty of every honest, and generous, and intelligent citizen. "As democrats, we protest most solemnly against such barefaced frauds, such palpable cupidity and covetousness being termed any thing but what they are. Democracy is a lofty and noble sentiment. It is just, and treats all men alike. It is not the friend of a canting legislation, but meaning right, dare act directly. There is no greater delusion than to suppose that true democracy has any thing in common with injustice or roguery. Nor is it any apology for anti-rentism, in any of its aspects, to say that leasehold tenures are inexpedient. The most expedient thing in existence is to do right. Were there no other objection to this anti-rent movement than its corrupting influence, that alone should set every wise man in the community firmly against it."

The Redskins: "You understand Latin then" demanded the parent, examining me over his spectacles from head to foot – "a leetle sir, just a ferry leetle."

Mr. Cooper's pecuniary interest in the question was very slight indeed ; but his was the far-seeing eye which in every illegal public act sees the danger which threatens eventually every family hearth-stone in the country. Acts of public violence, which may become justifiable under other forms of government, he considered as absolutely inexcusable in a democracy, without even the most feeble shadow of reason to support them. During those anti-rent disturbances, there was a degree of ferment in Otsego county, but no open defiance of law. There were two or three small pieces of artillery, kept in a very dilapidated arsenal on the lake-shore, and used hitherto solely for rejoicing and political victories ; these were removed for a time from the village, by orders from Albany, lest they should be seized by the anti-renters of the adjoining county of Delaware. Ammunition also passed through the valley on the way to Delhi. But beyond these few preliminary steps of caution, the good people of Otsego escaped all overt acts of disturbance. The victory which the honest supporters of the laws gained over the rebellious faction in Delaware county, which was placed for a time under martial law, will be remembered by the reader. The spirit of violence and insubordination was subdued. That it may, in every outbreak, be met and controlled with firmness, with wisdom, with upright impartiality and justice, must be the heartfelt wish of every honest citizen of the republic.

The legal knowledge and skill shown by Mr. Cooper in this series of works has been declared remarkable by distinguished jurists of the country. He was partial to legal reading, and often studied some questions of that nature with deep interest, and without any other object than the pleasure of the investigation itself.

REDSKINS.

THE following day was Sunday. I did not rise until nine, and when I withdrew the curtains and opened the shutters of my window, and looked out upon the lawn, and the fields beyond it, and the blue void that canopied all, I thought a lovelier day, or one more in harmony with the tranquil character of the whole scene, never shone from the heavens. I threw up the sash, and breathed the morning air which filled my dressing-room, pregnant with the balms and odors of the hundred sweet-smelling flowers and plants that embellished the shrubberies. The repose of the Sabbath seemed to rest on man and beast; the bees and humming-birds that buzzed about the flowers, even at their usual pursuits, seemed as if conscious of the sanctity of the day. I think no one can be insensible to the difference there is between a Sabbath in the country and any other day of the week. Most of this, doubtless, is the simple consequence of abstaining from labor; but, connected with the history of the festival, its usual observances, and the holy calm that appears to reign around, it is so very obvious and impressive, that a Sunday, in a mild day in June, is to me ever a delicious resting-place, as a mere poetical pause in the bustling and turmoil of this world's time. Such a day was that which succeeded the night through which we had just passed, and it came most opportunely to soothe the spirits, tranquillize the apprehensions, and afford a moment for sober reflection.

There lay the smouldering ruins of the barn, it is true; a blackened monument of a wicked deed; but the mood which had produced this waste and wrong appeared to have passed away; and, in all other respects, far and near, the farms of Ravensnest had never spread themselves before the eye in colors more in consonance with the general benevolence of a bountiful nature. For a moment, as I gazed on the broad view, I felt all my earlier interests in it revive, and am not ashamed to own that a profound feeling of gratitude to God came over me when I recollected it was by his providence I was born the heir to such a scene, instead of having my lot cast among the serfs and dependents of other regions.

After standing at the window a minute, in contemplation of that pleasing view, I drew back, suddenly and painfully conscious of the character and extent of the combination that existed to rob me of my rights in it. America no longer seemed America to my eyes; but, in place of its ancient submission to the law, its quick distinction bewteen right and wrong, its sober and discriminating liberty, which equally avoided submission to the injustice of power and the excesses of popular delusion, here had been substituted the rapacity of the plunderer, rendered formidable by the insidious manner in which it was interwoven with political machinery, and the truckling of the wretches entrusted with authority—men who were playing into the hands of demagogues, solely in order to secure majorities to perpetuate their own influence. Was, then, the state really so corrupt as to lend itself to projects as base as those openly maintained by the anti-renters? Far from it: four men out of five, if not a larger proportion, must be, and indeed are, sensible of the ills that their success would entail on the community, and would lift up heart and hand to-morrow to put them down totally and without pity; but they have made themselves slaves of the lamp; have enlisted in the ranks of *party*, and *dare* not oppose their leaders, who wield them as Napoleon wielded his masses, to further private views, apostrophizing and affecting a homage to liberty all the while! Such is the history of man!

When the family met in the breakfast-room, a singular tranquillity prevailed among us. As for my grandmother, I knew her spirit and early experience, and was not so much surprised to find her calm and reasonable; but these qualities seemed imparted to her four young companions also. Patt could laugh, and yield to her buoyant spirits, just the same as if nothing had occurred, while my uncle's other wards maintained a lady-like quiet, that denoted any thing but apprehension. Mary Warren, however, surprised me by her air and deportment. There she sat, in her place at the table, looking, if possible, the most feminine, gentle, and timid of the four. I could scarcely believe that the blushing, retiring, modest, pretty daughter of the rector could be the prompt, decided, and clear-headed young girl who had been of so much service to me the past night, and to whose coolness and discretion, indeed, we were all indebted for the roof that was over our heads, and some of us, most probably, for our lives.

Notwithstanding this air of tranquillity, the breakfast was a silent and thoughtful meal. Most of the conversation was between my uncle and grandmother, and a portion of it related to the disposal of the prisoners. There was no magistrate within several miles of the Nest, but those who were tainted with anti-rentism; and to carry Seneca and his companion before a justice of the peace of this character, would be, in effect, to let them go at large. Nominal bail would be taken, and it is more than probable the constable employed would have suffered a rescue, did they even deem it necessary to go through this parade of performing their duties. My uncle, consequently, adopted the following plan: he had caused the two incendiaries to be transferred to the old farm-house, which happened to contain a perfectly dry and empty cellar, and which had much of the security of a dungeon, without the usual defects of obscurity and dampness. The red-men had assumed the office of sentinels, one having his station at the door, while another watched near a window which admitted the light, while it was scarcely large enough to permit the human body to squeeze through it. The interpreter had received instructions from the agent to respect the Christian Sabbath; and no movement being contemplated for the day, this little duty just suited their lounging, idle habits, when in a state of rest. Food and water, of course, had not been forgotten; and there my uncle Ro had left that portion of the business, intending to have the delinquents carried to a distant magistrate, one of the judges of the county, early on Monday morning. As for the disturbers of the past night, no signs of them were any longer visible; and there being little extensive cover near the Nest, no apprehension was felt of any surprise.

We were still at breakfast, when the tone of St. Andrew's bell came floating, plaintively, through the air, as a summons to prepare ourselves for the services of the day. It was little more than a mile to the church, and the younger ladies expressed a desire to walk. My grandmother, attended by her son, therefore, alone used the carriage, while we young people went off in a body, on foot, half an hour before the ringing of the second bell. Considering the state of the country, and the history of the past night, I was astonished at my own indifference on this occasion, no less than at that of my charming companions; nor was it long before I gave utterance to the feeling.

"This America of ours is a queer place, it must be admitted," I cried, as we crossed the lawn to take a foot-path that would lead us, by pleasant pastures, quite to the church-door, without entering the highway, except to cross it once; "here we have the whole neighborhood as tranquil as if crime never disturbed it, though it is not yet a dozen hours since riot, arson, and perhaps murder, were in the contemplation of hundreds of those who live on every side of us. The change is wonderful!"

"But, you will remember it is Sunday, Hugh," put in Patt. "All summer, when Sunday has come, we have had a respite from disturbances and fears. In this part of the country, the people are too religious to think of desecrating the Sabbath by violence and armed bands. The anti-renters would lose more than they would gain by pursuing a different course."

I had little or no difficulty in believing this, it being no unusual thing, among us, to find observances of this nature clinging to the habits of thousands, long after the devout feeling which had first instilled it into the race has become extinct. Something very like it prevails in other countries, and among even higher and more intellectual classes, where it is no unusual thing to find the most profound outward respect manifested toward the altar and its rites, by men who live in the hourly neglect of the first and plainest commands of the decalogue. We are not alone, therefore, in this pharisaical spirit, which exists, in some mode or other, wherever man himself is to be found.

XXIII.

JACK TIER.

THIS is another tale of the sea—a very interesting book—full of original incident, the scene being laid in the Gulf of Mexico. The book was at first called Rose Budd, from the young girl of that name who plays an important part in the narrative, and was published in "Graham's Magazine." While writing it, the author was also occupied with a series of naval biographies, the lives of distinguished officers of the American marine, many of whom had been his own messmates and personal friends in early life. The character of Jack Tier is quite original, and very good. There are lovely heroines, of ancient times, figuring, in the guise of page or squire, in many a ballad and romance of the days of chivalry; but a plain, homely, hard-working creature, following a very indifferent sort of husband about the world, under the garb, and doing the work of a common sailor of our own times, is not exactly the personage one would look for as a heroine of romance. And yet, as we close this spirited and original tale, we feel a regard, and even a sort of affection for Jack, as we leave her, once more clad in womanly garments, by the side of her dying husband. The incidents connected with the sea, it is scarcely necessary to observe, are strikingly graphic and spirited.

Jack Tier: ...and he permitted Rose to escape from his
grasp in the effort to save himself from a fall. Turning
fiercely towards the assailant, he saw Tier standing
within a few yards, levelling a pistol at him.

THE REEF.

It is seldom that man is required to make an exertion as desperate and appalling, in all its circumstances, as that on which Harry Mulford was now bent. The night was starlight, it was true, and it was possible to see objects near by with tolerable distinctness; still, it was midnight, and the gloom of that hour rested on the face of the sea, lending its solemn mystery and obscurity to the other trying features of the undertaking. Then there was the uncertainty whether it was the boat at all of which he was in pursuit; and, if the boat, it might drift away from him as fast as he could follow it. Nevertheless, the perfect conviction that, without some early succor, the party on the wreck, including Rose Budd, must inevitably perish, stimulated him to proceed, and a passing feeling of doubt, touching the prudence of his course, that came over the young mate, when he was a few yards from the wreck, vanished under a vivid renewal of this last conviction. On he swam, therefore, riveting his eye on the "thoughtful star" that guided his course, and keeping his mind as tranquil as possible, in order that the exertions of his body might be the easier.

Mulford was an excellent swimmer. The want of food was a serious obstacle to his making one of his best efforts, but, as yet, he was not very sensible of any great loss of strength. Understanding fully the necessity of swimming easily, if he would swim long, he did not throw out all his energy at first, but made the movements of his limbs as regular, continued, and skilful as possible. No strength was thrown away, and his progress was in proportion to the prudence of this manner of proceeding. For some twenty minutes he held on his course, in this way, when he began to experience a little of that weariness which is apt to accompany an unremitted use of the same set of muscles, in a monotonous and undeviating mode. Accustomed to all the resources of his art, he turned on his back, for the double purpose of relieving his arms for a minute, and of getting a glimpse of the wreck, if possible, in order to ascertain the distance he had overcome. Swim long in this new manner, however, he could not with prudence, as the star was necessary in order to keep the direct line of his course. It may be well to explain to some of our readers that, though the surface of the ocean may be like glass, as sometimes really happens, it is never absolutely free from the long, undulating motion that is known by the name of a "ground swell." This swell, on the present occasion, was not very heavy, but it was sufficient to place our young mate, at moments, between two dark mounds of water, that limited his view in either direction to some eighty or a hundred yards; then it raised him on the summit of a rounded wave, that enabled him to see far as his eye could reach under that obscure light. Profiting by this advantage, Mulford now looked behind him, in quest of the wreck, but uselessly. It might have been in the trough, while he was thus on the summit of the waves; or it might be that it floated so low as to be totally lost to the view of one whose head was scarcely above the surface of the water. For a single instant, the young man felt a chill at his heart, as he fancied that the wreck had already sunk; but it passed away when he recalled the slow progress by which the air escaped, and he saw the certainty that the catastrophe, however inevitable, could not yet have really arrived. He waited for another swell to lift him on its summit, when, by "treading water," he raised his head and shoulders fairly above the surface of the sea, and strained his eyes in another vain effort to catch a glimpse of the wreck. He could not see it. In point of fact, the mate had swam much further than he had supposed, and was already so distant as to render any such attempt hopeless. He was fully a third of a mile distant from the point of his departure.

Disappointed, and in a slight degree disheartened, Mulford turned, and swam in the direction of the sinking star. He now looked anxiously for the boat. It was time that it came more plainly into view, and a new source of anxiety beset him, as he could discover no signs of its vicinity. Certain that he was on the course, after making a due allowance for the direction of the wind, the stout-hearted young man swam on. He next determined not to annoy himself by fruitless searches, or vain regrets, but to swim steadily for a certain time—a period long enough to carry him a material distance—ere he again looked for the object of his search.

For twenty minutes longer did that courageous and active youth struggle with the waste of waters, amid the obscurity and solitude of midnight. He now believed himself near a mile from the wreck, and the star which had so long served him for a beacon was getting near to the horizon. He took a new observation of another of the heavenly bodies nigh it, to serve him in its stead when it should disappear altogether, and then he raised himself in the water, and looked about again for the boat. The search was in vain. No boat was very near him, of a certainty, and the dreadful apprehension began to possess his mind of perishing uselessly in that waste of gloomy waters. While thus gazing about him, turning his eyes in every quarter, hoping intently to catch some glimpse of the much-desired object in the gloom, he saw two dark, pointed objects, that resembled small stakes, in the water, within twenty feet of him. Mulford knew them at a glance, and a cold shudder passed through his frame, as he recognized them. They were, out of all question, the fins of an enormous shark —an animal that could not measure less than eighteen or twenty feet in length.

It is scarcely necessary to say, that when our young mate discovered the proximity of this dangerous animal, situated as he was, he gave himself up for lost. He possessed his knife, however, and had heard of the manner in which even sharks were overcome, and that, too, in their own element, by the skilful and resolute. At first he was resolved to make one desperate effort for life, before he submitted to a fate as horrible as that which now menaced him ; but the movements of his dangerous neighbor induced him to wait. It did not approach any nearer, but continued swimming to and fro, on the surface of the water, according to the known habits of the fish, as if watching his own movements. There being no time to be wasted, our young mate turned on his face, and began again to swim in the direction of the setting star, though nearly chilled by despair. For ten minutes longer did he struggle on, beginning to feel exhaustion, however, and always accompanied by those two dark, sharp, and gliding fins. There was no difficulty in knowing the position of the animal, and Mulford's eyes were oftener on those fins than on the beacon before him. Strange as it may appear, he actually became accustomed to the vicinity of this formidable creature, and soon felt his presence a sort of relief against the dreadful solitude of his situation. He had been told by seamen of instances, and had once witnessed a case himself, in which a shark had attended a swimming man for a long distance, either forbearing to do him harm, from repletion, or influenced by that awe which nature has instilled into all of the inferior for the highest animal of the creation. He began to think that he was thus favored, and really regarded the shark as a friendly neighbor, rather than as a voracious foe. In this manner did the two proceed, nearly another third of a mile, the fins sometimes in sight ahead, gliding hither and thither, and sometimes out of view behind the swimmer, leaving him in dreadful doubts as to the movements of the fish, when Mulford suddenly felt something hard hit his foot. Believing it to be the shark, dipping for his prey, a slight exclamation escaped him. At the next instant both feet hit the unknown substance again, and he stood erect, the water no higher than his waist! Quick, and comprehending every thing connected with the sea, the young man at once understood that he was on a part of the reef where the water was so shallow as to admit of his wading.

Mulford felt that he had been providentially rescued from death. His strength had been about to fail him, when he was thus led, unknown to himself, to a spot where his life might yet be possibly prolonged for a few more hours or days. He had leisure to look about him, and to reflect on what was next to be done. Almost unwittingly, he turned in quest of his terrible companion, in whose voracious mouth he had actually believed himself about to be immolated a few seconds before. There the two horn-like fins still were, gliding about above the water, and indicating the smallest movement of their formidable owner. The mate observed that they went a short distance ahead of him, describing nearly a semi-circle, and then returned, doing the same thing in his rear, repeating the movements incessantly, keeping always on his right. This convinced him that shoaler water existed on his left hand, and he waded in that direction, until he reached a small spot of naked rock.

For a time, at least, he was safe! The fragment of coral on which the mate now stood, was irregular in shape, but might have contained a hundred feet square in super-ficial measurement, and was so little raised above the level of the water as not to be visible, even by daylight, at the distance of a hundred yards. Mulford found it was perfectly dry, however—an important discovery to him, as, by a close calculation he had made of the tides, since quitting the Dry Tortugas, he knew it must be near high water. Could he have even this small portion of bare rock secure, it made him, for the moment, rich as the most extensive landholder living. A considerable quantity of sea-weed had lodged on the rock, and, as most of this was also quite dry, it convinced the young sailor that the place was usually bare. But, though most of this sea-weed was dry, there were portions of the more recent accessions there that still lay in or quite near to the water, which formed exceptions. In handling these weeds, in order to ascertain the facts, Mulford caught a small shell-fish, and, finding it fresh and easy to open, he swallowed it with the eagerness of a famishing man. Never had food proved half so grateful to him as that single swallow of a very palatable testaceous animal. By feeling further, he found several others of the same family, and made quite as large a meal as, under the circumstances, was probably good for him. Then, thankful for his escape, but overcome by fatigue, he hastily arranged a bed of sea-weed, drew a portion of the plant over his body, to keep him warm, and fell into a deep sleep that lasted for hours.

Mulford did not regain his consciousness until the rays of the rising sun fell upon his eye-lids, and the genial warmth of the great luminary shed its benign influence over his frame. At first his mind was confused, and it required a few seconds to bring a perfect recollection of the past, and a true understanding of his real situation. They came, however, and the young man moved to the highest part of his little domain, and cast an anxious, hurried look around in quest of the wreck. A knowledge of the course in which he had swum, aided by the position of the sun, told him on what part of the naked waste to look for the object which he sought. God had not yet forsaken them! There was the wreck; or, it might be more exact to say, there were those whom the remaining buoyancy of the wreck still upheld from sinking into the depths of the gulf. In point of fact, but very little of the bottom of the vessel actually remained above water, some two or three yards square at most, and that little was what seamen term nearly awash. Two or three hours must bury that small portion of the still naked wood beneath the surface of the sea, though sufficient buoyancy might possibly remain for the entire day still to keep the living from death.

There the wreck was, however, yet floating; and, though not visible to Mulford, with a small portion of it above water. He saw the four persons only; and, what was more, they saw him. This was evident by Jack Tier's waving his hat like a man cheering. When Mulford returned this signal, the shawl of Rose was tossed into the air, in a way to leave no doubt that he was seen and known. The explanation of this early recognition and discovery of the young mate was very simple. Tier was not asleep when Harry left the wreck, though, seeing the importance of the step the other was taking, he had feigned to be so. When Rose awoke, missed her lover, and was told what had happened, her heart was kept from sinking by his encouraging tale and hopes. An hour of agony had succeeded, nevertheless, when light returned, and no Mulford was to be seen. The despair that burst upon the heart of our heroine was followed by the joy of discovering him on the rock.

It is scarcely necessary to say how much the parties were relieved on ascertaining their respective positions. Faint as were the hopes of each of eventual delivery, the two or three minutes that succeeded seemed to be minutes of perfect happiness. After this rush of unlooked-for joy, Mulford continued his intelligent examination of surrounding objects.

The wreck was fully half a mile from the rock of the mate, but much nearer to the reef than it had been the previous night. "Could it but ground on the rocks," thought the young man, "it would be a most blessed event." The thing was possible, though the first half hour of his observations told him that its drift was in the direction of the open passage so often named, rather than toward the nearest rocks. Still, that drift brought Rose each minute nearer and nearer to himself again. In looking round, however, the young man saw the boat. It was a quarter of a mile distant, with open water between them, apparently grounded on a rock, for it was more within the reef than he was himself. He must have passed it in the dark, and the boat had been left to obey the wind and currents, and to drift to the spot where it then lay.

Mulford shouted aloud when he saw the boat, and at once determined to swim in quest of it as soon as he had collected a little refreshment from among the sea-weeds. On taking a look at his rock by daylight, he saw that its size was quadrupled to the eye by the falling of the tide, and that water was lying in several of the cavities of its uneven surface. At first he supposed this to be sea water, left by the flood; but, reflecting a moment, he remembered the rain, and hoped it might be possible that one little cavity, containing two or three gallons of the fluid, would turn out to be fresh.

Kneeling beside it, he applied his lips in feverish haste, and drank the sweetest draught that had ever passed his lips. Slaking his thirst, which had begun again to be painfully severe, he arose with a heart overflowing with gratitude—could he only get Rose to that narrow and barren rock, it would seem to be an earthly paradise. Mulford next made his scanty, but, all things considered, sufficient meal, drank myderately afterward, and then turned his attention and energies toward the boat, which, though now aground and fast, might soon float on the rising tide, and drift once more beyond his reach. It was his first intention to swim directly for his object; but, just when about to enter the water, he saw with horror the fins of at least a dozen sharks, which were prowling about in the deeper water of the reef, and almost encircling his hold. To throw himself in the midst of such enemies would be madness, and he stopped to reflect, and again to look about him. For the first time that morning, he took a survey of the entire horizon, to see if any thing were in sight; for, hitherto, his thoughts had been too much occupied with Rose and her companions to remember any thing else. To the northward and westward he distinctly saw the upper sails of a large ship, that was standing on a wind to the northward and eastward. As there was no port to which a vessel of that character would be likely to be bound in the quarter of the Gulf to which such a course would lead, Mulford at once inferred it was the sloop-of-war, which, after having examined the islets, at the Dry Tortugas, and finding them deserted, was beating up, either to go into Key West, or to pass to the southward of the reef again, by the passage through which she had come as lately as the previous day. This was highly encouraging, and could he only get to the boat, and remove the party from the wreck before it sunk, there was now every prospect of a final escape.

The Oak Openings: There he sat, motionless as the
rock on which he had placed himself, a picture of
solitude and reflection.

XXIV.

THE OAK OPENINGS.

In the month of June, of the year 1847, the author of the Pathfinder made a pleasant excursion westward. The journey was not a long one, reaching only as far as Detroit, the prairies, and the beautiful open groves of southern Michigan. Beyond Seneca Lake, the ground, in its actual aspect, was quite new to him; recollections of the journey taken through the same region, in early youth, now giving additional interest to every mile of the way, as he moved along among well tilled lands—garden, orchard, and grain-field, all rich in full midsummer promise—and passed from one large and affluent town to another, where, forty years earlier, he had travelled through a wilderness. He had now reached his threescore years, but, full of vigor and spirit, still felt undiminished the interest he had always taken in the advancing movement of civilization. He saw Niagara again. The sublime character of the cataract impressed him very deeply on this occasion; it far surpassed his recollections, and, having now seen the most admired falls of Europe, he could better comprehend its dignity and grandeur— the out-pouring of great seas amid those ragged cliffs. The idea of an Indian narrative, connected with Niagara, occurred to him; he would have dated it a century earlier, and have carried a party of savages to Goat Island ere any bridge had been built, and while the whole adjoining country was still a forest. Would that the book had been written! What varied pictures of Niagara should we have had in its pages; what wild interest of adventure would he not have thrown over its scenes! With Buffalo and Detroit he was much pleased, from admiration of their growth and promise. But with the beautiful flowery prairies and natural groves of Michigan, he was quite charmed. Indeed, it would not be easy to say from which source he derived the greatest pleasure on this excursion—whether from the spirit of practical progress, or from the natural objects before him—the lakes, the cataracts, the prairies, and their groves. Here is a passage relating to this excursion:

"To get an idea of Prairie Round, the reader must imagine an oval plain of some five-and-twenty or thirty thousand acres in extent, of the most surprising fertility, without an eminence of any sort; almost without an inequality. There are a few small cavities, however, in which there are springs forming large pools of water that the cattle will drink. This plain, so far as we saw it, is now entirely fenced and cultivated. The fields are large—many containing eighty acres, and some one hundred and sixty; most of them being in wheat. We saw several fields of this size in that grain. Farm-houses dotted the surface, with barns, and the other accessories of rural life. In the centre of the prairie is an "island" of forest, containing some five or six hundred acres of the noblest native trees we remember ever to have seen. In the centre of this wood is a little lake, circular in shape, and exceeding a quarter of a mile in diameter. The walk in this wood, which is not an opening, but an old-fashioned virgin forest, we found delightful of a warm summer's day. One thing that we saw in it was characteristic of the country. Some of the nearest farmers had drawn their manure into it, where it lay in large piles, in order to get it out of the way of doing any mischief. Its effect on the land, it was thought, would be to bring too much straw!"

Mr. Cooper was absent from home but a few weeks. One morning, not long after his return, passing, as usual, his leisure hours at the mountain farm, in overlooking his laborers, he observed a little skiff leaving a point on the opposite shore of the lake, and moving directly toward an opening on his own lands, made originally for the purpose of rolling logs from the heights above, but which was now occasionally used as a landing-place. The adjoining shores on the western side of the lake were scarcely peopled for some miles from the village, with the exception of a small inn, a baiting place for teamsters, and here and there a log cabin beyond. Mr. Cooper believed the boatman to be coming over the lake on some errand to himself, connected with hemlock timber, with which he was then supplying the new plank road on the opposite bank. Presently a stranger, with a tin pail in his hand, made his appearance, coming slowly up the winding road to the hill-top, where Mr. Cooper was engaged with his workmen. Approaching the party, he inquired if a large swarm of bees had not been seen somewhere in that direction; he had lost a fine swarm, which had left the hive early in the morning, several days before, and, after looking for them in vain for a while, he had just learned that a farmer's wife in his neighborhood had seen them cross the lake in the direction of the Châlet. No such swarm had been seen by the workmen at the Châlet; one of them remarked, however, that bees had been "very plenty about the blossoms for a day or two." Learning this fact, the stranger began to look about him more closely, and, from the un-usual number of honey-bees coming and going about the flowering plants on the hill, he became convinced that his swarm was lodged somewhere within reach. A search for the lost bees began; Mr. Cooper, who was much interested by the little incident, assisting the stranger in his task. The farm was belted by wood on all sides, while a young grove skirted the cliffs, and on the height a number of tall scattered trees, some charred and lifeless, others still in full vigor, showed the remains of the original forest. The farmer from Highborough professed himself very knowing in the ways of bees; boasted of having one of the largest "bee-sheds" in the country, running along two sides of his garden; he knew the trees in which the bees would be most likely to lodge, and accord-ingly he went directly toward those gaunt old oaks and elms on the hill-top, in some hollow of which he was convinced that the swarms had alighted. Rustic jokes passed at the cost of the stranger, who was asked by the workmen which of all the old trees, with straight, branchless trunks perhaps sixty or eighty feet high, he would most fancy to climb; when he was ready, he must let them know, they would like to see the sight! Mr. Cooper had a word to say also: while wishing the search good success, he protested against receiving the treatment which a friend of his had lately met with—a pine tree, nearly two hundred feet high, and perhaps five hundred years old, having been deliberately felled by some lawless fellow, for the sake of a swarm of bees which had alighted on one of the topmost boughs. The Highborough farmer nodded his head, and declared that he did not mean to waste any time in climbing or in "chopping" that day, the weather was too warm; he meant to call his bees down—that was his fashion. And taking up his tin pail, he began to move about over a little spot of waste land, where many flowering plants grew at will; here he soon found a honey-bee sipping from the cup of a rose raspberry; he professed to know at once the face of one of his own bees, "to say nothin' of the critter's talk," as he termed the buzzing of the wings. A glass taken from the pail was placed over it, a few drops of sweet honey having been previously thrown into it; the captive bee, after moving about uneasily for a while, began to sip the honey; when its little bag was quite full, it was set at liberty, the course it took being carefully followed as far as the eye could reach. Again the farmer looked over the flowers for a second honey-bee, and one was soon found on a head of golden-rod; the little creature was captured, fed with honey, and set at liberty as the first had been; the stranger placing himself, however, at a different position, and at an opposite point of the compass from that where he had first stood. When the bee had taken wing, its course was closely watched until it had flown out of sight. In this way, some dozen bees were successively captured from the clover, or daisies, or wood flowers, found in mingled growth about the hill-top, until, at length, the general direction taken by them all, when set at liberty, was discovered. This process of "lining the bees," or tracking them by an air-line to the natural hive, proved that the farmer had been correct; an old, half-charred oak stub, some forty feet in height, with a single limb near the top, had been their alighting place; once beneath the tree, the little creatures might be seen flying about the blighted bough above. The stranger now went to his boat again, and brought a new hive to the hill-top, placing it at a short distance from the old trunk where his bees had housed themselves; honey was sprinkled about the little doorway of the hive, flowering plants were gathered and strewn around, and some were placed in water to preserve them in freshness. The good man then withdrew to a little distance, and seated himself on a stump, awaiting the result; it was not long before a line of communication was opened between the bee-company above, and the hive with its store of honey, and the flowering plants below; and when the sun set, the bees had of their own accord taken possession of their new abode; by moonlight they were rowed across the lake, and placed on the shelf in the farmer's garden, beside the mother swarm they had left a few days earlier on their adventurous journey to the Châlet.

This little incident interested Mr. Cooper very much, and in the course of the following autumn, while thinking over a new tale connected with the prairies of Michigan, he determined that a "bee-hunter" should be one of the principal characters. This book proved the last of a long series of Indian tales. In twelve different works of the imagination, from the same pen, the savages had held positions more or less prominent—among scenes of adventurous life in the Otsego hills, on the shores of the Horican, roaming over the far western prairies, on the waters of Lake Ontario, among the forests of New York, and now among the oak groves of Michigan. The last of the series is full of interest, original in incident, and different in spirit from those which preceded it. In the principal character, we see how the holy and peaceful influences of Christianity are made at length to triumph over that dearest passion of the American savage, the spirit of revenge.

The "Oak Openings" was commenced on New Year's day of 1848, and written in the course of the following winter and spring. A note, relating to the first pages of the book, occurs in a brief diary kept by the writer during that year:

"Saturday, January 1st, 1848.—Read St. John. No church. Weather very mild, though snow fell in the night. Walking very bad, and I paid no visits out of the family. Had ***, ***, ***, ***, and ***, at dinner. A very merry evening with the young people. Played chess with my wife. Wrote a little in 'Oak Openings' to begin the year with."

THE COUNCIL FIRE.

THE Indians already present were not seated. They stood in groups, conversing, or stalking across the arena, resembling so many dark and stately spectres. No sound was heard among them—a circumstance that added largely to the wild and supernatural aspect of the scene. If any spoke, it was in a tone so low and gentle, as to carry the sound no further than to the ears that were listening; two never spoke at the same time, and in the same group, while the moccasin permitted no foot-fall to be audible. Nothing could have been more unearthly than the picture presented in that little, wood-circled arena, of velvet-like grass and rural beauty. The erect, stalking forms, half naked, if not even more; the swarthy skins; the faces fierce in the savage conceits which were intended to strike terror into the bosoms of enemies; and the glittering eyes that fairly sparkled in their midst, all contributed to the character of the scene, which le Bourdon rightly enough imagined was altogether much the most remarkable of any he had ever been in the way of witnessing.

Our two spectators might have been seated on the fallen tree half an hour, all of which time they had been gazing at what was passing before their eyes; with positively not a human sound to relieve the unearthly nature of the picture. No one spoke, coughed, laughed, or exclaimed, in all that period. Suddenly, every chief stood sill, and all the faces turned in the same direction. It was toward the little gate-way of the rill, which being the side of the arena most remote from the bee-hunter and the corporal, lay nearly in darkness as respected them. With the red men it must have been different, for *they* all appeared to be in intent expectation of some one from that quarter. Nor did they have to wait long; for, in half a minute, two forms came out of the obscurity, advancing with a dignified and deliberate tread to the centre of the

arena. As these new-comers got more within the influence of the flickering light, le
Bourdon saw that they were Peter and Parson Amen. The first led, with a slow, imposing manner, while the other followed, not a little bewildered with what he saw. It
may be as well to explain here, that the Indian was coming alone to this place of
meeting, when he encountered the missionary wandering among the oaks, looking for
le Bourdon and the corporal, and, instead of endeavoring to throw off this unexpected
companion, he quietly invited him to be of his own party.

It was evident to le Bourdon, at a glance, that Peter was expected, though it was
not quite so clear that such was the fact as regarded his companion. Still, respect for
the great chief prevented any manifestations of surprise or discontent, and the medicine-
man of the pale faces was received with as grave a courtesy as if he had been an invited
guest. Just as the two had entered the dark circle that formed around them, a young
chief threw some dry sticks on the fire, which, blazing upward, cast a stronger light on
a row of as terrifically-looking countenances as ever gleamed on human forms. This
sudden illumination, with its accompanying accessories, had the effect to startle all the
white spectators, though Peter looked on the whole with a calm like that of the leafless
tree, when the cold is at its height, and the currents of the wintry air are death-like
still. Nothing appeared to move *him*, whether expected or not; though use had
probably accustomed his eye to all the aspects in which savage ingenuity could offer
savage forms. He even smiled, as he made a gesture of recognition, which seemed to
salute the whole group. It was just then, when the fire burned brightest, and when
the chiefs pressed most within its influence, that le Bourdon perceived that his old acquaintances, the head men of the Pottawattamies, were present, among the other chiefs
so strangely and portentously assembled in these grounds which he had so long possessed almost entirely to himself.

A few of the oldest of the chiefs now approached Peter, and a low conversation
took place between them. What was said did not reach le Bourdon, of course; for it
was not even heard in the dark circle of savages who surrounded the fire. The effect
of this secret dialogue, however, was to cause all the chiefs to be seated, each taking
his place on the grass; the whole preserving the original circle around the fire. Fortunately for the wishes of le Bourdon, Peter and his companions took their stations
directly opposite to his own seat, thus enabling him to watch every lineament of that
remarkable chief's still more remarkable countenance. Unlike each, and all, of the
red men around him, the face of Peter was not painted, except by the tints imparted
by nature; which, in his case, was that of copper a little tarnished, or rendered dull by
the action of the atmosphere. The bée-hunter could distinctly trace every lineament;
nor was the dark, roving eye beyond the reach of his own vision. Some attention was
given to the fire, too; one of the younger chiefs occasionally throwing on it a few
dried sticks, more to keep alive the flame, and to renew the light, than from any need
of warmth. One other purpose, however, this fire *did* answer; that of enabling the

young chiefs to light the pipes that were now prepared; it seldom occurring that the chiefs thus assembled without *smoking* around their council fire.

As this smoking was just then more a matter of ceremony than for any other purpose, a whiff or two sufficed for each chief; the smoker passing the pipe to his neighbor as soon as he had inhaled a few puffs. The Indians are models of propriety in their happiest moods, and every one in that dark and menacing circle was permitted to have his turn with the pipe, before any other step was taken. There were but two pipes lighted, and mouths being numerous, some time was necessary in order to complete this ceremony. Still, no sign of impatience was seen, the lowest chief having as much respect paid to his feelings, as related to this attention, as the highest. At length the pipes completed their circuit, even Parson Amen getting, and using, his turn, when a dead pause succeeded. The silence resembled that of a Quaker meeting, and was broken only by the rising of one of the principal chiefs, evidently about to speak. The language of the great Ojebway nation was used on this occasion, most of the chiefs present belonging to some one of the tribes of that stock, though several spoke other tongues, English and French included. Of the three whites present, Parson Amen alone fully comprehended all that was said, he having qualified himself, in this respect, to preach to the tribes of that people; though le Bourdon understood nearly all, and even the corporal comprehended a good deal. The name of the chief who first spoke at this secret meeting, which was afterward known among the Ojebways by the name of the "Council of the Bottom Land, near to the spring of gushing water," was Bear's Meat, an appellation that might denote a distinguished hunter, rather than an orator of much renown.

"Brothers of the many tribes of the Ojebways," commenced this personage, "the Great Spirit has permitted us to meet in council. The Manitou of our fathers is now among these oaks, listening to our words, and looking in at our hearts. Wise Indians will be careful what they say in such a presence, and careful of what they think. All should be said and thought for the best. We are a scattered nation, and the time is come when we must stop in our tracks, or travel beyond the sound of each other's cries. If we travel beyond the hearing of our people, soon will our children learn tongues that Ojebway ears cannot understand. The mother talks to her child, and the child learns her words. But no child can hear across a great lake. Once we lived near the rising sun. Where are we now? Some of our young men say they have seen the sun go down in the lakes of sweet water. There can be no hunting-grounds beyond *that* spot; and, if we would live, we must stand still in our tracks. How to do this, we have met to consider.

"Brothers, many wise chiefs and braves are seated at this council fire. It is pleasant to my eyes to look upon them. Ottawas, Chippeways, Pottawattamies, Menominees, Hurons, and all. Our Father at Quebec has dug up the hatchet against the Yankees. The war path is open between Detroit and all the villages of the red men. The prophets are speaking to our people, and we listen. One is here; he is about to speak. The council will have but a single sense, which will be that of hearing."

Thus concluding, Bear's Meat took his seat, in the same composed and dignified manner as that in which he had risen, and deep silence succeeded. So profound was the stillness, that, taken in connection with the dark lineaments, the lustrous eyeballs that threw back the light of the fire, the terrific paint, and the armed hands of every warrior present, the picture might be described as imposing to a degree that is seldom seen in the assemblies of the civilized. In the midst of this general but portentous calm, Peter arose. The breathing of the circle grew deeper, so much so as to be audible, the only manner in which the intensity of the common expectation betrayed itself. Peter was an experienced orator, and knew how to turn every minutiæ of his art to good account. His every movement was deliberate, his attitude highly digni-fied—even his eye seemed eloquent.

Oratory! what a power art thou, wielded, as is so often the case, as much for evil as for good. The very reasoning that might appear to be obtuse, or which would be overlooked entirely when written and published, issuing from the mouth, aided by the feelings of sympathy and the impulses of the masses, seems to partake of the wisdom of divinity. Thus is it, also, with the passions, the sense of wrong, the appeals to vengeance, and all the other avenues of human emotion. Let them be addressed to the cold eye of reason and judgment, in the form of written statements, and the mind pauses to weigh the force of arguments, the justice of the appeals, the truth of facts; but let them come upon the ear aided by thy art, with a power concentrated by sym-pathy, and the torrent is often less destructive in its course than that of the whirlwind that thou canst awaken!

"Chiefs of the great Ojebway nation, I wish you well," said Peter, stretching out his arms toward the circle, as if desirous of embracing all present. "The Manitou has been good to me. He has cleared a path to this spring, and to this council fire. I see around it the faces of many friends. Why should we not all be friendly? Why should a red man ever strike a blow against a red man? The Great Spirit made us of the same color, and placed us on the same hunting-grounds. He meant that we should hunt in company; not take each other's scalps. How many warriors have fallen in our family wars? Who has counted them? Who can say? Perhaps enough, had they not been killed, to drive the pale-faces into the sea!"

Here Peter, who as yet had spoken only in a low and barely audible voice, suddenly paused, in order to allow the idea he had just thrown out to work on the minds of his listeners. That it was producing its effect was apparent by the manner in which one stern face turned toward another, and eye seemed to search in eye some response to a query that the mind suggested, though no utterance was given to it with the tongue. As soon, however, as the orator thought time sufficient to impress that thought on the memories of the listeners had elapsed, he resumed, suffering his voice gradually to in-crease in volume, as he warmed with his subject.

"Yes," he continued, "the Manitou has been very kind. Who is the Manitou?

Has any Indian ever seen him? Every Indian has seen him. No one can look on the hunting-grounds, on the lakes, on the prairies, on the trees, on the game, without see-ing his hand. His face is to be seen in the sun at noon-day; his eyes in the stars at night. Has any Indian ever heard the Manitou? When it thunders, he speaks. When the crash is loudest, then he scolds. Some Indian has done wrong. Perhaps one red man has taken another red man's scalp!''

Another pause succeeded, briefer, and less imposing than the first, but one that sufficed to impress on the listeners anew the reat evil of an Indian's raising his hand against an Indian.

"Yes, there is no one so deaf as not to hear the voice of the Great Spirit when he is angry,'' resumed Peter. "Ten thousands of buffalo bulls, roaring together, do not ,make as much noise as his whisper. Spread the prairies, and the openings, and the lakes, before him, and he can be heard in all, and on all, at the same time. Here is a medicine-priest of the pale-faces; he tells me that the voice of the Manitou reaches into the largest villages of his people, beneath the rising sun, when it is heard by the red man across the great lakes, and near the rocks of the setting sun. It is a loud voice; woe to him who does not remember it. It speaks to all colors, and to every people, and tribe, and nation.

"Brothers, that is a lying tradition which says there is one Manitou for a Sac, and another for the Ojebway—one Manitou for the red man, and another for the pale-face. In this, we are alike. One Great Spirit made all; governs all; rewards all; punishes all. He may keep the Happy Hunting-Grounds of an Indian separate from the white man's Heaven, for he knows that their customs are different, and what would please a warrior would displease a trader; and what would please a trader would displease a warrior. He has thought of these things, and has made several places for the spirits of the good, let their colors be what they may. Is it the same with the places of the spirits of the bad? I think not. To me it would seem best to let *them* go together, that they may torment one another. A wicked Indian and a wicked pale-face would make a bad neighborhood. I think the Manitou will let *them* go together.

"Brothers, if the Manitou keeps the good Indian and the good pale-face apart in another world, what has brought them together in this? If he brings the bad spirits of all colors together in another world, why should they come together here, before their time? A place for wicked spirits should not be found on earth. This is wrong; it must be looked into.

"Brothers, I have now done: this pale-face wishes to speak, and I have said that you would hear his words. When he has spoken his mind, I may have more to tell you. Now, listen to the stranger. He is a medicine-priest of the white men, and says he has a great secret to tell our people—when he has told it, I have another for their ears, too. Mine must be spoken when there is no one near but the children of red clay.''

XXV.

THE SEA LIONS.

From the day when the little Ariel first sailed into view, and dropped her anchor in that gloomy bay of the German Ocean, where, at a later hour, Long Tom and herself were to close their career together, many a noble ship had been launched and sailed by the same master hand. Who, indeed, shall call over the names of all the vessels bearing his flag? Never admiral of the Ocean Sea held so great a fleet under command! Proud men-of-war are here, from the lofty three-decker to the light gun-boat, fighting his battles; merchantmen of every rig—brig, bark, schooner, and yacht—come and go, amid storm and tempest, with swift and skilful manœuvre, at his will; the light felucca flies wing-and-wing over the blue Mediterranean; the bark canoe glides over the lake, steals along the shadowy forest stream, or the reedy shore, doing his bidding. And how many brave and generous hearts, how many gallant spirits, are moving about those decks! What deeds of high adventure are wrought among them! What an atmosphere of picture and poetry lights up eye and arm, sail, and spar, and flag! Could he have gathered his full fleet together, and sailed at their head into port, that would have been, indeed, a gallant nautical gala, filling the proudest harbor in the land. And his ships are all from the best yards, well commanded, skilfully piloted. The poetical light which lingers about them is warm with reality; their iron anchors hold as firm a grasp of the bottom as those of the heaviest hulk that can be found in the harbor to-day.

During thirty long years his ships were coming and going over the high seas, good people ashore still following their movements with more or less of interest. But now we behold the last of that numerous fleet. His nautical pictures began with that craft especially American, the schooner; and in this, the latest of his marine writings, the interest is also thrown about two schooners, each bearing the name of "The Sea Lion," and both sailing from home waters on a voyage of daring adventure, into far distant seas toward the southern pole.

In his early married life, Mr. Cooper had paid repeated visits, during the summer months, to a relative of Mrs. Cooper, living on one of the islands off the eastern shore of Long Island. This gentleman led a sort of semi-aquatic life, which had great attractions for a young man still a seaman at heart. His estate covered an island of some size, inhabited by his own family and dependents only, and bearing the pleasing name of Shelter Island; and all communications with the main land were carried on by boats of different kinds. Here, cruising, fishing, shooting—and your true Long Islander of the old school was almost invariably a sportsman, and a good shot—Mr. Cooper had passed many a pleasant hour, remembered with pleasure through life. Familiarity with that part of the country now induced him to send abroad his two sealers from those waters.

The nautical plot of the book is peculiar, and is followed by the reader with much interest, the two rival schooners sailing in search of a very valuable but mysterious sealing-ground in the Antarctic Ocean. The whole spirit of the book, the history of the schooners, the course of their daring commanders, and, indeed, all the characters appearing in the narrative, are thoroughly American. The old, hard-fisted miser and religious formalist, Deacon Pratt, an important figure in the book, will be found well drawn throughout. Mary, his niece, the heroine of the story—though one dislikes that ambitious word when applied to a sweet, natural person like herself—is very pleasing; we readily love her, and we respect her truthful purity, and the enduring strength of her affections. While the outer movement of the plot is connected with the two schooners, there is a secret and a deeper spirit at work at the heart of the narrative. That gentle Mary, so sweetly pretty, so simply good, is overshadowed by a sorrow deep and true; she moves sadly beneath the low porch, about the great orchard, the thrifty garden, of the Long Island farm. Roswell Gardiner, the captain of "The Sea Lion," owned by the miserly deacon, loves Mary; the girl has given him her whole heart with that fulness and that fidelity of affection belonging to simple, truthful, unworldly natures like hers. But his wife she cannot be; there is a chasm between them. The religious education of young Gardiner has given him opinions directly at variance—as Mary, by her simple good sense, knows but too well—with the spirit of true Christianity. Where the young girl worships, with child-like piety—where the vast majority of the Christian world has worshipped, in devout and lowly adoration, and in living faith, for nineteen centuries—there the young man stands

The Sea Lions: "There must be life in him yet, sir. It's
not twenty minutes since he gave that last cry."

coldly erect, with covered head, scanning, doubting, debating; attempting, with the wretched inconsistency of human pride, to extinguish, with one hand, the light he upholds with the other—a light acknowledged by himself as a revealed gift from on high; daring, as it were, with his feeble, puny, sinful arm, to hold the Heavens in a balance! But this cold, soulless creed of Gardiner's is his by luck-less birthright only. Too honest to disavow it, even for the sake of his love, he is yet willing to be convinced of error, if error he can be made to see. Mary, though sad, still prays; and Mary hopes. The young man sails on his daring voyage; he reaches his mysterious bourne; and here, in those distant icy regions, comparatively alone with his Maker, amid shipwreck, and disaster, and suffering, his mind is enlightened by the fulness of truth.

Through life the religious convictions of the author of "The Pathfinder" had been clear and sincere. He not unfrequently spoke on sacred subjects, and always with reverence. He ever yielded a full and honest assent to the great doctrines of Christianity. Doubt and scepticism would seem never, for a moment, to have darkened that clear mind, that frank spirit, that upright heart. But, while through life he had never doubted, while he had ever acknowledged, ever revered, he had not until a comparatively late day fully submitted to those sacred influences. In the little parish church, however, which he had taken so much pleasure in improving; whose interests he had so faithfully and liberally upheld; in whose behalf he served at intervals as vestryman or warden for nearly forty years, and from whose sacred worship, when under his own roof, he was so rarely absent; here he had been gradually learning lessons the most precious while reverently joining in those devotions which he ever felt and acknowledged to be beautiful, sublime, holy. Eternal truths rose more clearly before him—filled a larger space in his heart and mind. The sorrows and disappointments of this life assumed their real character; he learned to look above them, beyond them. It was in this frame of mind that, in the year 1849, "The Sea Lions" was written. The point of religious doctrine connected with the narrative was one on which Mr. Cooper was frequently heard to speak with reverence, and the utmost fulness of conviction. To his clear mind, the positive denial of that one holy doctrine must inevitably be followed by the essential rejection of the whole system of Christianity; he considered that absolute infidelity was to a degree more capable of defence, less entirely inconsistent with itself, less at variance with its own assertions, than the doctrine which, in "The Sea Lions," he leads the young sailor to reject.

The book was written in the winter season, at a moment when the severe frosts of the Highlands may have given greater strength to his descriptions of the ice-berg and the snowdrift.   Had the many deeply interesting volumes relating to the arctic seas which we have all lately read been written at that day, the author's descriptions would no doubt have received many an additional detail.   Very possibly the departure of Sir John Franklin on his ill-fated expedition—a recent event at the date of "The Sea Lions"—may have induced the writer to turn his attention to similar scenes, and led him to launch the last of his own imaginary fleet into the waters of those mysterious polar seas.

SEALER'S LAND.

It was an enterprising and manly thing for a little vessel like the Sea Lion to steer, with an undeviating course, into the mysterious depths of the antarctic circle—mysterious, far more in that day than at the present hour. But the American sealer rarely hesitates. He has very little science, few charts, and those oftener old than new, knows little of what is going on among the savans of the earth, though his ear is ever open to the lore of men like himself, and he has his mind stored with pictures of islands and continents that would seem to have been formed for no other purpose than to meet the wants of the race of animals it is his business to pursue and to capture. Cape Horn and its vicinity have so long been frequented by this class of men, that they are at home among their islands, rocks, currents, and sterility; but, to the southward of the Horn itself, all seemed a waste. At the time of which we are writing, much less was known of the antarctic regions than is known to-day; and even now our knowledge is limited to a few dreary outlines, in which barrenness and ice compete for the mastery. Wilkes and his competitors have told us that a vast frozen continent exists in that quarter of the globe; but even their daring and perseverance have not been able to determine more than the general fact.

We should be giving an exaggerated and false idea of Roswell Gardiner's character, did we say that he steered into that great void of the southern ocean in a total indifference to his destination and objects. Very much the reverse was his state of mind, as he saw the high land of the cape sink, as it might be foot by foot, into the ocean, and then lost sight of it altogether. Although the weather was fine for the region, it was dark and menacing. Such, indeed, is usually the case in that portion of this globe, which appears to be the favorite region of the storms. Although the wind was no more than a good breeze, and the ocean was but little disturbed, there were those symptoms in the atmosphere and in the long ground-swells that came rolling in from the south-west, that taught the mariner the cold lessons of caution. We believe that heavier gales of wind at sea are encountered in the warm than in the cold months; but there is something so genial in the air of the ocean during summer, and something so chilling and repulsive in the rival season, that most of us fancy that the currents of air correspond in strength with the fall of the mercury. Roswell knew better than this, it is true; but he also fully understood where he was, and what he was about. As a sealer, he had several times penetrated as far south as the "Ne Plus Ultra" of Cook; but it had ever before been in subordinate situations. This was the first time in which he had the responsibility of command thrown on himself, and it was no more than natural that he should feel the weight of this new burden. So long as the Sea Lion of the Vineyard was in sight, she had presented a centre of interest and concern. To get rid of her had been his first care, and almost absorbing object; but, now that she seemed to be finally thrown out of his wake, there remained the momentous and closely approaching difficulties of the main adventure directly before his eyes. Roswell, therefore, was thoughtful and grave, his countenance offering no bad reflection of the sober features of the atmosphere and the ocean.

Although the season was that of summer, and the weather was such as is deemed propitious in the neighborhood of Cape Horn, a feeling of uncertainty prevailed over every other sensation. To the southward a cold mistiness veiled the view, and every mile the schooner advanced appeared like penetrating deeper and deeper into regions that nature had hitherto withheld from the investigation of the mariner. Ice, and its dangers, were known to exist a few degrees further in that direction; but islands also had been discovered, and turned to good account by the enterprise of the sealers.

It was truly a great thing for the Sea Lion of Oyster Pond to have thrown off her namesake of the Vineyard. It is true both vessels were still in the same sea, with a possibility of again meeting; but Roswell Gardiner was steering onward toward a haven designated in degrees and minutes, while the other craft was most probably left to wander in uncertainty in that remote and stormy ocean. Our hero thought there was now very little likelihood of his again falling in with his late consort, and this so much the more, because the islands he sought were not laid down in the vicinity of any other known land, and were consequently out of the usual track of the sealers. This last circumstance was fully appreciated by our young navigator, and gave him confidence of possessing its treasures to himself, could he only find the place where nature had hid them.

When the sun went down in that vast waste of water which lies to the southward of this continent, the little Sea Lion had fairly lost sight of land, and was riding over the long, south-western ground-swell like a gull that holds its way steadily toward its nest. For many hours her course had not varied half a point, being as near as possible to south-south-west, which kept her a little off the wind. No sooner, however, did night come to shut in the view, than Roswell Gardiner went aft to the man at the helm, and ordered him to steer to the southward, as near as the breeze would conveniently allow. This was a material change in the direction of the vessel, and, should the present breeze stand, would probably place her, by the return of light, a good distance to the eastward of the point she would otherwise have reached. Hitherto, it had been Roswell's aim to drop his consort; but, now it was dark, and so much time had already passed and been improved since the other schooner was last seen, he believed he might venture to steer in the precise direction he desired to go. The season is so short in those seas, that every hour is precious, and no more variation from a real object could be permitted than circumstances imperiously required. It was now generally understood that the craft was making the best of her way toward her destined sealing-ground.

No material change occurred during the night, or in the course of the succeeding day, the little Sea Lion industriously holding her way toward the south pole; making very regularly her six knots each hour. By the time she was thirty-six hours from the Horn, Gardiner believed himself to be fully three degrees to the southward of it, and consequently some distance within the parallel of sixty degrees south. Palmer's Land, with its neighboring islands, would have been near, had not the original course carried the schooner so far to the westward. As it was, no one could say what lay before them.

The third day out, the wind hauled, and it blew heavily from the north-east. This gave the adventurers a great run. The blink of ice was shortly seen, and soon after ice itself, drifting about in bergs. The floating hills were grand objects to the eye, rolling and wallowing in the seas; but they were much worn and melted by the wash of the ocean, and comparatively of greatly diminished size. It was now absolutely necessary to lose most of the hours of darkness, it being much too dangerous to run in the night. The great barrier of ice was known to be close at hand; and Cook's "Ne Plus Ultra," at that time the great boundary of antarctic navigation, was near the parallel of latitude to which the schooner had reached. The weather, however, continued very favorable, and after the blow from the north-east, the wind came from the south, chill, and attended with flurries of snow, but sufficiently steady, and not so fresh as to compel our adventurers to carry very short sail. The smoothness of the water would of itself have announced the vicinity of ice: not only did Gardiner's calculations tell him as much as this, but his eyes confirmed their results. In the course of the fifth day out, on several occasions when the weather cleared a little, glimpses were had of the ice in long mountainous walls, resembling many of the ridges of the Alps, though moving heavily under the heaving and setting of the restless waters. Dense fogs, from time to time, clouded the whole view, and the schooner was compelled, more than once that day, to heave-to, in order to avoid running on the sunken masses of ice, or fields, of which many of vast size now began to make their appearance.

Notwithstanding the dangers that surrounded our adventurers, they were none of them so insensible to the sublime powers of nature as to withhold their admiration from the many glorious objects which that lone and wild scene presented. The icebergs were of all the hues of the rainbow, as the sunlight gilded their summits or sides, or they were left shaded by the interposition of dark and murky clouds. There were instances when certain of the huge frozen masses even appeared to be quite black, in particular positions and under peculiar lights; while others, at the same instant, were gorgeous in their gleams of emerald and gold!

When the sun reappeared, on the morning of the sixth day after he had left the Horn, Roswell Gardiner believed himself to be far enough west for his purposes. It now remained to get a whole degree further to the south, which was a vast distance in those seas, and in that direction, and would carry him a long way to the southward of the "Ne Plus Ultra." If there was any truth in Daggett, however, that mariner had been there; and the instructions of the owner rendered it incumbent on our young man to attempt to follow him. More than once, that morning, did our hero regret he had not entered into terms with the Vineyard men, that the effort might have been made in company. There was something so portentous in a lone vessel's venturing within the ice, in so remote a region, that, to say the truth, Roswell hesitated. But pride of profession, ambition, love of Mary, dread of the deacon, native resolution, and the hardihood produced by experience in dangers often encountered and escaped, nerved him to the undertaking. It must be attempted, or the voyage would be lost; and our young mariner now set about his task with a stern determination to achieve it.

By this time the schooner had luffed up within a cable's length of the ice, along the margin of which she was running under easy sail. Gardiner believed himself to be quite as far to the westward as was necessary, and his present object was to find an opening, by means of which he could enter among the floating chaos that was spread, far and wide, to windward. As the breeze was driving the drifting masses to the northward, they became loosened, and more separated, every moment; and glad enough was Gardiner to discover, at length, a clear spot that seemed to favor his views. Without an instant's delay, the sheets were flattened in, a pull was taken on the braces, and away went the little Sea Lion into a passage that had a hundred fold more real causes of terror than the Scylla and Charybdis of old.

One effect of the vicinity of ice, in extensive fields, is to produce comparatively still water. It must blow a gale, and that over a considerable extent of open sea, to produce much commotion among the fields and bergs, though that heaving and setting which has been likened to the respiration of some monster, and which seamen call the "ground-swell," is never entirely wanting among the waters of an ocean. On the present occasion, our adventurers were favored in this respect, their craft gliding forward unimpeded by any thing like opposing billows. At the end of four hours, the schooner, tacking and waring when necessary, had worked her way to the southward and westward, according to her master's reckoning, some five-and-twenty miles. It was then noon, and the atmosphere being unusually clear, though never without fog, Gardiner went aloft, to take a look for himself at the condition of things around him.

To the northward, and along the very passage by which the vessel had sailed, the ice was closing, and it was far easier to go on than to return. To the eastward, and toward the south-east in particular, however, did Roswell Gardiner turn his longing eyes. Somewhere in that quarter of the ocean, and distant now less than ten leagues, did he expect to find the islands of which he was in quest, if, indeed, they had any existence at all. In that direction there were many passages open among the ice, the latter being generally higher than in the particular place to which the vessel had reached. Once or twice Roswell mistook the summits of some of these bergs for real mountains, when, owing to the manner in which the light fell upon them, or, rather, did not fall upon them directly, they appeared dark and earthy. Each time, however, the sun's rays soon came to undeceive him; and that which had so lately been black and frowning, was, as by the touch of magic, suddenly illuminated, and became bright and gorgeous, throwing out its emerald hues, or perhaps a virgin white, that filled the beholder with delight, even amid the terrors and dangers by which, in very truth, he was surrounded. The glorious Alps themselves—those wonders of the earth—could scarcely compete, in scenery, with the views that nature lavished, in that remote sea, on a seeming void. But the might and honor of God were there, as well as beneath the equator.

For one whole hour did Roswell Gardiner remain in the cross-trees, having hailed the deck, and caused the schooner's head to be turned to the south-east, pressing her through the openings as near the wind as she could go. The atmosphere was never without fog, though the vapor drifted about, leaving large vacancies that were totally clear. One spot, in particular, seemed to be a favorite resting-place for these low clouds, which just there appeared to light upon the face of the ocean itself. A wide field of ice, or, it were better to say, a broad belt of bergs, lay between this stationary cloud and the schooner, though the existence of the vapor early caught Roswell's attention; and, during the hour he was aloft, conning the craft through a very intricate and ticklish channel, not a minute passed that the young man did not turn a look toward that veiled spot. He was in the act of placing a foot on the ratlin below him, to descend to the deck, when he half-unconsciously turned to take a last glance at this distant and seemingly immovable object. Just then, the vapor, which had kept rolling and moving, like a fluid in ebullition, while it still clung together, suddenly opened, and the bald head of a real mountain, a thousand feet high, came unexpectedly into view! There could be no mistake; all was too plain to admit of a doubt. There, beyond all question, was land; and it was doubtless the most western of the islands described by the dying seaman. Every thing corroborated this conclusion. The latitude and longitude were right, or nearly so, and the other circumstances went to confirm the conjecture or conclusion. Daggett had said that one island, high, mountainous, ragged, and bleak, but of some size, lay the most westerly in the group, while several others were within a few miles of it. The last were lower, much smaller, and little more than naked rocks. One of these last, however, he insisted on it, was a volcano in activity, and that, at intervals, it emitted flames, as well as a fierce heat. By his account, however, the party to which he belonged had never actually visited that volcanic cauldron, being satisfied with admiring its terrors from a distance.

As to the existence of the land, Roswell got several pretty distinct and certain views, leaving no doubt of its character and position. There is a theory which tells us that the orb of day is surrounded by a luminous vapor, the source of heat and light, and that this vapor, being in constant motion, occasionally leaves the mass of the planet itself to be seen, forming what it is usual to term the "spots on the sun." Resembling this theory, the fogs of the antarctic seas rolled about the mountain now seen, withdrawing the curtain at times, and permitting a view of the striking and majestic object within. Well did that lone and nearly barren mass of earth and rock merit these appellations! The elevation has already been given; and a rock that is nearly perpendicular, rising out of the ocean for a thousand feet, is ever imposing and grand. This was rendered so much the more so by its loneliness, its stable and stern position amid floating and moving mountains of ice, its brown sides and bald summit, the latter then recently whitened with a fall of pure snow, and its frowning and fixed aspect amid a scene that might otherwise be said to be ever in motion.

Roswell Gardiner's heart beat with delight when assured of success in discovering this, the first great goal of his destination. To reach it was now his all-absorbing desire. By this time the wind had got round to the south-west, and was blowing quite fresh, bringing him well to windward of the mountain, but causing the icebergs to drift in toward the land, and placing an impassable barrier along its western shore. Our young man, however, remembered that Daggett had given the anchorage as on the north-eastern side of the island, where, according to his statements, a little haven would be found, in which a dozen craft might lie in security. To this quarter of the island Gardiner consequently endeavored to get.

There was no opening to the northward, but a pretty good channel was before the schooner to the southward of the group. In this direction, then, the Sea Lion was steered, and by eight bells (four in the afternoon) the southern point of the largest island was doubled. The rest of the group were made, and to the infinite delight of all on board her, abundance of clear water was found between the main island and its smaller neighbors. The bergs had grounded, apparently, as they drew near the group, leaving this large bay entirely free from ice, with the exception of a few small masses that were floating through it. These bodies, whether field or berg, were easily avoided; and away the schooner went with flowing sheets, into the large basin formed by the different members of the group. The smoke of a volcano arose from a rock to the eastward, that appeared to be some three or four miles in circumference, and which stood on the eastern side of the great basin, or some four leagues from Sealer's Land, as Daggett had at once named the principal island. This was, in fact, about the breadth of the main basin, which had two principal passages into it, the one from the south, and the other from the north-east.

Once within the islands, and reasonably clear of all ice, it was an easy thing for the schooner to run across the basin or great bay, and reach the north-eastern extremity of Sealer's Land. As the light would continue some hours longer, Roswell caused a boat to be lowered and manned, when he pulled at once toward the spot where it struck him the haven must be found, if there were any such place at all. Every thing turned out as it had been described by Daggett, and great was our young man's satisfaction, when he rowed into a cove that was little more than two hundred yards in diameter, and which was so completely landlocked as not to feel the influence of any sea outside. In general, the great difficulty is to land on any of the antarctic rocks, the breakers and surf opposing it; but, in this spot, the smallest boat could be laid with its bows on a beach of shingles, without the slightest risk of its being injured. The lead also announced good anchorage in about eight fathoms of water. In a word, this little haven was one of those small basins that so often occur in mountainous islands, where fragments of rock appear to have fallen from the principal mass as it was forced upward out of the ocean, as if purposely intended to meet the wants of mariners.

Nor was the outer bay, or the large basin formed by the entire group, by any means devoid of advantages to the navigator. From north to south this outer bay was at least six leagues in length, while its breadth could not much have fallen short of four. Of course, it was much more exposed to the winds and waves than the little harbor proper, though Roswell was struck with the great advantages it offered in several essential particulars. It was almost clear of ice, while so much was floating about outside of the circle of islands; thus leaving a free navigation in it for even the smallest boat. This was mainly owing to the fact that the largest island had two long, crescent-shaped capes—the one at its north-eastern, and the other at its south-eastern extremity—giving to its whole eastern side the shape of a new moon. The harbor just described was to the southward of, or within the north-eastern cape, which our young master at once named Cape Hazard, in honor of his chief mate's vigilance; that officer having been the first to point out the facilities probably offered by the formation of the land for an anchorage.

Though rocky and broken, it was by no means difficult to ascend the rugged banks on the northern side of the harbor, and Gardiner went up it, attended by Stimson, who of late had much attached himself to the person of his commander. The height of this barrier above the waves of the ocean was but a little less than a hundred feet, and when the summit was reached, a common exclamation of surprise, not to say delight, broke from the lips of both.   Hitherto not a seal of any sort had been seen, and Gardiner had felt some misgivings touching the benefits that were to be derived from so much hardship, exposure, and enterprise.   All doubts, however, vanished the instant he got a sight of the northern shore of the island.   This shore, a reach of several miles in extent, was fairly alive with the monsters of which he was in search.   They lay in thousands on the low rocks that lined that entire side of the island, basking in the sun of the antarctic seas.

While on the rocks, Roswell took such a survey of the localities as might enable him to issue his orders hereafter with discretion and intelligence.   The schooner was already making short tacks to get close in with the island, in obedience to a signal to that effect; and the second mate had pulled out to the entrance of the little haven, with a view to act as pilot.   Before the captain had descended from the summit of the northern barrier, the vessel came in under her jib, the wind being nearly aft, and she dropped two anchors in suitable spots, making another flying moor of it.

General joy now illuminated every face.   It was, in itself, a great point gained to get the schooner into a perfectly safe haven, where her people could take their natural rest at night, or during their watches below, without feeling any apprehension of being crushed in the ice; but here was not only security, but the source of that wealth of which they were in quest, and which had induced them all to encounter so many privations and so much danger.   The crew landed to a man, each individual ascending to the summit of the barrier, to feast his eyes on the spectacle that lay spread in such affluent abundance along the low rocks of the northern side of the island.